PEARSON CRIMINAL JUSTICE

CRJ 208 - Technologies in Criminal Justice
Custom Edition for Quinsigamond Community College

PEARSON

Please visit our website at *www.pearsonlearningsolutions.com*.

Attention bookstores: For permission to return any unsold stock, contact us at *pe-uscustomreturns@pearson.com*.

Pearson Learning Solutions, 501 Boylston Street, Suite 900, Boston, MA 02116
A Pearson Education Company
www.pearsoned.com

ISBN 10: 1-256-60541-7
ISBN 13: 978-1-256-60541-6

Table of Contents

TECHNOLOGY AND THE POLICE

The chapter begins with a discussion of Soulliere's (1999) stages of technological advancement, which loosely correlate with Kelling and Moore's (1991) eras of policing. The chapter then focuses primarily on two areas of policing where technology has been particularly influential: the development of forensic science and its impact on crime scene investigation and advances in crime analysis. With regard to forensics and crime scene investigation, particular attention is given to basic principles (i.e., Locard principle), developments in fingerprinting and DNA, and biometrics. The chapter also briefly touches upon profiling according to physical behavior and psychological makeup. The main thrust of the discussion on crime analysis involves the use of GIS and crime mapping, as well as geographic profiling. A number of other technological innovations are described, including the changing role of computers, closed circuit television, GPS, and imaging. The overriding theme of the chapter is that technological innovation has played a critically important role in enhancing the ability of police to accomplish their objectives. As we continue to progress through the twenty-first century, the role of technology is certain to remain important.

STAGES OF TECHNOLOGICAL ADVANCEMENT

Soulliere (1999) describes four different stages of technological developments: first stage (1881–1945), second stage (1946–1959), third stage (1960–1979), and the fourth stage (1980 – present).

The First Stage: 1881–1945

The first technological stage of policing encompasses two of the eras described by Kelling and Moore: the political and reform eras (Grant & Terry, 2005). In terms of technological advancement, the first stage involves the transformation of the police officer from the lone cop on foot patrol, completely disconnected from headquarters and responding only to what he sees or is brought to his attention by passersby, to the professional yet isolated officer on routine automobile patrol waiting for calls for service to come in to dispatch. The three critical advances in this stage that form the foundation of the reactive, preventive patrol philosophy are the automobile, the two-way radio, and the telephone. This stage is also defined by the other elements of August Vollmer's professional model including the first crime laboratory, fingerprinting, handwriting analysis, and the polygraph. Souillere (1999) notes that these advances had a number of important effects on policing including:

- Increased specialization within the organization (leading to more complex organizations).
- Increased mobility for officers on patrol.
- Increased officer safety (through better communications systems). (Grant & Terry, 2005)

The Second Stage: 1946–1959

Soulliere's (1999) second stage of technological advancement is the relatively brief period immediately following World War II when police departments became increasingly bureaucratic, in large part because of the innovations during the first stage. Also, there were important technological advances during this stage involving traffic enforcement, including the first speeding measures and early tools to assess levels of intoxication. These measures were the predecessors to radar and other automobile surveillance tools, as well as blood-alcohol measuring devices (Grant & Terry, 2005).

The Third Stage: 1960–1979

During this third stage, technology revolutionized the way police departments carried out their daily business. During the early part of this stage, police departments were lagging behind the rest of society with regard to technology, a major finding highlighted in the President's Commission on Law Enforcement and the Administration of Justice (1967, p. 125):

> The police, with crime laboratories and radio networks, made early use of technology, but most police departments could have been equipped 30 or 40 years ago as well as they are today. . . . Of all criminal justice agencies, the police have had the closest ties to

science and technology, but they have called on scientific resources primarily to help in the solution of specific serious crimes, rather than for assistance in solving general problems of policing. (see also Grant & Terry, 2005)

Despite the slow start, technology—especially computers—quickly became central components of policing in the late 1960s and 1970s. Examples include: the creation of the first 911 system in 1968; calls for service distribution centers; computerized databanks for criminal histories, warrants, offenders, and automobiles; computer-aided dispatch (CAD).

The Fourth Stage: 1980–Present

Soulliere's (1999) fourth stage is characterized by the enhanced access and use of information. Advances in computer technology, facsimile, the Internet, and telecommunications helped police departments store enormous amounts of information and allowed individual police officers to use that information is nearly real-time. Advances in **forensic sciences** have also redefined police investigations, particularly developments in DNA, fingerprinting, and imaging. Many of these technological advances will be described later in this chapter. The NYPD stores enormous amounts of information about police activities in a centralized database and uses that information to chart trends in crime and disorder. The department then realigns its deployment of resources to address the trends and problems identified through the **crime mapping** analysis. In July 2005, the NYPD announced the opening of its **Real Time Crime Center (RTCC).** The Center, staffed by 26 highly trained officers, offers real-time support to detectives and patrol officers investigating crimes. The Center accesses enormous amounts of data: 5 million New York state criminal records; 20 million New York City criminal complaints, summonses, and 311/911 calls; 31 million national crime records; and 33 billion public records (www.nyc.gov/html/nypd). When a crime occurs, the RTCC provides support to detectives through 911/311 call review, location analysis (mapping), victim analysis, crime pattern analysis, and offender analysis.

CRIME SCENE INVESTIGATION

As of the fall 2005 television season, there were three *CSI* shows—Las Vegas, Miami, and New York—as well as half a dozen others involving coroners, forensic anthropologists, and forensic scientists. The romanticized and sometimes inaccurate depiction of crime scene investigation on television has led to an entire generation of would-be forensic scientists through the "CSI-effect". In the real world of policing, forensic science has led to a slower but equally important revolution in police investigations.

Historical Perspective

Despite recent technological advances, crime scene investigation is not new. There are verified records of **fingerprints** being used as marks of authenticity in China more than 2,000 years ago (Gaensslen & Young, 2003). In the late nineteenth century, **Alphonse Bertillon** developed a system of criminal identification based on head size, finger length, and several other characteristics. In 1894, Juan Vucetich, employed by a police department in Argentina, wrote a book about the value of fingerprints as a means of identification of criminal offenders (Gaensslen & Young, 2003). In 1910, Thomas Jennings was arrested, tried, and convicted of murder, and fingerprints were the primary evidence against him. The professional reform movement, led by August Vollmer and others, placed a premium of using scientific methods of crime detection. During his tenure as Chief of the Berkeley, California, Police Department, Vollmer hired a Bertillon expert, urged the U.S. Congress to mandate the FBI to create a national fingerprinting bureau, hired a biochemist to operate a crime laboratory, and began handwriting analysis. Clearly, the seeds for forensic and scientific crime scene investigation were laid well before the turn of the twenty-first century.

The Locard Principle and Physical Evidence

The foundation of crime scene investigation rests on a single theoretical principle, called the **Locard exchange principle.** The Locard exchange principle states that:

> . . . whenever two objects come into contact, a mutual exchange of matter will take place between them. Linking suspects to victims is the most important and common type of linkage accomplished by physical evidence in criminal investigations. Linking victims and suspects to objects and scenes can also be accomplished by use of the physical evidence. (Miller, 2003, p. 116)

In simple terms, the principle maintains that criminal offenders leave behind trace physical evidence at the scene of the crime, through contact with either the victim or objects at the scene. This physical evidence can be any number of things, depending on the nature of the crime. The most common types of physical evidence and techniques for collecting it are described in the following sections.

Fingerprints. When a person grasps an item with reasonable pressure, grease oozing out of the pores under the ridges leaves latent fingerprints. No two persons have the same fingerprints, which are a combination of many possible patterns (i.e., arches, loops, and whirls). As a result, fingerprints left at the scene, once collected, can be compared to other known samples of fingerprints in an effort to identify a match. The comparison samples of fingerprints come from a variety of sources. Television and movies have shown us how people who are arrested are fingerprinted with the old-fashioned black ink and paper. Also, people serving in certain occupations are also fingerprinted either as routine, or as part of a background check (military, federal employees, teachers, etc.). In the past, investigators matched paper fingerprint cards from evidence collected at a crime scene with the fingerprints of persons previously arrested. While fingerprints provide clear and convincing evidence when a match occurs, the manual process of comparing fingerprints was extremely laborious and time consuming.

However, technology has dramatically altered this fingerprint matching process. First, in many jurisdictions the ink and paper approach has been replaced by digitized systems that scan the prints and store them in a computer. In 2000, the FBI began using the **Integrated Automated Fingerprint Identification System (IAFIS)**, a national database of nearly 40 million criminals' fingerprints and their criminal records (Champion & Hooper, 2003). Many states also operate their own automated fingerprint systems. These computerized fingerprint systems have revolutionized the utility of fingerprinting, as now a fingerprint collected at a crime scene can be entered in IAFIS and compared to 40 million other prints in a matter of hours (usually a two-hour turnaround), rather than weeks or months.

Blood, Saliva, Semen, Skin.   Technological advancements in the last twenty years have greatly expanded how police can use physical evidence in criminal investigations, and perhaps the most important advances have involved deoxyribonucleic acid—DNA. **DNA** is essentially a genetic fingerprint: No two people have the same (with the exception of identical twins). In the mid-1980s, forensic scientists developed and began to perfect a method for amplifying small amounts of DNA, called polymerase chain reaction, or PCR (Champion & Hooper, 2003). This technique allows scientists to compare DNA samples collected from crime scenes to other known DNA samples. DNA can be extracted from blood, hair, semen, and saliva, and advances in testing—single nucleotide polymorphism (SNP) analysis and mitochondrial DNA analysis—have increased the accuracy of DNA testing to over 95 percent. DNA testing gained worldwide attention as part of the O.J. Simpson murder trial in the early 1990s, where blood evidence at the scene linked Simpson to the crime: There was one chance in 240,000 that blood at the scene was NOT OJ's, and there was one chance in 1.2 million that blood in O.J.'s home was NOT his ex-wife's (the murder victim). Of course, O.J. Simpson was acquitted of all criminal charges, in large part because of problems in the chain of custody of the blood evidence (see below).

DNA evidence collected from a crime scene is not useful unless there are samples for comparison. As a result, the FBI developed and maintains a **Combined DNA Index System, or CODIS,** which became fully operation in 1998. By the start of 2001, CODIS held over 440,000 offender profiles, and the FBI estimated that the system would hold over one million by 2005 (Champion & Hooper, 2003). To determine whether physical evidence collected from a crime scene matches an existing offender, the crime laboratory technicians compare the collected sample to the database. Since the system is computerized, the matching process occurs very quickly. Of course, the testing helps the investigation only if there is a match, producing a known suspect. Nevertheless, each collected sample is entered in CODIS, and since federal law now allows police to take blood samples from convicted felons, CODIS is continually growing.

Weapon. Technology has also improved the ability of police to investigate crimes by linking weapons to crime scenes and individuals. Perhaps the best known field in this area is **ballistics,** which studies the motion of bullets. When a weapon is fired, the bullet picks up tiny imperfections of the bore of the gun that it passes through. Scratches are caused by the imperfections in the lands and grooves placed in the barrel at the time of manufacture and also through use. Experts can then determine if rounds are fired by the same gun by matching the imperfections on the round collected at the crime scene to other known samples (again, from databases created by states and the FBI such as IBIS, the Integrated Ballistics Identification System) (Grant & Terry, 2005). Class characteristics of a firearm can also be determined from expended cartridges (the part of the round that held the bullet and is expended from the gun after firing). These characteristics include caliber, shape of the firing pin, location of the firing pin, size of the firing pin, and size of extractors and ejectors (and the geometrical relationship between the two) (Rowe, 2003). Once the make and model of the firearm is determined, investigators can focus their search for that specific type of weapon.

A second area of weapon investigation involves **tool marks.** Rowe (2003) states that there are three types of tool marks: compression (indented), sliding, and cutting.

- Compression tool marks result when a tool is pressed into softer material. Such marks often show the outline of the working surface of the tool, so that class characteristics of the tool (such as dimensions) can be determined.
- Sliding tool marks are created when a tool slides along a surface; such marks usually consist of a pattern of parallel striations.
- Cutting tool marks are a combination of compression and sliding tool marks. The cutting tool indents the material being cut and, as it does so, the working surfaces of the tool slide over the cut surface. (pp. 349–350)

Once a tool mark has been documented and collected from a crime scene, the tool mark examiner in the laboratory compares the tool mark with tools collected at the crime scene. The tool mark examiner can use a tool collected at the crime scene to make a *test tool mark,* and then compare the test tool mark to the mark collected at the scene using a specialized microscope. This type of tool mark analysis can be used to identify weapons used in serious person crimes, but it is also quite useful in identifying tools used to commit break-ins and to crack safes (Rowe, 2003). Successful tool mark comparisons put investigators one step closer to the criminal by identifying a potential link between the offender and the crime scene (i.e., if it can be determined that the suspect owns or possessed the specific tool in question).

Other Developments in Forensic Science. Beyond the most common types of physical evidence and techniques to collect that evidence described above, technology has also led to the development of a wide range of new fields in forensic science. These include:

- *Forensic Pathology:* Study of the deceased through autopsy to determine cause of death; forensic pathologists, typically employed as coroners, also review witness statements, medical history, and examine the scene (in addition to autopsy) to determine cause of death (accident, suicide, or homicide).
- *Forensic Toxicology:* Examination of all aspects of toxicity that may have legal implications; three divisions of forensic toxicology are postmortem drug testing, workplace drug testing, and investigation (identification) of contraband materials.
- *Forensic Odontology:* Application of dentistry to the legal system via identification of individuals through comparison of unique features of teeth (victims to dental records) and comparison of bite mark patterns.
- *Forensic Anthropology:* Application of theory and methods of anthropology to forensic problems, most commonly involving the recovery and identification of human remains.
- *Forensic Taphonomy* and *Entomology:* Involves determining the history of a body after death (often for identifying the time of death); includes the death event, the interval of bone exposure through modification of soft tissue (decomposition), the potential interval of bone modification, and the point of body discovery. Forensic entomology involves the study of insect activity and death, particularly flies and beetles.
- *Recognition of Bloodstain Patterns:* Using knowledge about the biological and physical properties of blood to interpret bloodstain patterns—such as spatter, castoff, and transfer—at a crime scene and assist with reconstruction of the crime.
- *Microanalysis of Trace Evidence:* Microanalysis of minor components of some evidence collected at a crime scene, such as glass, fibers, paint, and soil. The purpose is to determine whether an association of persons, places, and things can be established (i.e., can fibers found on a suspect's coat be matched to carpet fibers in the victim's house).
- *Forensic Footwear Evidence:* As someone walks, his or her shoes track over a variety of surfaces, acquiring dust, dirt, grease, residue, oils, blood, and moisture. This material is then redeposited on subsequent surfaces that are walked upon. The contact between the shoe and the surface results in this transfer of materials, which can then be collected and compared to a suspect's shoes. Shoe impressions can also be analyzed and provide information regarding shoe type, shoe size, and gait characteristics (i.e., limp). A match between the collected footwear evidence and the suspect's footwear can prove that the suspect was at the crime scene. The FBI maintains a database of thousands of shoe designs.
- *Forensic Tire Impression and Tire Track Evidence:* Tire impressions or tire tracks at a crime scene can be compared to the tires on a suspect's vehicle, linking the suspect to the crime scene. Tire evidence typically is not definitive

about a specific vehicle; rather it helps identify a specific type of tire and vehicle, which can suggest the suspect's presence at the crime scene.

- *Document Examination:* Forensic document examination can involve a comparison of handwriting and signatures, typewriters and printing devices, alterations and obliterations to documents, counterfeiting, photocopies, rubber stamp impressions, inks, and paper.
- *Fire and Explosion Investigation:* Applying knowledge of fire, including chemistry and physics, to identify the origin and cause of a fire or explosion. Once origin and cause are identified, the fire or explosion is classified as one of the following: natural act (lightning), accidental, incendiary (intentional), or undetermined (cause unknown).
- *Vehicular Accident Reconstruction:* Applying laws of physics (Conservation of Momentum and Conservation of Energy), physical evidence, eyewitness testimony, and engineering knowledge to determine the nature and cause of automobile accidents. (James & Nordby, 2003)

Basic Procedures in Crime Scene Investigation

There are a number of well-established steps or procedures that, collectively, attempt to establish the physical link between the offender and the crime scene or victim. These include securing the scene, the crime scene survey (or walk-through), documentation, searching for evidence, collecting and preserving evidence, and crime scene reconstruction. A brief discussion of each step follows below (see James & Nordby, 2003, for a complete discussion).

Securing the Crime Scene. The first responder to a crime scene, almost always a patrol officer, has a number of important responsibilities, such as assisting the victim (i.e., emergency medical treatment), searching for and arresting the offender, and detaining and questioning witnesses. Another critical responsibility involves securing the crime scene. Based on the Locard principle (described earlier), anyone who enters the crime scene will alter and contaminate it by leaving additional evidence unrelated to the crime or by destroying evidence resulting from the crime (Miller, 2003). Thus, it is critical for the first officer on scene to block off the crime scene and control access to it. All movements into the scene and alterations to it should be recorded in a security log, and the crime scene investigator should review the security of the scene once he or she arrives (Miller, 2003).

Crime Scene Survey (Walk-Through). This stage represents the first examination of the crime scene by the investigator. Miller (2003) cites six objectives for a complete and accurate crime scene survey:

1. Begin to prepare a reconstruction theory (i.e., how it happened).
2. Note any transient evidence requiring immediate protection and processing.
3. Take precautions if weather conditions may change.

4. Note points of entry and exit to crime scene.
5. Record initial observations of who, what, where, when, and how.
6. Assess need for additional personnel, equipment, or other agencies.

Documentation. The documentation stage is perhaps the most important step in crime scene investigation. Documentation involves creating a permanent record of the crime scene and physical evidence as it currently exists (Miller, 2003). Once evidence is collected and processed, this documentation will represent the only existing evidence of the state of the crime scene upon discovery. Thus, this step is the most time consuming and laborious. There are four major tasks at this stage:

1. Note-taking: Emphasis on notification information (i.e., how the crime was discovered, time, etc.), arrival information (i.e., time, who was present), scene description, victim description, and the crime scene team (i.e., times of arrival and assignments).
2. Videotaping: No narration; should include the scene itself, surroundings, and the victim's viewpoint.
3. Photographs: Provide a still pictorial record of the crime scene and physical evidence; every photo must be recorded in a photo log; photograph everything.
4. Sketching: Assignment of units of measurement or correct perspective to the crime scene and the physical evidence within the scene.

Searching for Evidence. The investigators then engage in a thorough search for evidence throughout the crime scene. There are a variety of search patterns that can be used to ensure that the entire scene is covered, such as the link, grid, zone, wheel, and spiral. Once evidence is located, it should be marked so it can be collected once the search is complete. No evidence is collected at this stage (Miller, 2003).

Collecting and Preserving Evidence. The fifth stage of crime scene investigation involves the collection and processing of evidence. Transient or fragile evidence should be collected first, and one person should be assigned as the evidence collector to ensure consistency (Miller, 2003). Each piece of evidence should be collected and placed in a primary container, and the primary container should be stored in a secondary container. Each piece of evidence should be packaged separately, clearly marked, and sealed. Once all of the evidence has been collected and sealed, it can be transported back to the crime lab for analysis. The preservation of evidence and clear documentation of its transport, including all who are in control of it, is absolutely critical for maintaining the integrity of the investigation. Once this **chain of custody** is broken, the physical evidence is contaminated, and the defense counsel can challenge the validity of the evidence in court. This is what occurred in the O.J. Simpson trial and likely led to his acquittal. The blood evidence was overwhelming (statistics described above), but because of problems with the crime scene, collection of evidence, and handling of evidence at the scene and at the crime lab, much of the DNA evidence was considered suspect.

Crime Scene Reconstruction.   Crime scene reconstruction is the process of determining or eliminating events that occurred at the crime scene. It is the theory of what occurred based on analysis of the crime scene and physical evidence, forensic laboratory examination of physical evidence, logic, and experience and expertise of the crime scene investigator (Miller, 2003). The reconstruction process is both ongoing, beginning at the earliest stages of crime scene investigation, and fluid, changing as additional evidence is collected and analyzed. There are five basic steps to scene reconstruction:

1. Data collection: Organize and study all the evidence.
2. Conjecture: Formulate a possible explanation as the evidence is being studied.
3. Hypothesis formulation: Interpret the evidence and prepare a hypothesis about what happened.
4. Testing: Conduct additional testing to confirm/disprove the hypothesis (other alternatives are ruled out).
5. Theory formulation: Once the hypothesis is thoroughly tested and verified, establish the theory about what happened at the crime scene (Miller, 2003).

The Realities of Crime Scene Investigation

Although there is no question that technology has greatly advanced forensic science and crime scene investigation, the realities of the work are quite different from how they are portrayed on television (again, see Professor Hallett's scholarly perspective in the next chapter). First, it is a simple fact that crime scene investigation and forensic science are not relevant or necessary in many cases. This is perhaps best illustrated by the fact that patrol officers, not detectives, make the vast majority of arrests. When a patrol officer makes an arrest, it is usually because the suspect is still at the scene or the officer is given information about his or her immediate whereabouts (by the victim or an eyewitness). Also, keep in mind that most police departments are very small, with fewer than ten officers. These small police departments that dominate the landscape of U.S. policing simply do not have the resources to employ criminalists and forensic scientists. Moreover, the vast majority of convictions occur as a result of a plea bargain (where the offender willingly pleads guilty), not a criminal trial where the details of crime scene investigation and physical evidence are discussed.

Second, the depiction of crime scene investigators on television suggests that they are "jacks-of-all-trades," both sworn police officers and scientists who can interrogate suspects and make arrests, as well as conduct laboratory tests in ballistics, blood spatter analysis, and DNA. Again, this is simply not reality. In small departments, patrol officers and detectives often also act as crime scene investigators but lack the specialized skills to conduct laboratory analyses. In large departments, any number of models can be employed. Crime scene technicians who are civilian employees may be responsible for evidence collection and analysis. Specially trained detectives may serve as crime scene investigators, supplemented by crime scene scientists (in a laboratory) with superior skills and training. Many police departments, small and big, contract with county and state crime labs rather than employing their own personnel. And within the crime lab itself, technicians specialize in one particular field (such as ballistics or DNA testing), rather than working in all areas of crime scene analysis.

Third, television would have us think that all the steps of crime scene investigation, analysis of the evidence, and investigation concluding in an arrest can occur in a matter of hours. In direct contradiction to this portrayal, there is a huge backlog of cases waiting for DNA testing at crime labs across the United States (estimated delays in some jurisdictions are up to 18 months). Also, in a typical case, there is often so much evidence that the technicians are forced to pick and choose what they analyze, leaving many pieces of evidence unexamined. Last, there have recently been questions arising about the accuracy of some aspects of forensic science. Some of these questions involve the science itself, others focus on the human element and the potential for human error: either making mistakes in the investigation process or in expert testimony in court. In sum, while quantum leaps have been made in recent years with regard to forensic science and crime scene investigation, there are still formidable challenges to the field and its successful application in law enforcement.

CRIME ANALYSIS

Historical Perspective

The notion of police departments analyzing crime trends to help direct their deployment is certainly not a new concept. In fact, two of Sir Robert Peel's early principles of professional policing dealt specifically with that issue:

- The distribution of crime news is absolutely essential.
- The deployment of police strength both by time and area is essential. (Champion & Hooper, 2003, pp. 61–62)

Crime analysis and targeted deployment were also emphasized by Vollmer (and others) as part of the professionalism movement in the early twentieth century. Finally, O.W. Wilson's formula for deploying police personnel (Wilson, 1941) is based on analysis of calls for service, and assignment of the greatest number of officers to those areas producing the largest number of calls. While the idea of crime analysis by police itself is not new, the tools available to conduct such analysis have changed dramatically in recent years. Computers, **geographic information systems (GIS),** and advanced statistical analysis have revolutionized how police departments can review crime and call for service data, and can then modify deployment to more effectively achieve crime prevention, suppression, and investigation.

Crime Analysis in the Twenty-First Century

Crime analysis is defined as "the collection and analysis of data pertaining to a criminal incident, offender, and target" (Canter, 2000, p. 4). Police departments routinely collect enormous amounts of information on crime incidents, offenders, and victims as part of their day-to-day operations. In fact, one of the biggest myths surrounding policing involves the tremendous amounts of paperwork and report writing the job entails (not typically portrayed on television and in movies). Crime analysis involves taking advantage of available data and analyzing it to inform the department's strategies and deployment. O'Shea and Nicholls (2003) state that crime analysis serves three basic functions for police:

1. Assess the nature, extent, and distribution of crime in order to efficiently and effectively allocate resources and personnel.
2. Identify crime–suspect correlations to assist investigators.
3. Identify the conditions that facilitate crime and incivility so that policymakers may make informed decisions about prevention approaches. (p. 8)

In simpler terms, crime analysis helps police with their efforts to prevent and investigate crime, as well as how to deploy personnel to best achieve those objectives. Canter (2000) states that the functions of crime analysis for police fall into two basic categories: strategic and tactical. Strategic crime analysis involves examining data over a long period of time, often using past trends to attempt to predict what will happen in the future. This type of forecasting can be used to estimate future changes in crime trends or to assess changes in the community dynamics such as socioeconomic status, racial makeup, community attitudes, or risk factors associated with crime (Grant & Terry, 2005). The second category of functions, according to Canter (2000), involves tactical crime analysis. This type of analysis examines recent or real-time data to inform immediate decisions about deployment. This type of analysis often focuses on pattern detection—multiple offenses involving the same characteristics—and hotspots—multiple offenses in a single area. Based on recent shifts in crime patterns (recent meaning over the past few days), officers are then reassigned to targeted areas to prevent/suppress and more effectively respond to crime incidents.

Although departments have long engaged in crime analysis, the development of computers and their integration into U.S. law enforcement has allowed police to analyze available data in much greater amounts and to do so much more quickly. A survey in 2000 indicated that approximately one-third of local police departments in the United States were using computers to engage in crime analysis (Hickman & Reaves, 2003).

Of course, there are limitations to the utility of incident, offender, and victim data for police departments. For crime analysis to be successful, there are three essential criteria for the data that will be analyzed: timeliness, relevancy, and reliability (Grant & Terry, 2005). With regard to timeliness, if a police department is going to modify its deployment to targeted specific areas identified through crime analysis, the data must be up-to-date and show problems that currently exist. In simple terms, old data is useless for police. The relevancy issue refers to the accuracy of the data: Do the data truly reflect what is occurring in specific neighborhoods within the jurisdiction? If police officers consistently make mistakes when filing reports and entering information into the computer, the error-prone data will lead to faulty analysis, which will then lead to inappropriately deployed resources. The final data issue is reliability, or consistency. "Would the same data, interpreted by different people at different times, lead to the same conclusions?" (Grant & Terry, 2005, p. 330). If two people analyze the same data using the same techniques and produce different conclusions, the limitations of the data for police seem obvious. Quite simply, police departments cannot alter their deployment strategies if the data are suspect.

Geographic Information System (GIS)

One of the more recent and most useful developments in crime analysis involves the geographic information system (GIS). GIS is an automated system that captures, analyzes, and displays data using computerized maps of given jurisdictions. The visual images of crime and arrest locations on computerized maps facilitate the analysis of crime, particularly short-terms trends that may involve patterns or hotspots. GIS benefits police departments in two basic ways:

> First, by deploying officers in a more intelligent fashion, police agencies will have more officers available for proactive work (such as problem solving). Second, by identifying crime patterns and inferring where crime is likely to develop, police can engage in preventive work to reduce their future workload. (Pelfrey, 2005, p. 217)

The NYPD was employing pin maps through GIS as early as 1990, and a study by the National Institute of Justice in 1999 indicated that 13 percent of all local police departments were using GIS on a regular basis (NIJ, 1999). GIS is a foundational component of CompStat, and recent studies indicate that CompStat and similar programs have been widely adopted (especially by large departments) across the United States (Weisburd et al., 2003).

The mapping process is quite involved and requires departments to go through a number of important steps (Pelfrey, 2005). First, the department must collect the data that will eventually be displayed on the computerized maps. These data typically involve calls for service, crime reports, and arrest reports. Departments routinely collect this information, and have for some time now, but for crime mapping it is critical that the data be computerized. The second component of data collection involves the actual computerized maps, which can be purchased from a number of sources. These detailed maps, which need to be updated regularly, encompass an entire city or county and include all streets as well as important geographic features (lakes, rivers, etc.) (Pelfrey, 2005). The second stage of the crime mapping process involves **geocoding,** reducing the crime events into geographic reference points. These reference points are typically the address of occurrence. For each event (call for service, arrest, etc.), an analyst must enter the address information into the GIS system so the event can be "mapped." This geocoding process can be tedious, but accuracy is absolutely critical. Mistakes that are made at this stage will result in crime events not being displayed on the maps because the GIS takes the available address and matches it with known addresses on the computerized map. If there is no known address for a match, the event will not be displayed. For example, an address geocoded as

"110 Main Street" will be successfully displayed, but "110 Mani Street" will not (unless, of course, there is a Mani Street and then the event will be mapped in the wrong location).

The third part of the mapping process involves layer assembly, or the matching of geocoded information with computerized maps. Mapping software, such as Map-Info, is used to facilitate this process. Pelfrey (2005) states that the best way to understand this process is to think about the maps as layers:

> Imagine a series of transparencies with pieces of information on each one. These transparencies can be layered on top of each other to produce different maps or coverages. The first transparency has an outline of the city. The second transparency might have an outline of all the major streets. The third transparency might have labels of these streets. A fourth transparency might describe the major geographic landmarks (rivers, forest, etc.). With these base maps, different datasets of information can be layered on top. A map of all the drunken driving accidents may be the next layer. (p. 221)

The final stage in the mapping process is the production of the actual map. Once the above steps are completed, the map can be produced for a given period of time, for given parts of town, and for given events. For example, the department could produce a map of all burglaries in the 35th precinct in the last seven days. The time frame, location, and event can be altered to produce comparative maps, assessing change in the levels of given events in the same location over time. Has the number of burglaries in the 35th precinct in the last seven days increased or decreased since the previous week? Of course, the visual depiction of events (burglaries) also allows police to examine locations to identify hotspots and/or patterns. The department can then modify patrol allocation based on the findings produced on the maps. Under the CompStat model, the NYPD uses the prevalence of crime reports over time to document whether particular strategies are effective: Did the strategy deployed last week result in a reduction of the number of burglaries in the 35th precinct? GIS systems vary in their degree of sophistication, in their styles and format, and in terms of available options for mapping data.

Pelfrey (2005) describes five uses of crime mapping for police departments:

- *Description:* The most common use of crime maps is to describe crime for a given area. A descriptive map can show the locations, times, and suspect description to an officer who might not have been on duty when the offense happened but may have knowledge about the offender or area.
- *Identification of Patterns:* An observant officer or analyst who views a series of descriptive maps is likely to start looking for patterns. Crime maps are especially useful in this endeavor. By layering offenses from different periods of time, one can conduct trend analysis [i.e., the CompStat model].
- *Interaction of Factors:* Identification of factors that are related to the production, or prevention, of crime. There are many obvious examples of correlated factors that most departments have already explored—the locations of bars and

drunk driving accidents, thefts and the locations of pawn shops, abandoned houses and drug markets.

- *Projective Analysis:* These projective, or inferential, analyses estimate where crime is likely to occur based on a series of factors. For example, if we know that drug sales are likely to increase as the number of rental properties increase in an area (as homeowners move out and slum lords take over), once a certain threshold has been passed, police can begin to pay special attention to an area to *prevent* the expected increases in drug sales.
- ***Geographic Profiling:*** Using a technique called Criminal Geographic Targeting (CGT), Kim Rossmo, a Canadian police detective and scholar, suggests that serial criminals are likely to commit their crimes in a specific pattern, which can then be analyzed to predict where they live. This technique does not produce specific addresses of offenders. Instead, it identifies neighborhoods from which offenders probably traveled to commit their crimes. (pp. 244–227)

There are, of course, limitations to the use of GIS for crime analysis. First, the maps and mapping software can be quite expensive. Police department staff must also be trained in all aspects of the mapping process. Second, the GIS mapping systems are only as good as the data that are entered. If departments do not collect or keep data in an organized and computerized system, it may require a significant amount of work just to institute data collection procedures that produce usable data. There are ethical issues as well, such as problems arising from making crime maps available to the public that show addresses where individuals were victimized (i.e., sexual assaults). Last, crime analysis using GIS is limited in its utility if the findings do not become available to officers on the street who can use the information. Otherwise, it may simply be an interesting academic exercise. From earlier discussions, it is clear that the NYPD, through its CompStat meetings, makes use of the information and develops strategies to address identified problems. Also, the Camden (NJ) police department has made crime maps available to patrol officers through desktop computers in the precinct and wireless laptops in patrol cars (Grant & Terry, 2005).

OTHER TECHNOLOGICAL ADVANCES

Computers and the Internet

Many police departments have become fully computerized, ranging from the collection and storage of calls for service and crime data, performance measurement and early warning systems, to laptops and mobile digital terminals (MDTs) in patrol cars. The use of computers has greatly expanded police departments' use of data, particularly for crime analysis, as well as the speed in which data analyses can be conducted. Like any other business, computers have helped police departments with regard to administration of the organization including management, personnel and resource allocation. Computers in patrol cars have become increasingly common, from just

5 percent of local police departments in 1990 to 40 percent in 2000 (Hickman & Reaves, 2003). MDTs allow police officers to carry out a variety of functions such as:

- Communications with supervisors and other officers.
- Preparing field notes and reports.
- Obtain information about people and places from existing databases such as vehicle records, driving records, criminal histories, and calls for service. (Stroshine, 2005)

These systems greatly enhance the information available to police officers and have led to more effective police work and increased officer safety. For example, a police officer who has pulled over a motorist for speeding can find out quickly if the car is stolen or if the person is wanted on a warrant or other charges. Rather than simply issuing a ticket, the officer can call for back-up (if needed) and take the person into custody.

Police departments, like society as a whole, have begun to use the Internet in their day-to-day activities. Many police departments, particularly larger ones, have created websites that provide a wide range of information about the departments. Websites typically include a list of personnel, especially command staff, "most wanted" pages, crime prevention information, and crime data. Some departments have made crime maps like those discussed above available via the Internet. Some websites also allow citizens to file crime reports, citizen complaints, and officer commendations online, and many have begun to use the Internet to help with recruitment. Some of the larger departments—Miami-Dade, for example—allow citizens to download application forms from the website. And last, police departments are also increasingly using email as a method for communication between officers and between officers and their supervisors. With the advent of wireless Internet and placement of computers in patrol cars, officers can email back and forth with headquarters while in the field.

Computers and the Internet have also allowed law enforcement agencies in surrounding areas—and around the country—to integrate their systems. The fragmented nature of U.S. policing, with thousands of police departments across the country who function independently, has limited the ability of police to track criminals across jurisdictional boundaries, and more generally, has hampered cooperation among different agencies. Innovations in computers have facilitated the development of "interjurisdictional communication technolody" such as offender databases and radio communications (Grant & Terry, 2005, p. 345). Examples include the NCIC (National Crime Information Center, a national criminal history database), IAFIS and CODIS (described above), and the Advanced Generation of Interoperability for Law Enforcement program (AGILE), which provides direct connections across radio systems of neighboring law enforcement agencies (Grant & Terry, 2005).

Global Positioning Systems (GPS)

Law enforcement agencies have begun using **global positioning systems (GPS)** in a number of ways, mostly notably in the tracking of offenders and officer deployment (Grant & Terry, 2005). Offender monitoring systems allow police to track the movements of parolees and high-risk offenders such as sex offenders, to prevent them from congregating near or traveling through sensitive areas (schools, etc.). Police departments have also used GPS to:

- Track stolen property and vehicles
- Track movement of patrol cars
- Provide aerial views of crime scenes
- Track suspect movelents at a crime scene (Grant & Terry, 2005)

Closed Circuit Television (CCTV)

England has implemented an extensive system of **closed circuit television (CCTV)** cameras, particularly in London, and many policd departments in the United States have begun to adopt similar public-surveillance systems. These systems are traditionally common around transportation hubs, such as airports and train stations, banks, and government buildings, but they are increasingly being placed in other public areas. Many cities have attached surveillance systems to their traffic signals, and since these camera systems feed into a central control area, they offer a comprehensive monitoring system for automobile and pedestrian traffic throughout the jurisdiction. When a crime occurs, police can then examine the feeds from the CCTVs in the area to identify potential suspects and vehicles and to track their movements. Investigators in London used CCTV footage to track the movements of suspected terrorists responsible for the subway bombings in July 2005. Although too late, federal investigators later tracked the movements of the 9/11 terrorists through footage from airport surveillance cameras.

There are limitations with CCTV and other public surveillance systems. First, it is unknown whether these systems have any preventive or deterrent effect on crime. Instead, their value lies in the evidence they provide of suspect movements *after* a crime has occurred. Second, civil rights advocates warn against a "big brother" or "Orwellian" effect, where right to privacy is threatened by such surveillance systems. Last, these systems are still prone to human error; technology can only take us so far. After studying CCTV control rooms in England, Goold (2001) concluded that the effectiveness of surveillance had less to do with technology than with the attitudes and working culture of the camera operators.

 NIBRS

The National Incident Based Reporting System (NIBRS) was implemented in 1989 by the FBI to improve upon the UCR system. NIBRS collects data for multiple offenses, multiple victims, and multiple offenders as part of one crime incident. The system also divides crimes into two categories—Group A and Group B—involving 46 different criminal offenses. In sum, NIBRS overcomes many of the limitations of the traditional UCR system and presents a much more detailed and comprehensive picture of reported crime and arrests in the United States. Unfortunately, law enforcement agencies have not been as willing to adopt NIBRS as they were to report under the UCR system. To date, only about 3,000 law enforcement agencies consistently report NIBRS data (out of the more than 17,000 agencies in the United States).

Biometrics

A **biometric** is a unique personal or physiological characteristic that is measurable and can be used to identify a specific individual. A biometric system "compares a known set of individual characteristics, which must be stored in what is known as the reference template, with the person's actual characteristics" (Champion & Hooper, 2003, p. 580). While the primary biometric used by police involves fingerprints (see above), there are a variety of other biometric systems available for use by police. These include:

- Hand geometry software that uses a three-dimensional scan and nine-digit code that accounts for finger length and palm shapes.
- Face recognition software that scans individuals in a given area and compares them to known suspects and offenders in a stored database.
- Retinal and iris scanning systems that illuminate unique features of the eye and compare the features to known individuals. (Champion & Hooper, 2003)

Civil libertarians have voiced concerns about some of these biometric systems, particularly face recognition systems that are deployed in public places with the general population. Cost and limited availability have also prohibited widespread adoption of these types of biometric systems by U.S. police departments, with the exception of fingerprinting, which remains a central feature of police investigations.

Cold Case Squads

Many police departments across the United States have developed **"cold case squads"** to reinvestigate crimes that occurred in the past (this topic too has been romanticized on television). In 2001, for example, the West Virginia State Police created a nine-person Cold Case Unit to reinvestigate murder cases and other serious crimes (Champion & Hooper, 2003). The rationale for these units is quite simple. When the cases were originally investigated, police did not have the repertoire of technological innovations, forensic science, and crime scene investigation tools that exist today. Cold case squads reopen these old investigations and pursue leads with the now-available technological innovations, such as DNA testing (as long as the evidence is still viable). Detectives in these units can now submit physical evidence for DNA testing and attempt to match that evidence against known offenders in CODIS. Champion and Hooper (2003) state that CODIS has provided investigative leads in over 1,500 cold cases.

Less-than-Lethal Weapons

Technology has led to the development of a host of non-lethal or **less-than-lethal weapons** used by police. The intent of this class of weapons is to provide police officers with viable alternatives to the firearm to control combative and assaultive suspects. These weapons seek to protect officers from injury by reducing the occurrence of physical confrontations with suspects and to protect suspects from serious injury or death that would occur if the officer was forced to fire his or her gun. There is wide range of weapons including tear gas, mace, oleoresin capsicum (pepper spray), impact weapons, ballistic rounds, foams, nets, and electronic stun devices. The most commonly used less-than-lethal weapons include the baton (original PR-24 or the newer extendable versions), mace/pepper spray, and the Taser. Little research has been conducted to study the impact or relative effectiveness of less-than-lethal weapons, with the exception of oleoresin capsicum (Nowicki, 2001). The Taser is now undergoing extensive testing because of concerns about how and when it is being used by police (i.e., against children) and because of 70 deaths that have occurred following its use. Despite the lack of research on their effectiveness, police have generally been very receptive to these new weapons and view them as an additional tool to protect lives and combat crime.

Imaging

Imaging is "the enhancement of optical capabilities for law enforcement personnel, as well as the recording and documenting of crimes as they occur" (Champion & Hooper, 2003, p. 582). Imaging serves three basic functions for police departments:

- *Accountability:* Recording and monitoring police officer behavior in the field.
- *Recording and documenting crimes:* Cameras that are placed in specific locations to record potential criminal activity or law violations (at traffic intersections to identify speeders and cars that "run through" red lights).
- *Illumination:* Night vision and thermal systems that enhance police officers' vision of potential criminal activity.

The most common type of imaging used by police involves mobile video systems, which are video cameras attached to police vehicles. These systems provide a variety of functions for police departments including increased accountability (because the police officer's behavior is recorded), documentation (the officer can activate an audio recorder and record information during a car stop or car pursuit), and as a training tool (to observe officer's behavior and offer constructive criticism). These video systems also present important evidence that can verify or contradict citizen claims in complaints against police. The video footage can serve as evidence, leading to the dismissal of false complaints, and can be introduced in civil litigation to support police officer claims (or can be subpoenaed by defense counsel to support the plaintiff's claims).

Night vision and thermal imaging devices, developed for use in the military, are now being used by police to aid in their investigations. These devices are often used during surveillance operations, and they can also be used during searches for suspects or missing persons in wooded or overgrown areas. In *Kyllo v. United States,* the U.S. Supreme Court ruled that the use of thermal imaging to examine houses for heat signatures (in this case, heat lamps used to grow marijuana) constitutes a search under the Fourth Amendment of the Constitution and thus requires a warrant. Finally, the radar flashlight is another form of imaging that can be used to detect the presence of a person behind brick, wood, plasterboard and concrete (up to 10 inches thick) based on the individual's respiration.

SUMMARY

This chapter examines the important—and often defining—role of technology in policing. Given that this book focuses specifically on current issues and controversies in policing, there are discussions throughout each chapter that highlight the importance of technological innovation. The chapter begins by describing the development of technology in U.S. policing, setting aside Kelling and Moore's (1991) model, and using Soulliere's four stages of technological advancement. The chapter then turns to a few areas in policing where technology has been absolutely crucial. These include forensic science and its impact on crime scene investigation, and crime analysis through GIS and crime mapping.

Although the seeds of forensic science were planted long ago, much of the discussion focuses on recent developments in fingerprinting, DNA, and weapons analysis. The Locard exchange principle, which serves as the foundation for crime scene investigation, states that any time two objects come together there is an exchange of matter. For the police, this exchange of matter means that offenders leave behind trace or physical evidence that can be examined and provide a link between suspects, victims, and crime scenes. The FBI now maintains computer databases holding millions of fingerprints, DNA samples, and tool marks that can be used for comparison against evidence collected at a crime scene. Importantly, technology allows these comparisons to be made in a matter of hours, rather than weeks and months. The chapter also describes the basic steps of crime scene investigation, highlighting the complex and scientific nature of the process. However, the portrayal of forensic science and crime scene investigation on television has produced many misconceptions and perhaps exaggerated the importance of their role in police work. Nevertheless, the utility of this merger of science and investigation for police has been greatly enhanced by technological developments over the last two decades.

The chapter also discusses crime analysis and the emerging role of GIS and crime mapping for police. Again, the idea of crime analysis is not new, but technology has changed the face of this effort in recent years. The development of GIS and crime mapping, in particular, has served to revolutionize the manner in which police use information and, specifically, how that information is used to determine deployment patterns. Crime mapping allows police departments to make better use of limited resources, and to assess the impact of specific strategies designed to affect crime in given locations. This type of analysis is the "engine" that drives the CompStat model, which originated in New York but has been widely adopted elsewhere (Weisburd et al., 2003).

Finally, the chapter closes with brief discussions of other innovations such as computers and the Internet, closed circuit television, NIBRS, less-than-lethal weapons, and various forms of enhanced imaging. In sum, the message of this chapter is that technology has played—and will continue to play—a defining role in U.S. policing.

KEY TERMS

Ballistics

Bertillon, Alphonse

Biometrics

Chain of custody

Closed circuit television (CCTV)

Cold case squads

Combined DNA Index System (CODIS)

Crime mapping

DNA

Fingerprints

Forensic science

Geocoding

Geographic information system (GIS)

Geographic profiling

Global positioning system (GPS)

Imaging

Integrated Automated Fingerprint Identification System (IAFIS)

Integrated Ballistics Identification System (IBIS)

Less-than-lethal weapons

Locard exchange principle

Real Time Crime Center (RTCC, NYPD)

Tool marks

DISCUSSION QUESTIONS

1. Discuss Soulliere's four stages of technological advancement.

2. What is the Locard exchange principle? Explain its importance for police.

3. Describe how technology has influenced the utility of physical evidence recovered at crime scenes, particularly fingerprints and DNA.

4. Describe the six stages of crime scene investigation.

5. Explain how police can use geographic information systems to assist in crime analysis.

6. Describe how police have used computers to run their departments more efficiently and effectively.

REFERENCES

Canter, P. (2000). Using a geographic information system for tactical crime analysis. In V. Goldsmith, P. McGuire, J. Mollenkopf, & T. Ross (Eds.), *Analyzing crime patterns: Frontiers of practice.* Thousand Oaks, CA: Sage.

Champion, D.H., & Hooper, M.K. (2003). *Introduction to American policing.* New York: McGraw-Hill.

Gaensslen, R.E., & Young, K.R. (2003). Fingerprints. In S.H. James & J.J. Nordby (Eds.), *Forensic science: An introduction to scientific and investigative techniques.* New York: CRC Press.

Goold, B. (2001). *CCTV in the United Kingdom.* Unpublished dissertation. Oxford, United Kingdom: Oxford University.

Grant, H.B., & Terry, K.J. (2005). *Law enforcement in the 21st century.* Boston: Allyn and Bacon.

Hickman, M.J., & Reaves, B.A. (2003). *Local police departments, 2000.* Washington, DC: Bureau of Justice Statistics, U.S. Department of Justice.

James, S.H., & Nordby, J.J. (Eds.). (2003). *Forensic science: An introduction to scientific and investigative techniques.* New York: CRC Press.

Kelling, G.I., & Moore, M.H. (1991). From political to reform to community: The evolving strategy of the police. In J.R. Greene & S.D. Mastrofski (Eds.), *Community policing: Rhetoric or reality.* New York: Praeger.

Miller, M.T. (2003). Crime scene investigation. In S.H. James & J.J. Nordby (Eds.), *Forensic science: An introduction to scientific and investigative techniques.* New York: CRC Press.

National Institute of Justice (NIJ). (1999). *The use of computerized crime mapping by law enforcement: Survey results.* Washington, DC: U.S. Department of Justice.

Nowicki, E. (2001, June). OC spray update. *Law and Order,* 28–29.

O'Shea, T.C., & Nicholls, K. (2003). *Crime analysis in America: Findings and recommendations.* Washington, DC: U.S. Department of Justice.

Pelfrey, W.V. (2005). Geographic information systems: Applications for police. In *Critical issues in policing* (5th ed.). Long R.G. Dunham & G.P. Alpert (Eds.), Grove, Waveland Press.

President's Commission on Law Enforcement and Administration of Justice. (1967). *Task force report: The police.* Washington DC: US Government Printing Office.

Rowe, W.F. (2003). Firearm and tool mark examinations. In S.H. James & J.J. Nordby (Eds.), *Forensic science: An introduction to scientific and investigative techniques.* New York: CRC Press.

Soulliere, N. (1999). *Police and technology: Historical review and current status.* Ottawa: Canadian Police College.

Stroshine, M.S. (2005). Information technology innovations in policing. In R.G. Dunham & G.P. Alpert (Eds.), *Critical issues in policing* (5th ed.). Long Grove, IL: Waveland Press.

Weisburd, D., Mastrofski, S.D., McNally, A.M., Greenspan, R., & Willis, J.J. (2003). Reforming to preserve: CompStat and strategic problem-solving in American policing. *Criminology and Public Policy,* 2, 421–456.

Wilson, O.W. (1941). *Distribution of police patrol force.* Chicago: Public Administration Service.

SCHOLAR'S PERSPECTIVE

Crime Mapping—A Tool for Law Enforcement

Jennifer B. Robinson, Ph.D.[1]

*Assistant Professor of Criminal Justice and Director
of the Crime Pattern Research Laboratory
Northeastern University*

Crime mapping is a natural tool for law enforcement agencies. By the mid 1990s, crime mapping became more widely used and accepted in large police departments, most notably by the New York Police Department (NYPD) and the Chicago Police Department (CPD). Crime mapping is a primary tool of CompStat, computer-aided statistical analysis, which was first introduced to policing in 1994 by the NYPD. CompStat has been heralded as a successful tool for law enforcement, leading to increased communication between departmental units and outside agencies. The use of CompStat by police is related to reductions in crime and improvement in community policing (Weisburd, Mastrofski, Greenspan, & Willis, 2004).

Improvement in the capabilities of desktop computers is a fundamental reason for increased use of crime mapping by the police. The basic component of crime mapping is the Geographic Information System (GIS). The GIS spatially codes (geocodes) data and attaches attributes to the features stored to analyze these data based on those attributes and to map the result. Since a GIS is able to organize data in a way similar to maps, it is an excellent tool for examining multidimensional and multifaceted crime problems. The GIS is able to clarify the spatial relationships that exist between general social indicators in an environment and the crime patterns that also exist there (Rich, 1995).

The GIS relies primarily (in crime mapping) on police calls for service data and arrest data, although other types of data (i.e., census data) can also be used. Computer-aided dispatch (CAD) data can be linked to GIS software to automatically record addresses of calls in a format that is recognized by the GIS software. This linkage reduces the number of errors in the data and allows for more accurate mapping.

The GIS is used by the police for crime analysis and resource planning (Craglia, Haining, & Wiles, 2000), intelligence dissemination (Ratcliffe, 2000,

---

[1]Assistant Professor and Director of the Crime Pattern Research Laboratory, Northeastern University. Ph.D. Temple University.

p. 315), and to inform residents about crime problems in their areas (Mamalian & LaVigne, 1999:3). Crime mapping is also used by police departments ". . . to support court testimony, to plan and monitor traffic flow, and to facilitate special operations and hazardous material transport . . ." (Travis & Hughes, 2002, p. 3).

A 1997 survey of law enforcement agencies in the United States found that of the departments who do not use GIS, 20 percent reported having budgeted funds to purchase hardware and software in the following year (Mamalian & LaVigne, 1999, p. 1). Of the agencies who reported using GIS to map crime, 91 percent reported mapping offense data and 52 percent reported mapping vehicle recovery data (Mamalian & LaVigne, 1999, p. 2).

By 1998, 75 percent of law enforcement agencies performed at least some crime analysis, but only 13 percent of those agencies used some form of crime mapping (Mamalian & LaVigne, 1999). In 1999, approximately 11 percent of small police departments (50 to 99 sworn personnel) and 32.6 percent of large police departments (100 or more sworn personnel) had implemented a CompStat-like program. Approximately 60 percent of departments with 500 or more sworn personnel had implemented crime mapping by 1999 (Weisburd, et al., 2004, pp. 6, 12).

Crime mapping is also used in criminological research to describe a number of different phenomena including, but not limited to, gang activity (Block, 2000; Kennedy, Braga, & Riehl, 1998; Thrasher, 1927), nonresidential burglaries (Ratcliffe, 2000), drug arrests and incidents (Olligschlaeger, 1998; Robinson & Rengert, 2005), police interventions (Robinson & Rengert, 2005), crimes of serial rapists (Hubbs, 1998; LeBeau, 1992), robbery (Block & Skogan, 1995), residential burglary (Rengert & Wasilchik, 1985; Groff & LaVigne, 2001), the home addresses of juvenile delinquents (Shaw & McKay, 1969), and home and work addresses of serial murderers (Rossmo, 2000).

Robinson's (2003) research on drug-free zones in Portland, Oregon, is an example of research that utilizes crime mapping. The research examined the effects of drug-free zones on changing spatial patterns of drug sales arrests in Portland from 1990 through 1998. The research first characterized the drug-free zone initiative as a situational crime prevention strategy with explicit geographic crime reduction objectives. It then considered how the intervention may have altered spatial patterns and levels of drug crime in Portland over time.

The analysis of possible effects of the drug-free zone strategy engaged a variety of methods, including mapping, clustering, and multilevel analytic techniques. Together, these methods were employed to identify hypothesized impacts of the drug-free zone intervention, in the context of the effects of temporal shifts and community characteristics, on drug sales arrests. This study found some support for the drug-free zones in changing both the locations and numbers of drug sales arrests in the targeted areas. Findings from the research suggest that future consideration be given to the relationship between drug-free zone status and law enforcement practices and to understanding the nature of the places where drug-free zones are employed.

For crime mapping to remain a truly useful tool for the police, the proper infrastructure to support it must exist, including an efficient method for distributing the information to the officers and management and databases that integrate accurate and useful information from a variety of sources (Manning, 2001, p. 93). The development of professional standards is also becoming important as more agencies use GIS to map crime. Funding is another key concern for the future. Funding should be increased in general in order to ensure that exposure to crime mapping and expertise in crime mapping continues to grow. Public access to crime maps and crime data is key to maintaining crime mapping as a useful tool for the police. Last, the development of methods to predict (forecast) crime patterns rather than simply display and explain current patterns will ensure that crime mapping continues to evolve and meet the changing needs of law enforcement.

REFERENCES

Block, R. (2000). Gang activity and overall levels of crime: A new mapping tool for defining areas of gang activity using police records. *Journal of Quantitative Criminology, 16,* 36–51.

Block, R., & Skogan, W.G. (1995). *Dynamics of violence between strangers: Victim resistance and outcomes in rape, robbery and assault: Final report.* Washington, DC: National Institute of Justice.

Craglia, M., Haining, R., & Wiles, P. (2000). A comparative evaluation of approaches to urban crime pattern analysis. *Urban Studies, 37,* 711–729.

Hubbs, R. (1998). The Greenway rapist case: Matching repeat offenders with crime locations. In N. LaVigne & Wartell (Eds.), *Crime mapping case studies: Successes in the field.* Washington, DC: Police Executive Research Forum (pp. 93–97).

Groff, E.R., & LaVigne, N.C. (2001). Mapping an opportunity surface of residential burglar. *Journal of Research in Crime and Delinquency,* 38(3), 257–279.

Kennedy, D.M., Braga, A.A., & Piehl, A.M. (1998). The (un)known universe: Mapping gangs and gang violence in Boston. In D. Weisburd & T. McEwen (Eds.), *Crime mapping and crime prevention.* New York: Criminal Justice Press (pp. 219–262).

Kyllo v. United States (99-8508) 533 U.S. 27 (2001).

LeBeau, J. (1992). Four case studies illustrating the spatial-temporal analysis of serial rapists. *Police Studies, 15* (3), 124–145.

Mamalian, C., & LaVigne, N. (1999). *The use of computerized crime mapping by law enforcement: Survey results.* Washington, DC: National Institute of Justice, Research Preview.

Manning, P. (2001). Technology's ways: Information technology, crime analysis and the rationalization of policing. *Criminal Justice: the International Journal of Policy and Practice, 1,* 83–103.

Olligschlaeger, A.M. (1998). Artificial neural networks and crime mapping. In D. Weisburd & T. McEwen (Eds.), *Crime mapping and crime prevention.* New York: Criminal Justice Press (pp. 313–347).

Ratcliffe, J. (2000). Implementing and integrating crime mapping into a police intelligence environment. *Policing: An International Journal of Police Science and Management, 2,* 313–323.

Rengert, G., & Wasilchik, J. (1985). *Suburban burglary: A time and a place for everything.* Springfield, IL: Charles Thomas.

Rich, T. (1995). *The use of computerized mapping in crime control and prevention programs.* Washington DC: U.S. Department of Justice, Office of Justice Programs.

Robinson, J.B. (2003). *Drug free zones, the police, locations, and trends in drug sales in Portland, Oregon, 1990–1998.* Doctoral dissertation submitted to the graduate school at Temple University.

Robinson, J.B., & Rengert, G. (2005, Fall). Drug free zones: The geographic perspective. *Western Criminology Review.* (Forthcoming).

Rossmo, D.K. (2000). *Geographic profiling.* Boca Raton, FL: CRC Press.

Shaw, C., & McKay, H. (1969). *Juvenile delinquency and urban areas: A study of rates of delinquency in relation to differential characteristics of local communities in American cities.* Chicago: University of Chicago Press.

Thrasher, F. (1927). *The gang.* Chicago: University of Chicago Press.

Travis, L., & Hughes, K. (2002). Mapping in police agencies: Beyond this point there be monsters. *Overcoming the Barriers: Crime Mapping in the 21st Century, 2,* 1–16.

Weisburd, D., Mastrofski, S., Greenspan, R., & Willis, J. (2004). *The growth of CompStat in American policing.* Washington, DC: Police Foundation.

ZUMA Press/NewsCom.com

TECHNOLOGY AND CRIME

LEARNING OUTCOMES

After reading this chapter, you should be able to answer the following questions:

- How does advancing technology produce new forms of crime?

- How does high technology provide new criminal opportunities?

- What different types of cybercriminals does this chapter describe?

- What is identity theft, and how can identities be stolen?

- What new technologies are being used in today's fight against crime?

- What is being done to combat cybercrime and to secure the Internet today?

- What are some of the personal freedoms that are threatened by today's need for advanced security?

From Chapter 13 of *Criminology Today: An Integrative Introduction*, Sixth Edition, Frank Schmalleger. Copyright © 2012 by Pearson Education, Inc. Published by Pearson Prentice Hall. All rights reserved.

Follow the author's tweets about the latest crime and justice news at **http://twitter.com/schmalleger**.

Introduction

In 2010 a new term, *cyberbanging*—referring to the use of the Internet and social networking Web sites by street gangs to tout their exploits, recruit new members, post threats, and socialize—entered the law enforcement lexicon. Videos and lyrics glorifying gang activities can be found on Facebook, MySpace, and Twitter, and some gangs have their own home pages and even run their own servers.[1] "Gangs are going to use any form of communication they can," stated George W. Knox, director of the National Gang Crime Research Center, "including Twitter, including Facebook."[2] Law enforcement experts have said that gangs sometimes use social networking sites to circumvent court injunctions forbidding members from meeting face-to-face. Not to be outdone, police agencies and criminal prosecutors have begun scouring social networking sites looking for evidence they can use to disrupt gang activities or to prosecute gang members for crimes they've committed. "Five years ago we would find evidence in a gang case on the Internet and say, 'Wow!'" Bruce Riordan, director of antigang operations for the Los Angeles City Attorney's office commented. "Well, there's no more 'Wow' anymore. It's much more routine."[3]

The Advance of Technology

Technology and crime have always been closely linked. The con artist who uses a telephone in a financial scam, the robber who uses a firearm and drives a getaway car, even the murderer who wields a knife—all employ at least rudimentary forms of technology in the crimes they commit. Technology can be employed by both crime fighters and lawbreakers. Early forms of technology, including the telegraph, telephone, and automobile, were embraced by agents of law enforcement as soon as they became available. Evidence derived from fingerprint and ballistics analysis is routinely employed by prosecutors; and emerging technologies promise to keep criminologists and law enforcement agents in step with high-tech offenders.

As technology advances, it facilitates new forms of behavior, so we can be certain that tomorrow's crimes will differ from those of today. Personal crimes of violence and traditional property crimes will continue to occur, but advancing technology will create new and as-yet unimaginable opportunities for criminals positioned to take advantage of it and of the power it will afford.

Bret and Sammy of the Sammy4U show adult Web site, which broadcasts the daily activities of nudists on the Internet. Bret and Sammy (a former stripper) work out of their home in Florida using video-streaming technology. Should the federal government regulate such productions?
Source: Preston C. Mack

A frightening preview of such possibilities was seen during the collapse of the Soviet Union when the resulting social disorganization made the acquisition of fissionable materials, stolen from Soviet stockpiles, simple for even relatively small outlaw organizations. In what is a nightmare for authorities throughout the world, Middle Eastern terrorist groups are making forceful efforts to acquire former Soviet nuclear weapons and the raw materials necessary to manufacture their own bombs, and some evidence suggests that nuclear weapons parts may have already been sold to wealthy international drug cartels and organized criminal groups, who could hoard them to use as bargaining chips against possible government prosecution.

High Technology and Criminal Opportunity

The twenty-first century has been described by some as the epitome of the postindustrial information age. Information is vital to the success of any endeavor, and certain forms of information hold nearly incalculable value. Patents on new products, chemical compositions of innovative and effective drugs, corporate marketing strategies, and financial resources of competing corporations are all forms of information whose illegitimate access might

■ **TEMPEST**

A standard developed by the U.S. government that requires that electromagnetic emanations from computers designated as "secure" to be below levels that would allow radio-receiving equipment to read the data being computed.

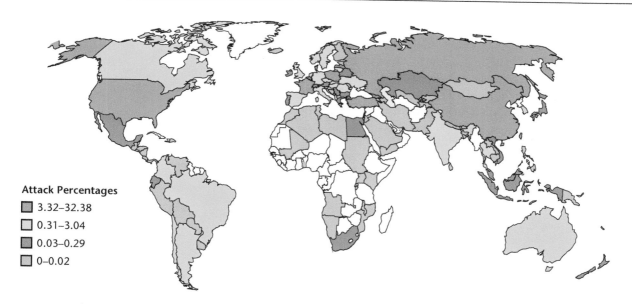

Attack Percentages
- 3.32–32.38
- 0.31–3.04
- 0.03–0.29
- 0–0.02

FIGURE 1 | Global Cyberthreat Map
Source: Courtesy Websense, Inc., *Global Threat Map 2010.*

bestow unfair advantages on unscrupulous competitors. Imagine the financial wealth and market share that would accrue to the first pharmaceutical company to patent a true AIDS cure or an effective treatment for bird flu and the potential profitability inherent in the information describing the chemical composition of that drug (especially to a competitor, who might be able to beat the legitimate originator of the substance to the patent desk or who might use stolen information in a later bid to challenge patents already issued).

High-tech criminals seeking illegitimate access to computerized information and to the databases that contain it have taken a number of routes (Figure 1). One is the path of direct access, by which office workers or corporate spies, planted as seemingly innocuous employees, violate positions of trust and use otherwise legitimate work-related entry to a company's computer resources to acquire wanted information, stealing data during business hours under the guise of normal work routines.

Another path of illegal access, called "computer trespass," involves remote access to targeted machines. Anyone equipped with a home computer and some knowledge about computer modems, telecommunications, and log-on procedures has easy access to numerous computer systems across the country because many of these systems have few (if any) security procedures in place. In one case, a Silicon Valley software company learned that a fired software developer had been using a telephone connection to enter the company's computers. By the time she was caught, she had copied several million dollars' worth of the company's programs.[5] It was later learned that the stolen software had been slated for illicit transmission to collaborators in Taiwan, and if the scheme had succeeded, thousands of pirated copies of the software would have been distributed at great financial loss to the legitimate copyright owners.

More exotic techniques used to steal data stored in computers extend to reading the electromagnetic radiation produced by electromagnetic field (EMF) decoders, which were originally developed for military purposes and can scan radio-frequency emanations generated by all types of computers; keystroke activity, internal chip-processed computations, disk reads, and the like can all be detected and interpreted at a distance under favorable conditions. Computers secured against such passively invasive practices are rarely found in the commercial marketplace because those available to commercial organizations generally conform to a security standard developed by the U.S. military called **TEMPEST**, created

> The cyberthreat is one of the most serious economic and national security challenges we face as a nation. . . .
>
> —President Barack Obama[6]

■ **hacker**
A person who uses computers for exploration and exploitation.
■ **computer virus**
A computer program designed to invade computer systems and either modify the way they operate or alter the information they store.

LIBRARY EXTRA 13–1

■ **cybercrime**
Any crime that involves the use of computers or the manipulation of digital data as well as any violation of a federal or state cybercrime statute.

under a U.S. Department of Defense program seeking to develop methods of reducing or eliminating unintended electronic emissions from computers and other electromagnetic devices. The newer wireless networking has rekindled fears of data theft.

Some cybercriminals intend simply to destroy or alter data without otherwise accessing or copying the information. Disgruntled employees, mischievous computer **hackers** (people who use a computer for exploration or exploitation), business competitors, and others have varied degrees of interest in destroying a company's records or computer capabilities.

In 1988, in the first criminal prosecution of a person accused of creating a **computer virus** (a computer program designed to secretly invade computer systems and modify the way they operate or alter the information they store), Texas programmer Donald Gene Burleson was arrested for allegedly infecting a former employer's computer with a program designed to destroy the information it contained. Since Burleson's arrest, many imitators have taken similar paths of revenge. According to Richard Baker, author of the respected *Computer Security Handbook*, "The greatest threat to your computers and data comes from inside your company, not outside. The person most likely to invade your computer is not a gawky youngster in some other part of the country but an employee who is currently on your payroll."[6]

> The person most likely to invade your computer is currently on your payroll.

Cybercrime refers to any crime that involves the use of computers or the manipulation of digital data as well as any violation of a federal or state cybercrime statute. Many argue that only those crimes that employ computer technology as central to their commission and that could not be committed without it may properly be called "cybercrimes."

A Federal Bureau of Investigation typology distinguishes among five types of computer crimes: (1) internal computer crimes, such as viruses; (2) Internet and telecommunications crimes, including illegal hacking; (3) support of criminal enterprises, such as databases supporting drug distribution; (4) computer-manipulation crimes, such as embezzlement; and (5) hardware, software, and information theft.[7] Table 1 lists these five categories, with additional examples of each. Learn more about cybercrime typologies by reading **Library Extra 13–1**.

An estimate by the U.S. Secret Service in conjunction with the Cybersecurity Center (CERT) at Carnegie Mellon University

TABLE 1 | **Categories of CyberCrime**

Internal Cybercrimes (Malware)
Trojan horses
Logic bombs
Trapdoors
Viruses
Internet and Telecommunications Crimes
Phone phreaking
Hacking
Denial of service attacks
Illegal Web sites
Dissemination of illegal material (such as child pornography)
Misuse of telephone systems
Theft of telecommunications services
Illegal eavesdropping
Illegal Internet-based gambling
Support of Criminal Enterprises
Databases to support drug distribution
Databases to support loan-sharking
Databases to support illegal gambling
Databases to keep records of illegal client transactions
Electronic money laundering
Communications in furtherance of criminal conspiracies
Computer-Manipulation Crimes
Embezzlement
Electronic fund-transfer fraud
Other fraud/phishing
Extortion threats/electronic terrorism
Hardware, Software, and Information Theft
Software piracy (Warez)
Theft of computers
Theft of microprocessor chips
Theft of trade secrets and proprietary information
Identity theft

put the annual cost of cybercrime at around $666 million.[8] Another industry group, the Computer Security Institute (CSI), surveyed 313 business organizations and found that cybercrimes

■ **software piracy**
The unauthorized and illegal copying of software programs.
■ **phone phreak**
A person who uses switched, dialed-access telephone services for exploration and exploitation.

WEB EXTRA 13-1

AMERICA'S PRIDE:
THE JOURNEY CONTINUES

Coincidence or espionage? Before the dissolution of the Soviet Union, Eastern bloc scientists succeeded in building a copy of the American space shuttle (pictured here). Experts suspected that the Soviet model would not have been possible without information stolen from U.S. research archives. Why is technology difficult to protect?
Source: Phil Sandlin-Canapress Photo Service/AP Wide World Photos (left); Terry Renna-Canapress Photo Service/AP Wide World Photos (right)

example, it is estimated that 82% has been illegally copied. Learn more about software piracy from the Business Software Alliance via **Web Extra 13–1**.

According to some experts, losses like these may be just the beginning. One technological visionary observed, "Our society is about to feel the impact of the first generation of children who have grown up using computers. The increasing sophistication of hackers suggests that computer crime will soon soar, as members of this new generation are tempted to commit more serious offenses."[13]

While the theft or damage of information represents one area of criminal activity, using different technologies in direct furtherance of criminal enterprises constitutes another and is as varied as the technologies themselves. Nuclear blackmail may represent the extreme technologically based criminal threat, whereas telephone fraud and phone phreaking are examples of low-end crimes that depend on modern technology for their commission.

One of the earliest forms of cybercrime was committed by **phone phreaks**, who use special dial-up access codes and other restricted technical information to avoid long-distance charges; some are able to place calls from pay phones, whereas others fool telephone equipment into billing other callers. "Many organizations discover they have been victims of telephone fraud only after their telephone bill arrives in a carton instead of an envelope."[14]

Another form of phone phreaking emerged that involved the electronic theft of cellular telephone numbers and access codes. Thieves armed with simple mail-order scanners and low-end computers can "literally grab a caller's phone number and identification number out of the air."[15] According to some experts, "Those numbers are [then] used to program computer

cost companies an average of $168,000 each in 2006.[9] A 2009 survey by the Ponemon Institute, however, found per-company losses as high as $6.7 million from data breaches at 43 large organizations in 2008.[10]

Software piracy, the unauthorized and illegal copying of software programs, is rampant, and global estimates of lost revenues due to pirated software (known as "Warez" in the computer underground) dwarfed those cybercrime amounts. The Software and Information Industry Association (SIIA) distinguishes among various forms of software piracy, including Internet piracy and software counterfeiting.[11]

According to the Business Software Alliance, global losses from software piracy totaled nearly $51.4 billion in 2009.[12] The Alliance notes that 43% of software in use worldwide is illegally copied. Some countries have especially high rates of illegal use. Of all the computer software in use in China, for

phishing
An Internet-based scam to steal valuable information such as credit-card numbers, Social Security numbers, user IDs, and passwords.

WEB EXTRA 13-2
LIBRARY EXTRA 13-2

chips, which are placed inside other cellular phones—or 'clones'—so the long-distance calls appear on the victim's bill."[16]

Developments in voice-over Internet protocol (VoIP) technology have made the theft of telecommunications services less lucrative but have also opened the door to new kinds of crimes. The U.S. Department of Justice (DOJ) has gone on record as being concerned about the fast growth of VoIP communications services because they make surveillance and wiretapping difficult and can facilitate "drug trafficking, organized crime and terrorism."[17] Laura Parsky, a deputy assistant attorney general in the DOJ, told investigators at a recent Senate hearing, "If legal loopholes allow criminals to use new technologies to avoid law enforcement detection, they would use these technologies to coordinate terrorist attacks, to sell drugs throughout the United States and to pass along national security secrets to our enemies." The hearing was held to consider changes to the proposed VoIP Regulatory Freedom Act, which might require telecommunications providers to build "back doors" into VoIP networks that would allow for court-ordered wiretaps to be successfully enforced.

Another form of high-technology fraud is termed **phishing** (pronounced "fishing"), a scam that uses official-looking e-mail messages to steal valuable information such as credit-card numbers, Social Security numbers, user IDs, and passwords from victims. The e-mail messages appear to come from a user's bank, credit-card company, retail store, or Internet service provider (ISP) and generally inform the recipient that some vital information in his or her account urgently needs to be updated. Those who respond are provided with an official-looking Web form on which they can enter their private financial information; once the information is submitted, it enters the phisher's database.

The Anti-Phishing Working Group—a coalition of banks and ISPs—estimated that a typical phishing scheme reaches up to 1 million e-mail inboxes and had identified more than 55,600 different phishing Web sites as of June 2007.[18] Some observers have noted that in addition to losses suffered by individuals and institutions, phishing has the potential to threaten the viability of e-commerce and to call into question the safety of all Web-based financial transactions.[19]

The federal Violent Crime Control and Law Enforcement Act of 1994 made it illegal to use interstate telephone lines in furtherance of telemarketing fraud and expanded federal jurisdiction to cover cases of insurance fraud and fraud committed against the elderly, even when such crimes do not

The world isn't run by weapons anymore, or energy, or money. It's run by ones and zeros—little bits of data—it's all electrons. . . .

—Sneakers

involve use of the mail or telephone. Learn more about telemarketing fraud and Internet-based fraud at the National Fraud Information Center via **Web Extra 13–2**; read an important criminological discourse on cybercrime via **Library Extra 13–2**.

Technology and Criminal Mischief

Not all cybercrime is committed for financial gain. Some types of cybercrime—the creation and transmission of destructive computer viruses, "worms," spyware, and other malicious forms of programming code (often called *malware*)—might better be classified as "criminal mischief." These types of activities are typically associated with young, technologically sophisticated males

Dr. Ali-Reza Ghasemi and his wife, Shahla Ghasemi, of Tampa (Florida). They lost $400,000 to an advance-fee scheme on the Internet. Advance-fee schemes (often called Nigerian e-mail fraud because many of the messages appear to come from Nigeria) promise victims a lot of money in return for advancing fees to cover legal services and transfer of funds. How can you tell when an e-mail message is likely to be a fraud?
Source: William S. Speer/Bloomberg News

TECHNOLOGY AND CRIME

1	Mydoom (2004) *Estimated damage: $38.5 billion*
2	Sobig.F (2003) *Estimated damage: $30 billion*
3	Klez (2001) *Estimated damage: $18.9 billion*
4	Sasser (2004) *Estimated damage: $14.8 billion*
5	ILOVEYOU, AKA Loveletter and The Love Bug (2000) *Estimated damage: $8.75–$15 billion*
6	Backdoor.Zagaban (2005) *Estimated damage: unknown, but thought to be in the billions of dollars*
7	Blaster (2003) *Estimated damage: $5 to $10 billion*
8	Code Red (2001) *Estimated damage: $2.6 billion*
9	Slammer (2003) *Estimated damage: unknown, but thought to total in the billions of dollars*
10	Storm (2007) *Estimated damage: $1 billion in lost productivity*

FIGURE 2 | The Ten Most Damaging Computer Viruses and Worms

References: Buzzle.com, "The Most Damage Causing Computer Viruses Revealed," http://www.buzzle.com/articles/the-most-damage-causing-computer-virusesrevealed.html (accessed October 22, 2010); Christopher Null, "The Worst Computer Viruses of All Time," Yahoo! Tech, http://tech.yahoo.com/blogs/null (accessed October 22, 2010); and George Jones, "The 10 Most Destructive PC Viruses of All Time," Tech Web, July 5, 2006, http://www.techweb.com/tech/160200005 (accessed June 26, 2010).

seeking a kind of clandestine recognition from their computer-savvy peers. Cybercrimes committed by youthful idealistic offenders may represent a new form of juvenile delinquency—one aimed at expressing dissatisfaction with the status quo (see **Library Extra 13–3**).

Computer viruses have shown signs of becoming effective terrorist-like tools in the hands of young, disaffected "technonerds" intent on attacking or destroying existing social institutions. A computer virus is simply a computer program that is designed to secretly invade computer systems, changing the way in which they run or the content they store.[20] Other types of destructive programs are called logic bombs, worms, and Trojan horse routines. Distinctions among these programs are based on either the way they infect targeted machines or the way they behave once they have managed to find their way into a computer. Figure 2 provides an overview of some of the most damaging computer viruses and worms.

Viruses may spread from one machine to another via modem or high-speed cable and digital subscriber line (DSL) connections (when files are downloaded) and through networks or direct links, DVDs, flash drives, CD-ROMs, or magnetic or optical backup media. Most viruses hide inside executable computer software, in the so-called boot sectors of storage media. Rogue codes known as "macro viruses" have also been secreted in text documents; the most famous of these, the Concept virus, affects users of Microsoft's Word software. Hypertext markup language (HTML) files, which form the backbone of the World Wide Web, may be infected with viruses lurking inside Java script or Macromedia Shockwave–generated code, and some users worry that "cookies" (small programs sent to users' machines by servers on the Web) may spread viruses.

Viruses infect not only desktop and laptop machines but also popular handheld devices, including personal digital assistants (PDAs) and mobile phones. In 2000, a Swedish software developer accidentally released Liberty Crack, a disabling software code that enters handheld devices like the Palm and Handspring products.[21]

Perhaps the most insidious forms of destructive programming making the rounds of the computer world are polymorphic viruses, which use advanced encryption techniques to assemble varied (yet entirely operational) clones of themselves and have the ability to alter themselves once they have infected a computer. This strategy is effective in circumventing most security devices that depend on scanning techniques to recognize viral signatures—when viruses change, they can no longer be recognized. In typical leapfrog fashion, as when crime-fighting techniques are overtaken and surpassed by new technologies favoring lawbreakers and then later regain ascendancy, polymorphic viruses have largely rendered signature-based antivirus-scanning technologies obsolete.

Although many hardware devices and software products now on the market offer some degree of virus protection to individual and commercial users, new viruses are constantly being created that may soon have the ability to circumvent all security procedures now in place. The only fully effective technique for

CRIME | in the NEWS

Gangs Turn to Social Media

Gang members in Oklahoma have begun using cell phones and text messaging to conduct criminal activities, and Internet social media such as Facebook and YouTube to recruit members as young as second-graders, according to a survey of gang activity in the state. The survey, a follow-up to a study in 2006, shows Oklahoma's increase in gang members the past three years is relatively small compared with the rest of the country. But youth in the state are joining gangs at an earlier age, and gang members are becoming more prone to violent actions.

As a result, the entire community, not just law enforcement, must address the gang issues facing Oklahoma, said Michael Wilds, an associate professor of criminal justice and legal studies at Northeastern State University, the author of the report. "You're seeing more recruiting done to the younger population," said Wilds.

Oklahoma City and Tulsa officers reported gang members as young as ten years old, compared with the youngest being identified as 12 years old three years ago. Oklahoma City officers reported that some youngsters are recruited as young as 8 years old, the survey states.

Officers reported Oklahoma gangs are becoming more sophisticated in conducting criminal operations by using Internet social networking sites to recruit new members. They are also using cell phones and text messaging for communications related to criminal activities such as drug manufacturing and distribution routes, the survey found.

Gang members are also using cell phones and international dialing to maintain contact with incarcerated gang members or gang members who have been deported to Mexico, Columbia, El Salvador, and other Central American countries.

State law enforcement agencies and district attorneys reported 1,026 gangs in 2009, a 2% increase compared with the 1,006 gangs reported in 2006, the report shows. Wilds also did the 2006 report.

Law officers reported 13,512 gang members in the state, an increase of 0.26% compared with the 13,477 gang members reported in 2006. Nationally, gang members increased 25%, according to the National Gang Threat Assessment.

Wilds said the 2009 numbers are more accurate because law enforcement officers have had increased training and are more accurate in identifying gang members.

"The officers that first thought four people walking around with a baseball bat were gang members—no, they were baseball players," he said.

About 60% of the police chiefs, sheriffs, and district attorneys who were mailed surveys responded, or 378 of 635, Wilds said. The survey was paid for by the state District Attorneys Council.

Similar to the 2006 survey, the newest survey shows the major criminal gangs operating in Oklahoma are the Crips, Bloods, Hoover Crips, white supremacist groups, and various Hispanic gangs.

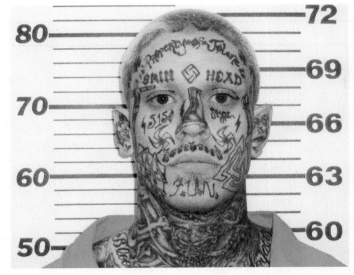

A prisoner charged with murdering a corrections officer who took him to a hospital appointment in Utah. Curtis Allgier, a neo-Nazi affiliated with the Aryan Brotherhood, is alleged to have wrestled the guard's gun from him and shot him; he then carjacked a vehicle and led police on a chase before being apprehended. Why are street gangs turning to the Internet?

Source: Splash News & Pictures/NewsCom.com

Oklahoma City and Tulsa officers reported "third-generation" gang members, where son, dad, and grandfather all belong to the same criminal gang.

Only 15 of the state's 77 counties reported no gangs in 2009 compared with 19 counties three years ago.

"They're not afraid of hurting people," Wilds said. "Now we're more aware that many of the drive-by shootings are in fact related to gang activity as well as meth activity–type drugs. Gangs are getting a little bit more lethal . . . more bold in their criminal activities."

Discussion Questions

1. How might criminal gangs make use of social media such as Facebook?

2. How might the use of social media by criminal street gangs potentially impact other users of social media?

---

avoiding viral contamination is the complete and total isolation of computer equipment—a strategy as unlikely to be maintained as it is to be implemented. Once certain forms of malicious software code have successfully invaded a computer, they can take over the machine and use it to either send additional copies of themselves or send spam and other information (including the

legitimate user's personal information) to various places on the Internet.

In 2010, international law enforcement and security officials shut down the Mariposa botnet, one of the largest networks of co-opted computers ever discovered.[22] At its peak, the Mariposa botnet, which used compromised computers to

■ **Cyber Security Enhancement Act (CSEA)**
A federal law found in the Homeland Security Act of 2002 that directs the U.S. Sentencing Commission to take specific factors into account in creating new sentencing guidelines for cybercriminals.

■ **Digital Theft Deterrence and Copyright Damages Improvement Act**
A 1999 federal law (Public Law 106–160) that amends Section 504(c) of the Copyright Act by increasing the amount of damages that could be awarded in cases of copyright infringement.

WEB EXTRA 13–3

■ **No Electronic Theft Act (NETA)**
A 1997 federal law (Public Law 105–147) that criminalizes the willful infringement of copyrighted works, including by electronic means, even when the infringing party derives no direct financial benefit from the infringement (such as when pirated software is freely distributed online).

identify and capture sensitive personal and financial information for malware creators, was able to install itself on 12.7 million computers worldwide. Learn more about botnets, computer viruses, and malware at **Web Extra 13–3**.

Cybercrime and the Law

In the early years of computer-based information systems, most U.S. jurisdictions often tried to prosecute unauthorized computer access under preexisting property-crime statutes, such as burglary and larceny laws. Because stealing a computer is quite different from simply copying or altering some of its information, juries frequently could not understand the applicability of such laws to high-tech crimes and computer criminals were exonerated. As a result, all states and the federal government developed cybercrime statutes specifically applicable to invasive activities aimed at illegally accessing stored information. Federal statutes included (1) the Cyber Security Enhancement Act of 2002;[23] (2) the Digital Theft Deterrence and Copyright Damages Improvemsent Act of 1999;[24] (3) the No Electronic Theft Act of 1997;[25] (4) the Communications Decency Act as amended; (5) the Computer Fraud and Abuse Act of 1984[26] and its amendments, especially Section 290001 of Title 29 of the Violent Crime Control and Law Enforcement Act of 1994, known as the Computer Abuse Amendments Act of 1994; (6) the Electronic Communications Privacy Act of 1986; (7) the National Stolen Property Act;[27] and (8) the Federal Wiretap Act of 1968.

Federal laws protect both equipment owned by the federal government or financial institutions and computers accessed across state lines without prior authorization.[28] The U.S. Criminal Code, Title 18, Section 1030(a), defined as criminal the intentional unauthorized access to a computer used exclusively by the federal government or any other computer used by the government when such conduct affects the government's use. It also made criminal the intentional and unauthorized access to two or more computers in different states and conduct that alters or destroys information and causes loss to one or more parties in excess of $1,000.[29] Punishment specified under federal law is a maximum sentence of five years and a fine of up to $250,000 upon conviction. The Computer Abuse Amendments Act of 1994 added the provision that "any person who suffers damage

or loss by reason of a violation of [this] section may maintain a civil action against the violator to obtain compensatory damages and injunctive relief or other equitable relief,"[30] which is intended to support civil actions in federal court against cybercriminals by those suffering monetary losses as a result of cybercrimes.

The 2002 **Cyber Security Enhancement Act (CSEA)**, part of the Homeland Security Act of 2002, directed the U.S. Sentencing Commission to take several factors into account in creating new sentencing guidelines for cybercriminals.[31] The commission should consider not only how large the financial losses caused by cybercrime were but also what the level of planning involved in the offense was, whether the crime was committed for commercial or private advantage, and whether malicious intent existed on the part of the perpetrator; cybercriminals can face life in prison if they put human lives in jeopardy. The law intends to help deter cybercrime by subjecting cybercriminals to substantial criminal penalties, makes it easier for law enforcement agencies to obtain investigative information from ISPs, and shields from lawsuits ISPs that hand over user information to law enforcement officers without a warrant—but that information should pose an immediate risk of injury or death.

> The 2002 Cyber Security Enhancement Act (CSEA), provides substantial new penalties for cybercriminals.

The 1999 **Digital Theft Deterrence and Copyright Damages Improvement Act** amended Section 504(c) of the Copyright Act and increased the amount of damages that could be awarded in cases of copyright infringement, a crime intimately associated with software piracy. Enacted in 1997, the **No Electronic Theft Act (NETA)** criminalized the willful infringement of copyrighted works, including by electronic means, even when the infringing party derives no direct financial benefit from the infringement (such as when pirated software is freely distributed online). In keeping with requirements of NETA, the U.S. Sentencing Commission enacted amendments to its guidelines on April 6, 2000, to increase penalties associated with electronic theft.

■ **Communications Decency Act (CDA)**
A 1996 federal statute labeled Title 5 of the federal Telecommunications Act of 1996 (Public Law 104–104, 110 Stat. 56) that seeks to protect minors from harmful material on the Internet and that criminalizes the knowing transmission of obscene or indecent messages to any recipient under 18 years of age. In 1997, in *Reno* v. *ACLU* (521 U.S. 844), the U.S. Supreme Court found the bulk of the CDA to be unconstitutional, ruling that it contravenes First Amendment free speech guarantees.

In 1996, President Bill Clinton signed into law the **Communications Decency Act (CDA)**, Title 5 of the Telecommunications Act of 1996, to protect minors from harmful material on the Internet.[32] A portion of the CDA criminalized the knowing transmission of obscene or indecent messages to any recipient under 18 years of age. Another section prohibited the sending or displaying to a person under age 18 any message "that, in context, depicts or describes, in terms patently offensive as measured by contemporary community standards, sexual or excretory activities or organs." The law provided acceptable defenses for those who took "good faith effective actions" to restrict access by minors to prohibited communications and for those who restricted such access by requiring certain designated forms of age proof, such as a verified credit card or an adult identification number.

Shortly after the law was passed, the American Civil Liberties Union (ACLU) and a number of other plaintiffs filed suit against the federal government, challenging the constitutionality of the law's two provisions relating to the transmission of obscene materials to minors. In 1996, a three-judge federal district court entered a preliminary injunction against enforcement of both challenged provisions, ruling that they contravened First Amendment guarantees of free speech. The government then appealed to the U.S. Supreme Court. The Court's 1997 decision in ***Reno* v. *ACLU*** upheld the lower court's ruling and found that the CDA's "indecent transmission" and "patently offensive display" provisions abridged "the freedom of speech" protected by the First Amendment.[33] Justice John Paul Stevens wrote for the majority: "It is true that we have repeatedly recognized the governmental interest in protecting children from harmful materials. But that interest does not justify an unnecessarily broad suppression of speech addressed to adults."

Most other federal legislation aimed at keeping online pornography away from children has not fared any better when

The cybercrime laws of individual states contain great variation.

reviewed by the Court, so it remains to be seen whether the 1998 Child Online Protection Act (COPA) can be modified to meet Court muster. Although the Children's Internet Protection Act (CIPA), which requires public and school libraries receiving certain kinds of federal funding to install pornography filters on their Internet-linked computers, was approved, most observers acknowledge that the Court has placed the Internet in

the same category as newspapers and other print media, where almost no regulation is permitted.

The cybercrime laws of individual states are rarely modeled after federal legislation, so they contain great variation. Texas law criminalized "breach of computer security," which occurs when an individual "knowingly accesses a computer, computer network, or computer system without the effective consent of the owner [or when someone] intentionally or knowingly gives a password, identifying code, personal identification number, debit card number, bank account number, or other confidential information about a computer security system to another person without the effective consent of the person employing the computer security system to restrict access to a computer, computer network, computer system, or data."[34]

Virginia specifically defined *cybercrime* according to the following categories: "theft of computer services, computer invasion of privacy, computer trespass, computer fraud, [and] personal trespass by computer" (via which physical injury accrues to someone by virtue of unauthorized access to a computer, as may happen in the case of disruption of utility services).[35]

Ambiguities in existing cybercrime laws, complicated by rapid changes in technology, can make it difficult even to tell when a crime has occurred. In 1995, 20-year-old University of Michigan student Jacob Alkhabaz (aka Jake A. Baker) became the first person ever indicted for writing something on the Internet when he was arrested by the FBI and charged with five counts of interstate transmission of threats;[36] he had posted a series of stories on the Internet about his fantasy of torturing, raping, and murdering a female classmate. His messages contained the following: "Just thinking about it anymore doesn't do the trick. I need to do it." "Torture is foreplay, rape is romance, snuff (killing) is climax."[37]

Although Alkhabaz might have been punished by a sentence of up to five years in prison, Detroit U.S. District Judge Avern Cohn threw out the charges after Alkhabaz had spent 29 days in jail, ruling that Alkhabaz's violent-sounding Internet writings were protected under the free speech clause of the U.S. Constitution.[38] Alkhabaz had been charged with communicating threats rather than cybercrime because his activities were not specifically covered under federal cybercrime laws. If they had been, a different verdict might have resulted.

Future illegitimate activities employing computer equipment may not always be adequately covered by existing laws, but

■ **computer-related crime**
An illegal act using computer technology in its perpetration, investigation, or prosecution.

■ **computer abuse**
An unlawful incident associated with computer technology in which a victim suffers loss or a perpetrator reaps benefit.

WEB EXTRA 13-4
LIBRARY EXTRA 13-4

■ **cyberspace**
The computer-created matrix of virtual possibilities, including online services, in which human beings interact with one another and with the technology itself.

some crimes committed with the use of a computer may be more appropriately prosecuted under traditional laws. For that reason, some experts distinguish among cybercrime (defined earlier) and two other types. **Computer-related crime** is "any illegal act for which knowledge of computer technology is involved for its investigation, perpetration, or prosecution," whereas **computer abuse** is said to be "any incident without color of right associated with computer technology in which a victim suffered or could have suffered loss and/or a perpetrator by intention made or could have made gain."[39] Learn more about digital crime of all kinds from the Computer Crime and Intellectual Property Section (CCIPS) of the Criminal Division of the DOJ via **Web Extra 13-4**.

A Profile of Cybercriminals

In 1997, FBI agents arrested Adam Quinn Pletcher, age 21, and charged him with trying to extort $5.25 million from Microsoft founder and chairman, Bill Gates.[40] Pletcher, a loner from Illinois who spent hour after hour in front of his computer, allegedly sent several letters to Gates demanding money and threatening to kill him or his wife, Melinda, if Gates did not respond to an America Online service known as "NetGirl." The service, an online dating forum, was to serve as a secure medium for the exchange of messages between Gates and the extortionist. FBI agents nabbed Pletcher after he sent a disk to Gates that held erased files containing the names of Pletcher's parents. By all accounts, Pletcher was a hacker—a technologically sophisticated loner.

It is from hacker subculture that cybercriminals tend to come because hackers and hacker identities are the products of **cyberspace**, a realm that exists only within electronic networks where computer technology and human psychology meet. For many hackers, cyberspace provides the opportunity for impersonal interpersonal contact, technological challenges, and game playing. Fantasy role-playing games are popular among hackers and may engross many "wave riders," who appear to prefer what is called "virtual reality" to the external physical and social worlds around them: "Cyberspace is hacker heaven."[41]

No one knows the actual identity of many of these people, but computer-security experts have come up with a rough profile of the average hacker.[42] He is a male between the ages

Simon Vallor, the 22-year-old Welsh Web site designer who was sentenced to two years in prison in 2002 for creating mass-mailer computer viruses. His viruses, named Gokar, Redesi, and Admirer, infected more than 27,000 computers and spread to 42 different countries. Should those who write malicious computer code be sent to prison?
Source: Stefan Rousseau/PA Photos

of 16 and 25 who lives in the United States, is a computer user but not a programmer, and hacks with software written by others; his primary motivation is to gain access to Web sites and computer networks, not to profit financially (see the Who's to Blame box).

The History and Nature of Hacking

Some authors have suggested that computer hacking began with the creation of the interstate phone system and direct dialing, implemented by AT&T in the late 1950s.[43] Early switching devices used audible tones that were easily duplicated by electronics hobbyists, and "blue boxes" capable of emulating such tones quickly entered the illicit marketplace. A form of illegal telephone access that has come to the fore is voice-mail hacking. Private voice-mail boxes used for storing verbal messages have become the targets of corporate raiders and young vandals alike. See **Library Extra 13-4** for a discussion of self-defense in cyberspace.

WHO'S TO BLAME—The Individual or Society?

Criminal Activity or Mischievous Gaming?

Late last year, Kelvin Mutchnak was arrested and charged under federal law with interfering with the operation of computers owned by the federal government. The computers, mostly Apple Mac Pros, ran Apple's latest operating system, popularly referred to as Mac OS X Snow Leopard, and were located in Veterans Administration (VA) hospitals across the country.

Mutchnak was especially taken with the long-standing popular impression that Apple's operating system was secure and impenetrable—a myth that computer hackers had long known was untrue, but which Apple corporate officials had done little to dispel. The feeling of those who worked for Apple, Mutchnak concluded, was that the popular myth could help sell computers. Nonetheless, most hackers continued to focus their efforts on Microsoft's Windows operating system because of its greater popularity, and because it was easier to hack. Since the advent of Windows Vista in 2006, however, and with the introduction of Macintosh computers able to dual-boot both Vista and Leopard, and able to run both simultaneously, attention in the hacker community had increasingly turned to identifying backdoors into the Macintosh operating system.

Soon Mutchnak was devoting all of his spare time to dispelling Apple's myth of invincibility, and to writing malware—malicious software code—that could successfully invade almost any of Apple's higher-end computers that were connected to the Internet.

After writing a malicious script that he could insert into a tiny QuickTime video, Mutchnak sent the video as an e-mail attachment to VA hospital computers, making the e-mail look as though it contained administrative data that would be of significance to people in charge of the facilities. Although the e-mail had to be opened and the video file clicked on, and although the person reading the e-mail had to be logged in under an administrative account (most, he found, were), Mutchnak's plan was very successful, and soon most Macintosh computers in federally run hospitals across the country were infected. Unfortunately for Mutchnak, however, federal anticyberterrorism officials had been running a drill responding to a mock cyberterrorism attack when his e-mail made its way onto the Net. Within minutes of its release, Mutchnak's malicious e-mail had been traced to the IP address assigned to his home by his ISP.

A warrant for his arrest was drawn up, and Mutchnak was arrested by federal agents who charged him with violating various federal computer crime laws, including one meant to deter terrorists.

Think about it:

1. Do you believe that Mutchnak saw his activity as criminal? As terrorist activity? If not, how did he perceive it?

2. Was Mutchnak, as he claimed, doing a service by showing weaknesses in parts of the nation's computer infrastructure?

3. Might there have been other ways for Mutchnak to make his point? Would those ways have been as effective as the computer mischief in which he engaged? Why or why not?

Note: Who's to Blame boxes provide fictionalized critical thinking opportunities, and are not actual cases.

Voice-mail fraud, another form of telephone crime, involves schemes in which mailbox access codes are shared in such a way that callers to toll-free numbers can leave messages for one another in voice-mail boxes, thereby avoiding personal long-distance charges.[44] Companies that provide access to voice-mail systems through toll-free numbers often learn of the need for access-code security only after they have been victimized by such schemes.

Hackers can be distinguished both by their purpose and by their method of operation, but such categorization is descriptive; distinctions can also be made on the basis of personality and lifestyle. Some experts have suggested that hackers can be grouped according to psychological characteristics:[45]

- **Pioneers**. Individuals who are fascinated by the evolving technology of telecommunications and explore it without knowing exactly what they are going to find are called pioneers; few hard-core criminals are found among this group.

- **Scamps**. Hackers with a sense of fun, with no intention to harm, are referred to as scamps.

- **Explorers**. Explorers are hackers motivated by their delight in discoveries associated with breaking into new computer systems—the farther away geographically such systems are from the hackers' physical locations or the more secure such systems are, the greater the excitement associated with breaking into them.

- **Game players**. Game players enjoy defeating software or system copy protection and may seek to illegally access computer systems with games to play. Hacking itself becomes a game for this sort of hacker.

- **Vandals**. Malicious hackers who deliberately cause damage with no apparent gain for themselves are called vandals. The original 414 Gang in Milwaukee, which broke into the Sloan-Kettering Cancer Institute's computers and wiped out patient records, is an example of this type of hacker.

WEB EXTRA 13-5

- **Addicts**. Classic computer nerds who are addicted to hacking and to computer technology are addicts. They may also be addicted to illicit drugs (some hacker bulletin board systems post information on drugs as well as on modems, passwords, and vulnerable systems).

Psychologist Percy Black argued for the existence of an underlying theme in all cases of hacking, calling it "the search for a feeling of power, possibly stemming from a deep-seated sense of powerlessness."[46] Hacking may serve as compensation for feelings of personal inferiority; by challenging the machine and by winning against machine culture, hackers go through a kind of rite of passage into adulthood, whereby they prove themselves capable of success.

Because most hackers are young adolescent males, it is important to realize that "their other favorite risky business is the time-honored adolescent sport of trespassing. They insist on going where they don't belong. But then teen-age boys have been proceeding uninvited since the dawn of human puberty. It seems hard-wired. The only innovation is in the new form of the forbidden zone and the means of getting in it."[47]

Unfortunately, not all computer hackers are simply kids trying their hand at beating technological challenges. Many are "high-tech computer operators using computers to engage in unlawful conduct."[48] Learn more about hackers and information security at the CERT Coordination Center, which can be reached via **Web Extra 13–5**.

Many technologically sophisticated professional criminals are also operating today by using diverse types of high technology for serious criminal activity, the theft of money being one major goal. Some years ago, technologically sophisticated thieves in New York City rolled a fake automated teller machine (ATM) into the local Buckland Hills shopping mall. Although the machine did not dispense money, it did record the information contained on the magnetic strips of legitimate banking cards as well as the personal information numbers (PINs) inserted by would-be customers. Armed with the necessary codes for legitimate accounts, the thieves then fabricated their own cards and used them to withdraw thousands of dollars from real ATM machines across the city.

Most people probably think of money as dollar bills, but money today is really only information—information stored in a computer network, located within the physical confines of a bank but also as bits and bytes of data on ISP machines. Typical financial customers give little thought to the fact that very little "real" money is held by their bank, brokerage house, mutual fund, or commodities dealer, nor do they consider the threats to their financial well-being by activities like electronic theft or the sabotage of existing accounts. Unfortunately, that threat is very real. Cybercriminals who are equipped with enough information or are able to ferret out the data they need can quickly and easily send vast amounts of money anywhere in the world. Although billions of dollars' worth of electronic transactions occur every day, no reliable estimates exist on the losses suffered in such transactions due to the activities of technologically adept criminal perpetrators because sophisticated high-tech thieves are so effective at eluding apprehension and even detection that reliable loss figures are impossible to ascertain.

Web sites can also facilitate criminal activity. U.S. Customs Service agents involved in Operation Longarm carried out raids on child pornographers and suspected pedophiles in 18 states using names taken from a pedophile site. According to the Customs Service, the computerized transmission of illegal pornography among pedophiles is rapidly becoming more popular than smutty magazines.[49] On June 18, 2007, British police, aided by U.S. investigators, arrested 200 suspects in an Internet pornography ring that streamed live video of children being sexually abused. The ring involved more than 700 suspects worldwide, and authorities in 35 countries participated in the investigation; 31 children were rescued as a result of the operation, some of them only a few months old.[50]

> Money today is really only information stored in a computer network as bits and bytes of data.

Cybercrime as a Form of White-Collar Crime

A number of analysts have suggested that cybercrime is merely a new form of white-collar crime or maybe its ultimate expression. Donn B. Parker, author of the National Institute of Justice (NIJ) *Computer Crime: Criminal Justice Research Manual*, compared white-collar criminals with computer criminals, stating that both share certain "common criminal behavior-related issues":[51]

- Both types of acts are often committed through nonviolent means, although certain industrial-, consumer-, and environment-related crimes have life-threatening consequences.

- Access to computers or computer storage media, through employment-related knowledge or technical skills, is often needed.

- These acts generally involve information manipulations that either directly or indirectly create profits or losses.

■ **identity theft**
The unauthorized use of another individual's personal information to commit fraud.

- These crimes can be committed by an individual, by several individuals working in collusion, or by organizations, with the victims in the last case ranging from individual clients to customers to employees in other organizations.

See the Criminal Profiles box for the story of a convicted hacker who became an author.

According to Parker, cybercrime and white-collar crime also share the following similarities:

- These crimes are difficult to detect, with discovery often started by accident or by customer complaint rather than as the result of direct investigation.
- The general public views many of these acts as less serious than crimes involving physical violence.
- These crimes cost individuals, organizations, and society large amounts of money and other resources.
- Prevention of these crimes requires a combination of legal, technical, managerial, security, and audit-monitoring controls.

Identity Theft

Identity theft—the misuse of another individual's personal information to commit fraud—is a special kind of larceny that often makes headlines and that appears to be rapidly growing in both scope and frequency.[52] It involves obtaining credit, merchandise, or services by fraudulent personal representation.

The DOJ notes that "the advent of information technology and computer literacy has joined with the accessibility of personal information to produce a rapid increase in identity theft as the method of choice for criminals."[53] The DOJ also says that the lack of severe consequences and the inconsistencies in investigation and in prosecution have all added to the value of identity theft for offenders. Individuals often learn that they are victims of identity theft only after they are denied credit or employment or when a debt collector seeking payment for a debt they did not incur contacts them. One of the most threatening aspects of identity theft is its potential relationship to international terrorism, and even where terrorism is not involved, identity theft could be used by transnational crime rings.

The misuse of stolen personal information can be classified into two broad categories: existing account fraud and new account fraud. *Existing account fraud* occurs when thieves obtain account information involving credit, brokerage, banking, or utility accounts that are already open; it is typically less costly but more prevalent. A stolen credit card may lead to thousands of dollars in fraudulent charges, but the card generally will not provide a thief with enough information to establish a false identity. Moreover, most credit-card companies do not hold consumers liable for fraudulent charges, and federal law caps liability of victims of credit-card theft at $50.

In *new account fraud*, identity thieves use personal information, such as a Social Security number, birth date, and home address, to open new accounts in the victim's name, make charges indiscriminately, and then disappear. While this type of identity theft is less likely to occur, it imposes much greater costs and hardships on the victim. In addition, identity thieves sometimes use stolen personal information to obtain government, medical, or other benefits to which the criminal is not legally entitled.

In addition to the losses that result when identity thieves misuse existing accounts or fraudulently open new accounts, monetary costs of identity theft include indirect costs to businesses for fraud prevention and for mitigation of any harm (for example, mailing notices to consumers and upgrading systems). Individual victims often suffer indirect financial costs, such as paying the costs incurred in civil litigation initiated by creditors and overcoming the many obstacles they face in obtaining or retaining credit. Victims of nonfinancial identity theft such as health-care-related or criminal-record fraud, face other types of harm and frustration.

Consumers' fears of becoming victims of identity theft can also harm the digital economy. In a 2006 online survey conducted by the Business Software Alliance and Harris Interactive, nearly 30% of adults interviewed said that security fears caused them to shop online less or not at all during the 2005–2006 holiday season.[54] A Cyber Security Industry Alliance survey found that 48% of consumers avoided making purchases on the Internet because they feared that their financial information might be stolen.[55]

> Consumers' fears of becoming victims of identity theft can harm the digital economy.

Identity theft became a federal crime in 1998 with the passage of the Identity Theft and Assumption Deterrence Act, which made it a crime whenever anyone "knowingly transfers or uses, without lawful authority, a means of identification of another person with the intent to commit, or to aid or abet, any unlawful activity that constitutes a violation of federal law, or that constitutes a felony under any applicable state or local law."[56]

The 2004 Identity Theft Penalty Enhancement Act added two years to federal prison sentences for criminals convicted of using stolen credit-card numbers and other personal data to commit crimes.[57] It also prescribed prison sentences for those who use identity theft to commit other crimes, including terrorism, and increased penalties for defendants who exceed or abuse the authority of their position to unlawfully obtain or misuse means of personal identification.

CRIMINAL | PROFILES

Kevin Mitnick

At the time of his arrest in February 1995, Kevin Mitnick was the most wanted computer criminal in U.S. history. His crimes included wire fraud, computer fraud, and wire communication interception, and the cost to his victims included millions of dollars in lost licensing fees, marketing delays, lost research and development, and the costs of repairing compromised computer systems.[i]

Cloned cellular telephones, hacker software programs, "sniffer" devices, and so-called social engineering were the tools Mitnick used to conduct the computer crime spree that launched a lengthy investigation beginning in 1992. The evidence amassed by the FBI during its three-year probe was sufficient to force Mitnick to accept a plea bargain rather than risk more severe penalties by going to trial.[ii] His corporate victims included a number of Fortune 500 companies, and he used University of Southern California computer systems to hide software code and obscure his identity.

Born August 6, 1963, and a product of a blue-collar upbringing in California's San Fernando Valley, Mitnick's 1981 juvenile arrest for stealing computer manuals led to his being placed on probation. The experience had little deterrent effect, however, as evidenced by his subsequent arrests in 1989 (for possession of unauthorized access devices) and in 1992 (for allegedly hacking into California Department of Motor Vehicles computers).[iii]

It is said that Mitnick served as the inspiration for the 1983 film *War Games* by breaking into the U.S. Department of Defense's North American Defense Command (NORAD) computers in 1982.[iv]

An intriguing element of Mitnick's case was the manner in which he was finally caught. Computer expert Tsutomu Shimomura, infuriated after Mitnick hacked into and stole information from his home computer, employed a dramatic cybersleuthing effort to track Mitnick down, resulting in Mitnick's arrest by the FBI in a Raleigh, North Carolina, apartment complex.

As a result of his 1995 arrest, Mitnick spent more than five years in prison, with more than eight months of it in solitary confinement. Now in his early forties, a significantly matured Mitnick has done a 180-degree turnaround in his approach to computer security. On March 1, 2000, he testified before the U.S. Senate's Governmental Affairs Committee, during which he suggested that the millions of dollars corporations spend on firewalls and secure access devices are negated by the "the weakest link in the security chain: the people who

Hacker-turned-author Kevin Mitnick posing for a portrait in 2002 in Las Vegas. Barred by the terms of his probation from using computers, ex-convict Mitnick turned to writing about them, baring the tricks of his former trade of hacking in a book titled *The Art of Deception.* Mitnick was granted an exemption to use a computer to write his book. What is he doing today?
Source: Joe Cavaretta/AP Wide World Photos

use, administer and operate computer systems."[v] Mitnick regaled the committee with tales of his use of "social engineering" (what he defines as "using manipulation, influence, and deception to get a trusted insider to release information and to perform some sort of action item") that enables a hacker to successfully attack the insider's own computer system.

Mitnick now heads up a highly successful computer consulting firm which specializes in advising on computer security issues. He suggests that it is easier to hack today than it was years ago, citing social engineering as still an extraordinarily effective technique for computer exploit. Mitnick's message is clear: Notwithstanding tremendous advances in both hardware and software security measures, the weak link is still the human element.[vi]

Notes

i. "Kevin Mitnick Sentenced to Nearly Four Years in Prison," U.S. Department of Justice Press Release, August 9, 1999; and "Computer Hacker Ordered to Pay Restitution to Victim Companies Whose Systems Were Compromised," U.S. Attorney's Office, Central District of California, August 9, 1999, http://www.cybercrime.gov/mitnick.htm (accessed June 2, 2010).

ii. Ibid.

iii. John Christensen, "The Trials of Kevin Mitnick," CNN, March 18, 1999, http://www.cnn.com/SPECIALS/1999/mitnick.background (accessed June 2, 2010).

iv. Ibid.

v. Elizabeth Wasserman, "Mitnick Schools Feds on Hacking 101," CNN, March 3, 2000, http://archives.cnn.com/2000/TECH/computing/03/03/mitnick.the.prof/mitnick.the.prof.html (accessed June 2, 2007).

vi. "A Convicted Hacker Debunks Some Myths," CNN, October 13, 2005, http://www.cnn.com/2005/TECH/internet/10/07/kevin.mitnick.cnna (accessed June 2, 2010).

The Incidence of Identity Theft

In 2007, the Bureau of Justice Statistics (BJS) reported its second statistical overview of identity theft in information derived from the National Crime Victimization Survey (NCVS).[58] For statistical-reporting purposes, BJS defined *identity theft* to include the following three behaviors: (1) the unauthorized use or attempted use of existing credit cards; (2) the unauthorized use or attempted use of other existing accounts such as checking accounts; and (3) the misuse of personal information to obtain new accounts or loans or to commit other crimes.

BJS surveyors found that at least one member of 5.5% of all households had been the victim of identity theft during the previous year, and the most common type of identity theft uncovered was the unauthorized use of credit cards, experienced by 2.96 million households in the 12-month period covered by the survey. About 1.6 million households reported being victimized by the theft of an existing account other than a credit-card account, such as the use or attempted use of a cell phone account, bank account, or debit/check card account without permission. Approximately 1 million households were victimized by the use of personal information to obtain new credit cards or loans, run up debts, open other accounts, or otherwise commit theft, fraud, or some other crime; the identity theft experienced by more than 790,000 households encompassed two or more types of thefts.

The BJS survey also revealed that about one in six victimized households had to pay higher interest rates as the result of identity theft, and one in nine households was denied phone or utility ser-

At least one member of 5.5% of all households has been the victim of identity theft during the previous year.

vice as a consequence of being victimized. About 7% of victimized households were turned down for insurance or had to pay higher rates, 5% became the subject of a civil suit or judgment, 4% became the subject of a criminal investigation, and about 20% reported other kinds of problems.

Among households sustaining a loss whose amount was known, about 5% reported losing more than $5,000, but 66% reported losing less than $500; the average amount of money involved in any type of identity theft in which there was a loss was put at $1,620. For households experiencing misuse of personal information, the average loss was $4,850, and it was $2,460 for households experiencing multiple types of theft at the same time. Learn more about identity theft from the Bureau of Justice Assistance at **Library Extra 13–5**.

Who Are Identity Thieves?

Unlike some groups of criminals, identity thieves cannot be readily classified because victims are not usually in a position to know who stole or misused their information.[59] Based on the Federal Trade Commission (FTC) survey of identity theft, only 14% of victims claim to know the perpetrator, who may be a family member, friend, or in-home employee. Identity thieves can act alone or as part of a criminal enterprise, and each poses unique threats to the public.

According to law enforcement agencies, identity thieves often have no prior criminal background and sometimes have pre-existing relationships with the victims. Identity thieves have been known to prey on people they know, including coworkers, senior citizens for whom they are serving as caretakers, and even family members. Some identity thieves rely on unsophisticated techniques, such as stealing mail from homeowners' mailboxes or taking trash containing financial documents, and in some jurisdictions, identity theft by illegal immigrants has resulted in passport, employment, and Social Security fraud. Occasionally, small clusters of individuals with no significant criminal records work together in a loosely knit fashion to obtain personal information and even to create false or fraudulent documents.[60]

Law enforcement agencies around the country have observed a steady increase in the involvement of groups and organizations of repeat offenders or career criminals in identity theft. Some of these groups—including national gangs such as the Hell's Angels and MS-13—are formally organized, have a hierarchical structure, and are well known to law enforcement because of their long-standing involvement in other major crimes such as drug trafficking. Other groups are more loosely organized but have taken advantage of the Internet to contact each other and then organize and coordinate their identity thefts more efficiently; members of these groups often are located in different countries and communicate primarily via the Internet. Some groups have a real-world connection with one another and share a nationality or ethnic group.

What Can Be Done about Identity Theft?

In 2006, the federal Office of Community Oriented Policing Services (the COPS Office), in conjunction with the Major Cities Chiefs Association (MCCA), released a report titled *A National Strategy to Combat Identity Theft*, which is available as **Library Extra 13–6**. It recognized identity theft as a pervasive crime that requires cooperation among law enforcement agencies, the federal and state governments, and citizens in order to

WEB EXTRA 13-6
LIBRARY EXTRA 13-7
LIBRARY EXTRA 13-8
LIBRARY EXTRA 13-9

develop a comprehensive and effective response and suggested six components of an effective national strategy for preventing and responding to the crime of identity theft:

1. **Public-awareness campaigns.** Public education has proven highly successful in the past to curtail national levels of alcohol and cigarette use.

2. **Victim assistance.** Frequently, victimization focuses on dollar loss and dismisses the emotional trauma or time needed to restore records and identity.

3. **Partnership and collaboration.** A staple for police departments, private industry, and others following the September 11 terrorist attacks, collaboration is also vital to the issue of identity theft. Many permutations and combinations are available when one considers the different functions within a jurisdiction—a single function across jurisdictions, such as a statewide or regional collaboration, or multiple functions across several jurisdictions.

4. **Legislation.** Legislative action is needed for several reasons: Private industry may not be willing to enact certain protections without a federal government mandate, or local police agencies may overlook the significance of taking identity theft reports, no matter how minor, to feed into a larger data bank for analysis.

5. **Information protection.** Protecting information is critical, and those combating identity theft should be as imaginative as needed.

6. **Training.** There was no doubt throughout the project that training is paramount, especially for police officers, investigators, and prosecutors.

On May 10, 2006, President George W. Bush established the President's Task Force on Identity Theft via Executive Order 13402. In forming the task force, the president called for a coordinated approach among government agencies to combat identity theft and to craft a strategic plan to make the federal government's efforts regarding identity theft more effective and efficient in the areas of awareness, prevention, detection, and prosecution. The task force, chaired by (then) Attorney General Alberto R. Gonzales and cochaired by FTC Chairman Deborah Platt Majoras, released its report in mid-2007 that said, "Identity theft depends on access to consumer data. Reducing the opportunities for thieves to get the data is critical to fighting the crime. Government, the business community, and consumers have roles to play in protecting data."[61] The task force made a number of recommendations to combat identity theft:

- Decrease the unnecessary use of Social Security numbers in the public sector by developing alternative strategies for identity management.

- Establish national standards to require private-sector entities to safeguard the personal data they compile and maintain and to provide notice to consumers when a breach occurs that poses a significant risk of identity theft.

- Have federal agencies implement a broad, sustained awareness campaign to educate consumers, the private sector, and the public sector on deterring, detecting, and defending against identity theft.

- Create a National Identity Theft Law Enforcement Center to allow law enforcement agencies to coordinate their efforts and information more efficiently and to investigate and prosecute identity thieves more effectively.

- Ensure that government agencies work together to provide victims with the knowledge, tools, and assistance needed to minimize the damage and begin the recovery process.

- Provide specialized training about victim recovery to first responders and others offering direct assistance to victims of identity theft.

- Create and distribute an ID Theft Victim Statement of Rights.

- Amend criminal restitution statutes to ensure that victims recover the value of time spent in trying to remediate the harms suffered.

- Assess whether to implement a national system that allows victims to obtain an identification document for authentication purposes.

Learn more about identity thieves and how they operate via the Identity Theft Resource Center at **Web Extra 13–6**, and read about how to prevent your own victimization and what to do if your identity is stolen via **Library Extras 13–7**, **13–8**, and **13–9**.

Technology in the Fight against Crime

Technology is a double-edged sword: It arms evildoers with potent new weapons of crime commission, yet it provides police agencies and criminal justice personnel with powerful tools useful in the battle against crime. Criminally useful or evasive technologies and law enforcement capabilities commonly leapfrog one another. Consider traffic radar, which has gone from early always-on units through trigger-operated radar devices to today's sophisticated laser-based speed-measuring apparatus—each change being an attempt by enforcement agencies to keep a step ahead of increasingly sophisticated radar-detection devices marketed to drivers.

> ■ **DNA profiling**
> The use of biological residue found at a crime scene for genetic comparisons in aiding the identification of criminal suspects.

Although cutting-edge laser units are invisible to most radar detectors, laser radar detectors *do* exist; their usefulness is open to debate because they generally alert the speeding driver too late. Radar-jamming devices and laser jammers are also now used by people apparently intent on breaking speed-limit laws. Not to be outdone, suppliers to law enforcement agencies have created radar-detector detectors, which are used by authorities in states where radar detectors have been outlawed.[62]

Other potent technologies in law enforcement today are computer databases of known offenders (including public access to sex-offender databases), machine-based expert systems, cellular communications, video surveillance (often combined with face-recognition technology), electronic eavesdropping, deoxyribonucleic acid (DNA) analysis, and less-lethal weapons.

Transponder-based automated vehicle location (AVL) systems now use patrol car–based transmitters in tandem with orbiting global positioning satellites (GPS) to pinpoint locations of police vehicles to within 50 feet so that dispatchers can better allocate available resources on a given shift and be able to substantially reduce police response times in crisis situations. (Chip-based transponders are also installed in private vehicles to deter thieves and to help trace stolen automobiles.)

> Criminal technologies and law enforcement capabilities leapfrog one another.

In jurisdictions with computer-aided dispatch (CAD) systems, police dispatchers are prompted by computers for important information that allows them to distinguish a location (such as a particular McDonald's). CAD systems also quickly provide information about how often officers have been called to a given site and can tell responding officers what they might expect to find based on past calls from that location.

More innovative crime-fighting technologies are becoming available. The "Spiderman snare," being tested for its usefulness in incapacitating fleeing suspects, is a 16-foot-wide net that is compressed into a small shotgun-like shell. The net has small weights at its circumference and wraps itself around its target after being fired. The snare's impact is harmless, and test subjects report being able to watch with open eyes as the net wraps around them. A special-frequency disco-like strobe light quickly disorients human targets by causing intense dizziness, leaving subjects unable to resist cuffing and arrest (operators wear special glasses designed to counter the influence of the light). Because high-speed chases pose a substantial danger to the public, scientists have developed an electromagnetic pulsing device that can be used to temporarily disable a vehicle's electrical system, causing the engine to stall.

The prototype is said to be safe enough to use on vehicles driven by those wearing pacemakers.

As new technologies are developed, their potential usefulness in law enforcement activities is evaluated by the FBI, the NIJ, and other agencies. NIJ's Technology Assessment Program (TAP) focuses on four areas of advancing technology: protective equipment, such as bullet-proof vests and other body armor; forensic sciences, including advances in DNA technology; transportation and weapons, such as electronic stun guns and other less-lethal weapons; and communications and electronics, including computer security and electronic eavesdropping. Other groups, such as the National Computer Security Association, the American Cryptography Association, and the American Society for Industrial Security, bring more specialized high-tech expertise to the private-security and public law enforcement professions.

DNA Technology ⤸

On January 16, 2001, Christopher Ochoa, age 34, was released from a Texas prison after serving 13 years for a murder he did not commit.[63] Ochoa had confessed to the rape and murder of 20-year-old Nancy DePriest at a Pizza Hut in Austin in 1988; although Ochoa later said he had been coerced by homicide detectives into confessing, no one believed him. A decade after he began serving a life sentence, law students at the Wisconsin Innocence Project at the University of Wisconsin–Madison took an interest in his case, studied surviving information, and concluded that DNA evidence conclusively proved that someone else had killed DePriest. The students and their law professor took the evidence to District Judge Bob Perkins, who called the case "a fundamental miscarriage of justice" and ordered Ochoa set free. According to authorities, evidence of DePriest's murder now points to Texas inmate Achim Joseph Marino, who confessed to her murder in 1996 following a religious conversion. Marino, currently serving three life sentences for other crimes, has provided investigators with the gun and handcuffs used to commit the crime. The law students involved in the case used DNA profiling, matching DNA samples taken from mouth swabs of Marino with the DNA found in semen taken from the victim's body. Without DNA profiling, Ochoa would still be in prison, and DePriest's real killer would be unknown.

A person's genetic code is contained in his or her DNA, whose composition is unique to each individual (except in the case of identical twins). DNA samples can be taken from blood, hair, semen, saliva, or even small flakes of skin left at the scene of a crime. After processing, DNA profiles appear like bar codes on film negatives, codes that can exonerate a suspect or provide nearly irrefutable evidence of guilt.

■ *Daubert* **standard**
A test of scientific acceptability applicable to the gathering of evidence in criminal cases.

DNA evidence is long lasting—fossilized DNA is now being used to reconstruct genetic maps of long-extinct plant and animal species. Although DNA analysis is theoretically possible using only a single cell, most reputable DNA laboratories require a considerably greater quantity of material to conduct an effective analysis, but that could change. Using a Nobel Prize–winning technique called "polymerase chain-reaction technology," minute strands of DNA can be effectively amplified so that even the identity of a person taking a single puff from a cigarette can be accurately established. Although the cost and complexity are prohibitive, these technological advances are expected to be available to a range of forensic analysts.

The National Research Council called DNA profiling "a highly reliable forensic tool" but admits that it is not infallible.[64] Obvious differences in scrutinized DNA samples can easily eliminate a suspect, but testing provides less certainty with positive identification, with human error in conducting the tests being perhaps the greatest threat to reliable results. At least 20 states and the federal government generally accept DNA evidence in criminal trials. Other jurisdictions, including California, are less clear in their recognition of DNA testing, and trial judges in those states may offhandedly exclude the use of such evidence when experts disagree as to its validity.

In 1993, the U.S. Supreme Court, in the civil case of ***Daubert* v. *Merrell Dow Pharmaceuticals, Inc.***, revised the criteria for the admissibility of scientific evidence;[65] the ruling rejected the previous admissibility standard established in the 1923 case of ***Frye* v. *United States***.[66] The *Daubert* Court ruled that the older *Frye* standard, requiring "general acceptance" of a test or procedure by the relevant scientific community, "is not a necessary precondition to the admissibility of scientific evidence," which is established by Rule 402 of the *Federal Rules of Evidence*, published after *Frye* and superseding it. Rule 402 says that "all relevant evidence is admissible [in a trial], except as otherwise provided by the Constitution of the United States, by Act of Congress, by these Rules, or by other rules prescribed by the Supreme Court pursuant to statutory authority."[67] The Court said that although "the *Frye* test was displaced by the Rules of Evidence, [it] does not mean that the Rules themselves place no limits on the admissibility of purportedly scientific evidence. Nor is the trial judge disabled from screening such evidence. To the contrary, under the Rules the trial judge must ensure that any and all scientific testimony or evidence admitted is not only relevant, but reliable." The real test for the admissibility of scientific expert testimony is for the trial judge to decide "at the outset whether the expert is proposing to testify to (1) scientific knowledge that (2) will assist the trier of fact to understand or determine a fact in issue." The Court

concluded that the trial judge's task is one of "ensuring that an expert's testimony both rests on a reliable foundation and is relevant to the task at hand. Pertinent evidence based on scientifically valid principles will satisfy those demands."

The plaintiffs in *Daubert* were not arguing the merits of DNA testing but were claiming that the drug Bendectin caused birth defects, but the ***Daubert* standard** eased the criteria for the introduction of scientific evidence at both civil and criminal trials—and effectively cleared the way for the use of DNA evidence in the courtroom.[68] The *Daubert* Court found that the following factors may be used to determine whether a form of scientific evidence is reliable:

- It has been subjected to testing.
- It has been subjected to peer review.
- It has known or potential rates of error.
- It has standards controlling application of the techniques involved.

One observer, discussing the quality of DNA identification methods, noted, "The challenges today are no longer technical; instead they lie in taking the technology and building a meaningful legal infrastructure around it."[69] As DNA evidence is accepted throughout jurisdictions nationwide and worldwide, digitized forensic DNA databases (similar to widely used fingerprint archives) are useful at the state and national levels, and a number of states and the federal government (through the FBI laboratory) already have them. In 1998 the FBI announced that its National DNA Index System (NDIS)—which enables U.S. forensic laboratories to exchange and compare DNA profiles electronically, thereby linking unsolved serial violent crimes to each other and to known offenders—had begun operation.[70] By June 1998, all 50 states had passed legislation requiring convicted offenders to provide samples for DNA databases, and all states have been invited to participate in NDIS. The federal DNA Identification Act of 1994 authorized the FBI to establish DNA indexes for (1) offenders convicted of crimes, (2) samples recovered from crime scenes, and (3) samples recovered from unidentified human remains.[71] There is the potential for coordination between the federally funded multibillion-dollar Human Genome Project and forensic DNA programs, which could lead to explosive growth in the use of DNA in criminal case processing.

In 1995 the British police, operating under a new nationwide crime bill, became the first national police force in the world to begin routine collection of DNA samples from anyone involved in a "recordable" offense (a serious crime).[72] It appears that genetic profiling will become one of the most significant crime-fighting

LIBRARY EXTRA 13–10
LIBRARY EXTRA 13–11

technologies of the twenty-first century. "Genetic profiling—the use of biotechnology to identify the unique characteristics of an individual's DNA—is about to become as prevalent as the Breathalyzer and more important than the fingerprint."[73]

In 1996, the NIJ released a comprehensive report, titled *Convicted by Juries, Exonerated by Science*, on the applicability of DNA testing to criminal case processing, calling DNA testing "the most important technological breakthrough of twentieth-century forensic science" and providing a detailed review of 28 cases in which postconviction DNA evidence exonerated defendants who had been sentenced to lengthy prison terms.[74] The 28 cases were selected on the basis of a detailed examination of records that indicated the convicted defendants might have actually been innocent. The men in the study had served, on average, seven years in prison, and most had been tried and sentenced prior to the widespread availability of reliable DNA testing. "Momentum is growing, spurred in part by the public's education from the Simpson trial, for DNA testing in criminal cases. Juries may begin to question cases where the prosecutor does not offer 'conclusive' DNA test results if the evidence is available for testing. More defense attorneys in court-appointed cases may file motions for DNA testing and request the State to pay for the tests."[75] Learn more about the science behind forensic DNA testing and how it has been used to convict as well as exonerate criminal defendants at **Library Extra 13–10**. An assessment of its likely future is available as **Library Extra 13–11**.

> Genetic profiling will become one of the most significant crime-fighting technologies of the twenty-first century.

Computers as Crime-Fighting Tools

The widespread use of computers and computer applications in a diversity of professions has been one of the most far-reaching social phenomena of recent years. Computers assist in the design of new technologies and aid in the assignment of resources to problem areas: Police departments, prisons, and courts now employ computer software to schedule facilities and personnel; to keep track of defendants, witnesses, and cases; and to keep account of budgetary matters.

Computers also connect people. The Internet contains a large number of law enforcement–oriented blogs and discussion groups and provides access to United Nations and worldwide crime data through its link to the United Nations Criminal Justice Information Network (uncjin.org). Other computer services offer access to security information and to software useful in law enforcement administration. Specialized Web sites, such as the Society of Police Futurists International's home page (policefuturists.org), the International Association of Chiefs of Police site (theiacp.org), and the SEARCH Group (search.org), link law enforcement professionals and criminologists throughout the country.

Other innovative computer technologies—the automated fingerprint identification system (AFIS) with interstate and international links, a computerized crime-scene simulation and reenactment, expert systems, and online clearinghouses with data on criminal activity and offenders—facilitate the work of law enforcement agents. AFIS allows investigators to match a suspect's fingerprints against stored records in a matter of minutes (instead of weeks or months) because its computers are able to compare and eliminate many thousands of fingerprints per second, sometimes leading to the identification of a suspect in a short time. "Live-scan" technology permits easy inkless digitizing of fingerprints from suspects, and the Bureau of Alcohol, Tobacco, and Firearms has new software that takes a 360-degree picture of a bullet's ballistic characteristics and then compares them with others stored in a database to isolate a small universe of potential matches.

Once crime-related information or profiles of criminal offenders have been generated, they are typically stored in a database and made accessible to law enforcement agencies at other sites. Some widely used online criminal information services include the FBI's National Crime Information Center, the Violent Criminal Apprehension Program, and the Police Executive Research Forum's information-sharing network called METAPOL. Other specialized database programs now track inner-city gang activity and gang membership, contain information on known sexual predators, and describe missing children.

PC radios, combinations of laptop computers and police radios, provide another high-tech weapon in the "war on crime." These devices were initially tested by the Baltimore (Maryland) Police Department, and mobile data terminals placed in police cars are proving useful in the apprehension of both traffic violators and more serious offenders. Officers use PC radios to (1) obtain motor vehicle information, (2) get detailed information when answering a call, and (3) report incidents either by saving

---

■ **expert system**
A system of computer hardware and software that attempts to duplicate the decision-making processes used by skilled investigators in the analysis of evidence and in the recognition of patterns that such evidence might represent.

■ **data encryption**
The process by which information is encoded, making it unreadable to all but its intended recipients.

■ **threat analysis**
A thorough assessment of the perils facing an organization.

■ **audit trail**
A record of computer activities that enables auditors to reconstruct and review the sequence of activities surrounding each event in one or more related transactions from inception to output of final results back to inception.

---

data on disk or by transmitting them to other locations such as police headquarters. PC radios have also helped mislead drug dealers, who routinely use police scanners to keep abreast of enforcement activities, because the digitized transmissions consist of machine code that cannot be easily read by drug dealers or other criminals trying to outguess the police.

Expert systems deploy machine-based artificial intelligence to duplicate decision-making processes used by skilled investigators in the analysis of evidence and in the recognition of patterns that such evidence might represent to draw conclusions and make recommendations to police investigators and others interested in solving problems related to crime and its commission. One system being used by the FBI's National Center for the Analysis of Violent Crime (NCAVC) attempts to profile serial killers by matching clues left at a crime scene with individual personality characteristics. While the NCAVC system is becoming increasingly sophisticated, it has not yet replaced human investigators. "There is certainly no possibility that the system we are devising will ever replace skilled human profilers. Rather, the system will function as a profiler's assistant or consultant."[76] A number of other specialized computer programs, such as ImAger (by Face Software, Inc.) and Compusketch (by Visatex Corporation), assist police artists in rendering composite images of suspects and missing victims.

Combating Cybercrime

In 1982, sales of information security software products to private companies and government agencies totaled only $51 million; by 1997, expenditures exceeded $425 million; and by 2003, they had grown to $1.17 billion.[77] Research conducted by Infonetics Research indicated that worldwide network-security appliance and software sales reached more than $4.5 billion in 2006 and surpassed $5.6 billion in 2009.[78] Among the products are **data encryption** (the process of encoding information so that it is unreadable to all but its intended recipients), keylog detectors, and Web servers supporting major security protocols.

Software alone is not enough—any effective program intended to secure an organization's operation against the threat of high-tech crime must be built on a realistic **threat analysis** (also called *risk analysis*) involving a thorough assessment of the perils facing the organization. Some risks, such as floods, tornadoes, hurricanes, and earthquakes, arise from natural events and

are often unpredictable. Others, including fires, electrical outages, and disruptions in public services, may be of human origin but are equally difficult to presage. Theft, employee sabotage, and terrorist attacks constitute yet another category of risk—those brought about by intentional human intervention. Responses to unpredictable threats can nonetheless be planned, and strategies for dealing with almost any kind of risk can be implemented. Unless an organization adequately assesses the threats to its continuing operation, it will be unable to formulate a plan to deal effectively with such risks, so threat analysis is a must for organizations preparing to meet the many diverse challenges of today's world.

Once specific threats are identified, strategies tailored to dealing with them can be introduced. One powerful tool useful in identifying instances of computer crime is the **audit trail**, "a sequential record of system activities that enables auditors to reconstruct, review, and examine the sequence of states and activities surrounding each event in one or more related transactions from inception to output of final results back to inception."[79] Audit trails, which are recorded in computer memory, trace and record the activities of computer operators and facilitate the apprehension of cybercriminals.

Although most large companies and financial institutions have fairly extensive computer-security programs, few small businesses, schools, hospitals, and individuals have any real understanding of their need for computer security. "What is surprising about computer crime," explained computer-security expert Kenneth Rosenblatt, "is how little is being done to deter it: Industry will not beef up security, the police are not equipped to catch electronic thieves, and judges do not hand down the kind of sentences that will impress would-be computer criminals. New strategies are urgently needed."[80]

Police Investigations of Cybercrime and Cybercriminals

In the past, few police departments had either the time or the qualified personnel to effectively investigate crimes committed by cybercriminals, even with new laws for backup. When it comes to cybercrime investigations, one technology expert concluded, "Police departments are simply unsuited to the task."[81] Although specialized cybercrime units have been created in some jurisdictions, they are often poorly funded and seriously understaffed.

WEB EXTRA 13-7
LIBRARY EXTRA 13-12

■ **DCS–3000**
An FBI-developed network diagnostic tool that is capable of assisting in criminal investigations by monitoring and capturing large amounts of Internet traffic. It was originally called *Carnivore.*

Most state and local police departments do not have personnel skilled in the investigation of cybercrimes, most officers know little about tracing the activities of cybercriminals, and some police investigators find it difficult to understand how a crime can actually have occurred when nothing at the scene appears to be missing or damaged. Police departments also sometimes intentionally avoid cybercrime investigations because they can be complex and demanding, thinking that the amount of time and money spent on cybercrime investigations could better be spent elsewhere. Cybercrime investigations can also cross state lines, involving a number of telecommunications companies and other services. Additionally, investigators who spend a lot of time on cybercrimes tend to not be promoted as readily as those in homicide and property-crime divisions, and personnel who are truly skilled in computer applications are apt to take jobs with private industries where pay scales are far higher than in police work. As a consequence, many police departments and their investigators frequently accord cybercrime a low priority, focusing instead on highly visible offenses, such as murder and rape, and seeing cybercrime victims as too wealthy to be seriously affected by the crimes they experience.

But the situation has been changing, thanks to federal intervention. In 1992, the FBI formed a National Computer Crime Squad (NCCS);[82] its job was to investigate violations of the federal Computer Fraud and Abuse Act of 1984 and other federal cybercrime laws.[83] Most of the FBI's larger offices established their own cybercrime squads to conduct high-tech investigations in the areas they served. Prior to the creation of the Department of Homeland Security (DHS), the FBI's Washington Field Office housed the agency's Infrastructure Protection and Computer Intrusion Squad (IPCIS), which was responsible for investigating unauthorized intrusions into major computer networks belonging to telecommunications providers, private corporations, U.S. government agencies, and public and private educational facilities;[84] the squad, whose duties have now been transferred to DHS, also investigated the illegal interception of signals (especially cable and satellite signal theft) and the infringement of copyright laws related to software.

The Computer Crime and Intellectual Property Section (CCIPS) began in 1991 as the DOJ's Computer Crime Unit. The CCIPS staff consisted of about two dozen lawyers focusing exclusively on the issues raised by cybercrime and intellectual-property crime. They worked closely on cybercrime cases with assistant U.S. attorneys known as "computer and telecommunications coordinators" in U.S. attorney's offices around the country.[85] CCIPS attorneys have taken a leading role in litigating some cybercrime and intellectual-property investigations and

> **Police departments sometimes intentionally avoid cybercrime investigations because they can be complex and demanding.**

a coordinating role in some national investigations, and U.S. assistant attorneys have advised federal prosecutors and law enforcement agents, commented on and proposed legislation, coordinated international efforts to combat cybercrime, litigated cases, and trained federal law enforcement groups. One of the first large-scale federal cybercrime operations took place in 1997 when FBI agents raided the homes and offices of about a dozen Web masters suspected of pirating software in eight cities across the country. The operation, code-named Cyber Strike, resulted from NCCS monitoring of Internet chat channels and file transfers over the Internet.[86] Visit CCIPS via **Web Extra 13–7**.

Automated monitoring of network traffic is an area of considerable interest to law enforcement officials. One network "sniffer" created by the FBI called DCS–1000 (previously known as "Carnivore") was a diagnostic tool intended to assist in criminal investigations by monitoring and capturing large amounts of Internet traffic. DCS–1000 was installed by FBI agents in ISP data centers as the need arose to monitor the electronic communications of individuals suspected of federal crimes like terrorism. The Carnivore/DCS–1000 initiative was later renamed **DCS–3000** and changed its focus to intercepting suspect personal communications services delivered via wireless services. Learn more about the challenges facing American law enforcement agencies when it comes to cybercrime and Internet-related crime by reading **Library Extra 13–12**.

While any effective policy for dealing with cybercrime and high-tech crime must recognize the issues associated with personal freedoms and individual rights in the information age, a second aspect of effective policy necessarily relates to crime control: How can high-tech criminals be deterred? If they succeed in committing criminal acts, how can they be reformed? Kenneth Rosenblatt, who focused on cybercrimes during his work as a California district attorney, suggested three effective sanctions to deter high-tech offenders:[87] confiscating equipment used to commit cybercrimes, limiting the offender's use of computers, and restricting the offender's freedom to accept jobs involving computers. Such penalties could be supplemented by a few days or weeks in a county jail, with longer periods of incarceration applicable in serious cases. "In my experience, one of the best ways to hurt computer offenders, especially young hackers, is to take away their toys."[88]

■ **Internet**
The world's largest computer network for moving data and
making information accessible.

WEB EXTRA 13–8

Cybercrime and Internet Security

America is a service-oriented, information-rich society. John Naisbitt, author of *Megatrends*, explained it this way: "The transition from an industrial to an information society does not mean manufacturing will cease to exist or become unimportant. Did farming end with the industrial era? Ninety percent of us produced 100 percent of the food in the agricultural era; now 3 percent of us produce 100 percent. In the information age, the focus of manufacturing will shift from the physical to more intellectual functions on which the physical depends."[89]

Although goods and materials will always need to be created, transported, and distributed, it is information that forms the lifeblood of the new world order and is a very valuable resource, comparable to (or exceeding) natural resources like oil, gas, coal, and gold. According to Naisbitt, "Information is an economic entity because it costs something to produce and because people are willing to pay for it."[90] Nations that are able to effectively manage valuable information and make it accessible to their citizens experience enhanced productivity and greater wealth. Moving information safely and securely is important, and today a large part of that is done on the **Internet**, the world's largest computer network. It began with the linkage of military and scientific computer facilities already existing on the Arpnet and Milnet and today consists of a vast resource of tens of thousands of computers around the world all linked together as a way of moving data quickly and making information accessible to masses of citizens.

The Internet provides some amazing and constantly growing capabilities: Web sites, e-mail, mailing lists, newsgroups, and file-transfer capability. Internet access was originally restricted to commercial users, researchers, and university personnel, but access to the Internet is now routinely available through ISPs that furnish Internet access to anyone able to pay the monthly fee. Web browsers combine with search engines like Google to make it easy to search the tremendous amount of information on the Web and to interact with other Internet users.

As the Internet has grown, it has been targeted by hackers and cybercriminals, some of whom have introduced rogue computer programs into the network's machines. In 1988, the infamous Internet "worm" written by Cornell University graduate student Robert T. Morris, Jr., circulated through computers connected to the Internet, effectively disabling many of them. Morris was later arrested, sentenced to 400 hours of community service and three years of probation, and was fined $10,000. Since then, many other hackers have exploited loopholes in the software and hardware supporting the Internet.

In response to the growing threat to the nation's information systems, President Clinton created the Commission on Critical Infrastructure Protection, which was charged with assessing threats to the nation's computer networks and recommending policies to protect them.[91] Security issues related to information systems that control the nation's telecommunications, electric power, oil and gas, banking and finance, transportation, water supply, emergency services, and government operations were studied by the commission. Its October 1997 report proposed (1) establishing an Information Analysis and Warning Center to collect information on computer-security breaches in industry and government; (2) creating legislation to permit private companies to conduct special background checks when hiring computer experts for sensitive positions; (3) creating a White House office to coordinate the information security roles of government, including the departments of Commerce, Defense, Energy, Justice, Treasury, and Transportation; and (4) quadrupling research on cyberspace security to $1 billion by the year 2004.[92]

The National Infrastructure Protection Center (NIPC), created in 1998 and located at the FBI's headquarters in Washington, D.C., served as the federal government's center for threat assessment, warnings, investigation, and response for threats or attacks against the nation's critical infrastructures. Its successor, the Office of Infrastructure Protection (IP), operates today within the DHS. Visit the IP Office via **Web Extra 13–8**.

In February 2000, the President's Working Group on Unlawful Conduct on the Internet released a report titled *The Electronic Frontier: The Challenge of Unlawful Conduct Involving the Use of the Internet*.[93] The group reported that "similar to the technologies that have preceded it, the Internet provides a new tool for wrongdoers to commit crimes, such as fraud, the sale or distribution of child pornography, the sale of guns or drugs or other regulated substances without regulatory protections, or the unlawful distribution of computer software or other creative material protected by intellectual property rights."

The group said that "although the precise extent of unlawful conduct involving the use of computers is unclear, the rapid growth of the Internet and e-commerce has made such unlawful conduct a critical priority for legislators, policymakers, industry, and law enforcement agencies." Because of the Internet's potential to reach vast audiences easily, the potential scale of unlawful conduct is equally wide.

Cybercriminals are no longer hampered by the existence of national or international boundaries because information and property can be easily transmitted through communications and data networks. A computer server running a Web page designed to defraud senior citizens might be located in Thailand, but

WEB EXTRA 13-9
WEB EXTRA 13-10
LIBRARY EXTRA 13-13
LIBRARY EXTRA 13-14

victims of the scam could be scattered throughout the world. Evidence of a crime can be stored at a remote location, either for concealment of the crime from law enforcement or due to the design of the network. "A cyberstalker in Brooklyn, New York, may send a threatening e-mail to a person in Manhattan. If the stalker routes his communication through Argentina, France, and Norway before reaching his victim, the New York Police Department may have to get assistance from the Office of International Affairs at the Department of Justice in Washington, D.C., which, in turn, may have to get assistance from law enforcement in (say) Buenos Aires, Paris, and Oslo just to learn that the suspect is in New York." In this example, the working group points out, the perpetrator needs no passport and passes through no checkpoints as he commits his crime, while law enforcement agencies are burdened with cumbersome mechanisms for international cooperation—mechanisms that often derail or slow investigations. Because the gathering of information in other jurisdictions and internationally is crucial to investigating and prosecuting cybercrimes, the President's Working Group concluded that "all levels of government will need to develop concrete and reliable mechanisms for cooperating with each other." Read the entire text of *The Electronic Frontier* via **Web Extra 13-9**.

In September 2003, the U.S. government established the United States Computer Emergency Readiness Team (US–CERT), a partnership between DHS and public and private sectors to protect the nation's Internet infrastructure and to coordinate defenses against cyberattacks across the nation. US–CERT is in charge of the National Cyber Alert System: "America's first cohesive national cyber security system for identifying, analyzing, and prioritizing emerging vulnerabilities and threats."[94] The Cyber Alert System relays computer-security updates and warning information to anyone who subscribes to its bulletins and provides all citizens—from computer-security professionals to home-computer users with basic skills—with free, timely, actionable information to better secure their computer systems. Visit US–CERT at **Web Extra 13-10**.

After taking office, President Barack Obama identified cybersecurity as one of the most serious economic and national-security challenges facing the United States and noted that the country was not adequately prepared to counter cybersecurity threats. In May 2009, the president decided to implement recommendations from the Comprehensive National Cybersecurity Initiative (CNCI), which had been launched by President George W. Bush in January 2008.[95] In December 2009, President Obama announced the appointment of Howard A. Schmidt as White House Cybersecurity Coordinator.[96] Schmidt, who served as chief security officer for Microsoft and eBay, was charged with coordinating cybersecurity activities across the federal government. Learn more about the CNCI at **Library Extra 13-13**, and read about new legislation to address the problem of cybercrime at **Library Extra 13-14**.

Policy Issues: Personal Freedoms in the Information Age

The continued development of telecommunications resources has led not only to concerns about security and data integrity but also to expanding interest in privacy, free speech, and personal freedoms. While the First and Fourth Amendments of the Constitution guarantee each of us freedom of speech and security in our "persons, houses, papers, and effects, against unreasonable searches and seizures," it is understandably silent on the subject of electronic documents and advanced forms of communication facilitated by technologies that did not exist at the time of the Constitutional Convention.

Within the context of contemporary society, we are left to ask, "What is speech? What are papers? Do electronic communications qualify for protection under the First Amendment?" In an era when most houses are wired for telephones and many support data links that extend well beyond voice capabilities, it becomes necessary to ask what constitutes someone's "speech" or "home." Questions abound: Does e-mail qualify as speech? Where does the concept of a home begin and end for purposes of constitutional guarantees? Do activities within the home that can be accessed from outside it (as when a Web site is run out of a home) fall under the same constitutional guarantees as a private conversation held in the physical confines of a house?

These and questions like them will be debated for years to come. In 1990, concerned individuals banded together to form the Electronic Frontier Foundation (EFF), a citizens' group funded by private contributions with the task of actively assisting in refining notions of privacy and legality as they relate to telecommunications and other computer-based media. Mitch Kapor, EFF cofounder and former president of Lotus Development Corporation, explained, "It is becoming increasingly obvious that the rate of technology

> Do electronic communications qualify for protection under the First Amendment?

advancement in communications is far outpacing the establishment of appropriate cultural, legal and political frameworks to handle the issues that are arising."[97]

The EFF, which also supports litigation in the public interest, has been an active supporter of the advocacy group Computer Professionals for Social Responsibility (CPSR), which maintains a Computing and Civil Liberties Project much in keeping with EFF's purpose. Visit the EFF on the Web via **Web Extra 13–11**.

SUMMARY

Technology and criminology have always been closely linked—as technology advances, it facilitates new forms of criminal behavior.

- High-technology offenses can dramatically change our understanding of crime. Some forms of high-tech crime, committed without regard for national borders or even the need for physical travel, hold dangers never before imagined.

- High technology provides new criminal opportunities by making available to perpetrators new tools and advanced techniques useful in the commission of crime, and by contributing to the development of items of value, like computer codes, that did not previously exist.

- Hackers can be pioneers (those fascinated by the evolving technology of telecommunications and its exploration), scamps (those with a sense of fun and no intent to harm), explorers (those motivated by personal delight in discoveries associated with breaking into new systems), game players (those whose joy is in defeating software or copyright protection), vandals (those with the goal of intentional damage without personal apparent gain), and/or addicts (those computer nerds addicted to hacking and computer technology).

- The combination of information technology and easy accessibility of personal information has produced a rapid increase in identity theft (misuse of another individual's personal information to commit fraud).

- Technology in law enforcement today involves computer databases of known offenders, expert systems, cellular communications, video surveillance and face-recognition technology, electronic eavesdropping, DNA analysis, and less-lethal weapons.

- Any effective program to combat cybercrime and secure an organization against the threat of high-tech crime must use threat analysis. Once specific threats are identified, strategies tailored to dealing with them can be implemented.

- Efforts to control high-tech crime through criminal investigation and prosecution impact issues of individual rights, from free speech to technological privacy in the context of digital interconnectedness. There will need to be an acceptable balance between constitutional guarantees of continued freedom of access to legitimate high-tech activities and effective enforcement initiatives for the massive threat high-tech crimes represent.

KEY TERMS

audit trail	Digital Theft Deterrence and Copyright Damages Improvement Act
Communications Decency Act (CDA)	
computer abuse	DNA profiling
computer-related crime	expert system
	hacker
computer virus	identity theft
cybercrime	Internet
Cyber Security Enhancement Act (CSEA)	No Electronic Theft Act (NETA)
cyberspace	phishing
data encryption	phone phreak
Daubert standard	software piracy
DCS–3000	TEMPEST
	threat analysis

QUESTIONS **FOR REVIEW**

1. How does advancing technology produce new forms of crime?

2. How does high technology provide new criminal opportunities?

3. What different types of cybercriminals does this chapter describe?

4. What is identity theft, and how can identities be stolen?

5. What new technologies are being used in today's fight against crime?

6. What is being done to combat cybercrime and to secure the Internet today?

7. What are some personal freedoms that are threatened by today's need for advanced security?

QUESTIONS **FOR REFLECTION**

1. This discussion emphasizes the theme of social problems versus social responsibility. Which perspective better explains the involvement of capable individuals in criminal activity necessitating high-tech skills? What is the best way to deal with such criminals?

2. What is the difference between high-tech crime and traditional forms of criminal activity? Will the high-tech crimes of today continue to be the high-tech crimes of tomorrow? Why?

3. What forms of high-tech crime can you imagine that this chapter has not discussed? Describe each briefly.

4. Do you believe that high-tech crimes will eventually surpass the abilities of enforcement agents to prevent or solve them? Why?

5. What different kinds of high-tech offenders can you imagine? What is the best way to deal with each type of offender? Give reasons for your answers.

CHAPTER **NOTES**

1. Tony Castro, "Valley Gangs Leave Trail on Web," *Los Angeles Daily News*, December 5, 2009, www.dailynews.com/news/ci_13931149 (accessed May 12, 2010).

2. Ibid.

3. Ibid.

4. The White House, *The Comprehensive National Security Initiative*, http://www.whitehouse.gov/cybersecurity/comprehensive-national-cybersecurity-initiative.

5. Kenneth Rosenblatt, "Deterring Computer Crime," *Technology Review*, Vol. 93, No. 2 (February/March 1990), pp. 34–41.

6. Richard H. Baker, *The Computer Security Handbook* (Blue Ridge Summit, PA: TAB Books, 1985).

7. Catherine H. Conly and J. Thomas McEwen, "Computer Crime," *NIJ Reports*, January/February 1990.

8. David McGuire, "Study: Online Crime Costs Rising," *Washington Post*, May 24, 2004, http://www.washingtonpost.com/wp-dyn/articles/A53042-2004May24.html (accessed July 30, 2005).

9. Dan Briody, "Keep Out," *Inc.*, March 2007, http://www.inc.com/magazine/20070301/technology-security.html (accessed June 17, 2007).

10. Ponemon Institute, *Fourth Annual U.S. Cost of Data Breach Study: Benchmark Study of Companies* (Traverse City, MI: Ponemon Institute, January 2009), p. 4.

11. Software and Information Industry Association, *Report on Global Software Piracy 2000*, http://www.siia.net/piracy/pubs/piracy2000.pdf, p. 7.

12. Business Software Alliance, *Seventh Annual BSA/IDC Global Software Piracy Study* (BSA, May 2010), http://portal.bsa.org/globalpiracy2009/index.html (accessed August 28, 2010).

13. Gary H. Anthes, "Software Pirates' Booty Topped $13B, Study Finds," *Computerworld*, January 6, 1997, p. 24.

14. Stephen R. Purdy, "Protecting Your Telephone Systems against Dial-Tone Thieves," *Infosecurity News*, July/August 1993, p. 43.

15. Paul Keegan, "High Tech Pirates Collecting Phone Calls," *USA Today*, September 23, 1994, p. 4A.

16. Ibid.

17. Fraser Lovatt, "U.S. Department of Justice: VoIP Fosters Crime, Drugs and Terrorism," Digital-Lifestyles.info, June 18, 2004, http://digital-lifestyles.info/display_page.asp?section=business&id=1318 (accessed August 1, 2006).

18. The Anti-Phishing Working Group, "Phishing Activity Trends," http://www.antiphishing.org/reports/apwg_report_april_2007.pdf (accessed June 17, 2007).

19. Gregg Keizer, "Gartner: Phishing Attacks Threaten E-Commerce," Security Pipeline.com, www.securitypipeline.com/news/20000036 (accessed July 30, 2007).

20. This and most other definitions related to cybercrime in this chapter are taken from Donn B. Parker, *Computer Crime: Criminal Justice Resource Manual* (Washington, DC: National Institute of Justice, 1989).

21. "Palm, Other Handheld Devices to Face Virus Threats," Reuters, August 31, 2000, http://www.bostonherald.com/business/technology/palm08312000.htm (accessed January 11, 2006).

22. Joseph Menn, "Police Shut Down Hacker Ring," *Financial Times*, March 4, 2010.

23. Public Law 107–296 (Homeland Security Act), Section 225.

24. Public Law 106–160.

25. Public Law 105–147.

26. U.S. Code, Title 18, Section 1030.

27. Public Law 104–294 as amended by the National Information Infrastructure Protection Act of 1996.

28. U.S. Code, Title 18, Section 1029.

29. M. Gemiganni, "Viruses and Computer Law," *Communications of the ACM*, Vol. 32 (June 1989), p. 669.

30. Section 290001(a) of Pub. L. 103-322, as amended by Pub. L. 104-294, title VI, Sec. 604(b)(34).

31. Section 225 of the Homeland Security Act of 2002 (H.R. 5710).

32. The following quotes are taken from Public Law 104–104, 110 Stat. 56.

33. *Reno v. ACLU*, 521 U.S. 844 (1997).

34. Texas Penal Code, Section 33.01.

35. Virginia Criminal Code, Sections 18.2–152.2 through 18.2–152.7.

36. Brian S. Akre, "Internet-Torture," Associated Press, February 10, 1995.

37. Ibid.

38. Jim Schaefer and Maryanne George, "Internet User's Charges Dismissed—U.S. Criticized for Pursuing U-M Case," *Detroit Free Press*, June 22, 1995.

39. Parker, *Computer Crime*.

40. Steve Miletich, no title, *Seattle Post-Intelligencer*, via Simon & Schuster NewsLink Online, May 21, 1997.

41. Paul Saffo, "Desperately Seeking Cyberspace," *Personal Computing*, May 1989, p. 247.

42. John Markoff, "Cyberpunks," *New York Times Upfront*, Vol. 132, No. 15 (March 27, 2000), pp. 10–14.

43. J. Bloombecker, "A Security Manager's Guide to Hacking," *DATAPRO Reports on Information Security*, Report IS35–450–101, 1986.

44. For more information, see Ronald R. Thrasher, "Voice-Mail Fraud," *FBI Law Enforcement Bulletin*, July 1994, pp. 1–4.

45. J. Maxfield, "Computer Bulletin Boards and the Hacker Problem," *EDPACS: The Electric Data Processing Audit, Control and Security Newsletter* (Arlington, VA: Automation Training Center, October 1985).

46. Percy Black, personal communication, 1991, as cited in M. E. Kabay, "Computer Crime: Hackers" (undated electronic manuscript).

47. John Perry Barlow, "Crime and Puzzlement: In Advance of the Law on the Electronic Frontier," *Whole Earth Review* (fall 1990), p. 44.

48. Ibid.

49. "Computer Porn," *Time*, March 15, 1993, p. 22.

50. Details for this story come from "Britain, U.S. Break Up Online Pedophile Ring," http://www.msnbc.msn.com/id/19288057 (accessed June 18, 2007).

51. Parker, *Computer Crime*.

52. President's Identity Theft Task Force, *Combating Identity Theft: A Strategic Plan* (Washington, DC: U.S. Department of Justice, 2007), from which much of the information comes and some of the wording is taken or adapted.

53. Office of Community Oriented Policing Services, *A National Strategy to Combat Identity Theft* (Washington, DC: COPS Office, 2006), from which the quote and some of the material in this section are taken.

54. See Business Software Alliance, "Consumer Confidence in Online Shopping Buoyed by Security Software Protection, BSA Survey Suggests," January 12, 2006, http://www.bsacybersafety.com/news/2005-Online-Shopping-Confidence.cfm (accessed May 10, 2010).

55. See Cyber Security Industry Alliance, "Internet Security Voter Survey," June 2005, https://www.csialliance.org/publications/surveys_and_polls/CSIA_Internet_Security_Survey_June_2005.pdf (accessed May 10, 2010).

56. U.S. Code, Title 18, Section 1028.

57. H.R. 1731 (2004).

58. Katrina Baum, *Identity Theft, 2005* (Washington, DC: Bureau of Justice Statistics, 2007).

59. The information and some of the wording in this section are taken from *Combating Identity Theft: A Strategic Plan*.

60. U.S. Attorney's Office, Southern District of Florida, press release, July 19, 2006, http://www.usdoj.gov/usao/fls/PressReleases/060719-01.html (accessed May 9, 2009).

61. Ibid., pp. 22–51.

62. For insight into how security techniques often lag behind the abilities of criminal perpetrators in the high-technology arena, see James A. Fagin, "Computer Crime: A Technology Gap," *International Journal of Comparative and Applied Criminal Justice*, Vol. 15, Nos. 1 and 2 (spring/fall 1991), pp. 285–297.

63. "DNA Frees Man Sentenced to Life," Associated Press, January 16, 2001, www.msnbc.com/news/517172.asp (accessed January 17, 2005).

64. Michael Schrage, "Today, It Takes a Scientist to Catch a Thief," *Washington Post*, March 18, 1994.

65. *Daubert v. Merrell Dow Pharmaceuticals, Inc.*, 509 U.S. 579 (1993).

66. *Frye v. United States*, 54 App. D.C. 46, 47, 293 F. 1013, 1014 (1923).

67. Federal Rules of Evidence, Article IV, Rule 402.

68. For the application of *Daubert* to DNA technology, see Barry Sheck, "DNA and *Daubert*," *Cardozo Law Review*, Vol. 15 (1994), p. 1959.

69. Schrage, "Today, It Takes a Scientist to Catch a Thief."

70. FBI press release, October 13, 1998, http://www.fbi.gov/pressrm/pressrel/pressrel98/dna.htm (accessed January 22, 2003).

71. U.S. Code, Title 42, Section 14132.

72. "British Police to Use DNA to Catch Burglars," Reuters, June 16, 1994.

73. Schrage, "Today, It Takes a Scientist to Catch a Thief."

74. Edward Connors et al., *Convicted by Juries, Exonerated by Science: Case Studies in the Use of DNA Evidence to Establish Innocence after Trial* (Washington, DC: National Institute of Justice, 1996).

75. Ibid.

76. Roland Reboussin, "An Expert System Designed to Profile Murderers," in Frank Schmalleger, ed., *Computers in Criminal Justice: Issues and Applications* (Bristol, IN: Wyndham Hall Press, 1990), p. 239.

77. Japan Electronics Industry Association, *Industry Monitor: High-Tech Sector*, "Security Software Demand to Show Strong Growth—Week Ended June 27, 2004," http://www.irstreet.com/top/im/im20040627.pdf (accessed July 30, 2006).

78. Infonetics Research, "Strong Growth Expected for Security Appliance and Software Markets," March 9, 2009 http://www.infonetics.com/pr/2010/4Q09-Network-Security-Content-Security-Market-Highlights.asp (accessed October 2, 2010).

79. Parker, *Computer Crime*, p. xiii.

80. Kenneth Rosenblatt, "Deterring Computer Crime," *Technology Review*, Vol. 93, No. 2 (February/March 1990), pp. 34–41.

81. Ibid.

82. The NCCS can be found at http://www.fbi.gov/programs/nccs/comcrim.htm.

83. Ibid., as modified in 1986, 1988, and later years.

84. This is adapted from the FBI's Washington Field Office Infrastructure Protection and Computer Intrusion Squad home page at http://www.fbi.gov/programs/ipcis/ipcis.htm.

85. This is adapted from the Computer Crime and Intellectual Property Section of the Criminal Division of the U.S. Department of Justice's home page at http://www.cybercrime.gov.

86. Wylie Wong, "FBI Targets BBS Operators, Seizes Hardware in Software Piracy Sting," *Computerworld*, February 3, 1997, p. 24.

87. Rosenblatt, "Deterring Computer Crime."

88. Ibid.

89. John Naisbitt, *Megatrends: Ten New Directions Transforming Our Lives* (New York: Warner, 1982), p. 36.

90. Ibid.

91. Gary H. Anthes, "White House Launches Cybershield," *Computerworld*, July 22, 1996, p. 29.

92. M. J. Zuckerman, "Clinton to Get Cyberterror Plan," *USA Today*, October 9, 1997, p. 1A.

93. The quotations attributed to the President's Working Group in this section are from President's Working Group on Unlawful Conduct on the Internet, *The Electronic Frontier: The Challenge of Unlawful Conduct Involving the Use of the Internet* (Washington, DC: White House, 2000), http://www.usdoj.gov/criminal/cybercrime/unlawful.htm (accessed April 16, 2007).

94. United States Computer Emergency Readiness Team, "About Us," http://www.us-cert.gov/aboutus.html (accessed August 1, 2007).

95. National Security Presidential Directive 54; Homeland Security Presidential Directive 23 (NSPD-54/HSPD-23).

96. "Introducing the New Cybersecurity Coordinator," White House Blog, December 22, 2009, http://www.whitehouse.gov/blog/2009/12/22/introducing-new-cybersecurity-coordinator (accessed May 12, 2010).

97. S. Mace, "Kapor and Wozniak Establish Electronic Policy Foundation," *InfoWorld*, Vol. 12, No. 29 (July 16, 1990), p. 6.

Traditional Sources of Information

Traditional Sources
of Information

KEY TERMS

consensual crimes

doctrine of informer privilege

documentary information

electronic surveillance

entrapment

Freedom of Information Act

informants with ulterior motives

National Crime Information Center

National Criminal Justice Reference Service

paid informants

Privacy Act

reward programs

voluntary informant

LEARNING OBJECTIVES

1. to appreciate the importance of informational sources to the investigative process;
2. to be able to list and define human information sources;
3. to be aware of legal considerations regarding the informant;
4. to be able to list and define documented information sources;
5. to be aware of privacy considerations that influence information gathering;
6. to have a thorough knowledge of federal legislation that has recently influenced information gathering and record keeping;
7. to understand the issues pertaining to electronic information gathering; and
8. to be familiar with recently developed scientific aids that have expanded criminal justice information gathering.

INTRODUCTION

Information is absolutely essential to the investigative process. Sources of information have always been the structural framework upon which the investigation is built. In media presentations, the investigator's information-gathering efforts are generally ignored. The hours (often weeks) of examining documents, interviewing informants, and searching files simply do not provide sufficient excitement for movies or television. However, all effective investigators have mastered information-gathering techniques. They know where and how to obtain information. In some cases, the information gathered dictates whether to follow an investigative lead or to scrap it, thereby determining the direction of the inquiry. Information is frequently necessary to identify an offender or to provide background on a probable suspect. Finally, information gathered from a multitude of sources is essential for the prosecution of the suspect.

HUMAN SOURCES OF INFORMATION

Although not always the most reliable sources of information, people are the most frequent sources. Human beings vary considerably in their motivation, accuracy, and willingness to reveal their knowledge to the authorities. Each individual who reports a crime to the police or answers an investigator's inquiry is providing information. Although some people give information only if paid to do so, the majority of people volunteer information through a sense of civic duty. The general reliability of human informational sources is questionable. Various factors can affect a person's accuracy of perception. Physiological abilities, emotional state, physical conditions, maturity, and a host of other factors play a part in information processing so that no two people experience an object or event in precisely the same way.

Voluntary Informants

It is unfortunate that the term *informant* has acquired such a negative connotation. As children, we learn to disapprove of "tattletales," or those who inform on others. In fact, an entire terminology has evolved, used by citizens and police alike, to describe the informant. "Snitch," "fink," "rat," "stoolie," and many other descriptors are all too common. Yet, few citizens consider themselves "stoolies" when they phone the police to report a loud party or a suspicious individual loitering in the street. The source of information can be a citizen with an impeccable background or an individual with a long criminal history. In either case, information has been obtained through an informant. The stigma attached to the term only serves to complicate the information-gathering process. Many individuals who wish to provide information to the police hesitate to do so for fear of being somehow connected with the criminal element. Anyone, regardless of a criminal or law-abiding background, who provides information to the police without ulterior motive or payment is a **voluntary informant**.

Voluntary informants run the entire social and economic spectrum. This type of informational source may be a garbage collector who observes a strange car parked in front of a home or a physician who treats an individual with a gunshot wound. The only common denominator is the voluntariness of the information. Civic responsibility, fear, or general suspicion often motivate voluntary informants to contact a police agency without being solicited, but much valuable information would never reach the police if the investigator failed to take the initiative. For a variety of reasons, some people will gladly relate information to police officers, but only if the officer initiates the contact. Thus, it is necessary for the investigator to pursue voluntary informants actively during the course of an investigation.

The nature of the crime, its location, and the probable identity of the perpetrator all serve to guide the investigator in contacting the voluntary informant. Obviously, if an offense occurs in front of a bar, the investigator will seek information within. A burglary offense calls for the questioning of known burglars or those who associate with such individuals. If the officer has an indication of the identity of the suspect, associates, relatives, and others are contacted for information. People in certain occupations have traditionally been found to have a high probability of yielding valuable information. Bartenders, pawnshop operators, taxi drivers, massage parlor personnel, and street vendors in general are some of them. Generally, those associated with businesses in used goods or entertainment, or who operate "in the street" in some manner are sources worth cultivating.

Investigators obtain voluntary information from informants in three general ways: by *personal cultivation*, by *departmental reference*, and by *unsolicited contact*. All officers should attempt to cultivate voluntary informants. Often, contacts made during a past investigation prove to be useful to the present case. If, for example, an officer conducted a past interview with a nightclub owner in a professional manner, the owner might be predisposed to provide information at a later date when solicited by the officer. A friendly, nonbelligerent, concerned attitude invites respect and confidence. An officer known for a positive attitude and reliability will find that reputation helpful in establishing rapport. Police officers often overlook a major source of voluntary information—the very suspects they arrest. An arrest does not have to be antagonistic. Of course, there will be some suspects who hate the police on general principle, but a surprisingly large number do not view an arrest as a personal affront. If treated fairly and in a professional manner, these suspects often voluntarily provide investigative information. The offer of a cigarette or an extra phone call to a suspect's relative can go far toward establishing a friendly rapport.

Many police agencies have established files listing voluntary informants cultivated in prior investigations. The file may be cross-referenced by name, type of information obtained, and occupation. Such information may prove to be very useful or of no value at all, depending on the informant. Although some informants will voluntarily provide information to any investigator, many will talk only to officers with whom a personal rapport has been established. Again, the stigma of being labeled an informant may prohibit the recontacting of some individuals.

Unsolicited contacts are voluntary informants who self-initiate the police contact. Identified subjects who report criminal activity without being solicited or subjects who give anonymous tips over the phone or by letter fall into this category. Anonymity may be essential for some voluntary informants. Many people wish to provide the police with information, yet the apprehension of being publicly identified stifles contact. Other individuals, for seemingly irrational reasons, fear face-to-face contact with an officer. They will provide information only on a totally anonymous basis. Some informants fear reprisal and simply do not trust the police to safeguard their identity. For these reasons, subjects who phone the police with information should not be pressured to reveal their identity. When asked, "May we have your name?" and the subject states, "I would rather not say," no further demand should be made.

Numerous police agencies have wisely instituted programs that recognize the necessity of guaranteed anonymity. One such program, known as the

Robotphone, was developed in Northern Ireland by the Royal Ulster Constabulary. When an informant dials the well-publicized Robotphone number, a recording device takes the information. This program has been highly successful in aiding officers in criminal investigations and in identifying terrorist suspects.[1] An important element of the program is the absence of a live police interviewer at one end of the telephone. Apparently, many voluntary informants will provide information to a machine much more readily than to a human being, either in person or over the phone. This method has been adopted by many American police agencies with equal success. TIP (Turn In a Pusher) and Secret Witness are two that have shown dramatic results.

In addition to newspaper programs or anonymous Web sites, television series currently dramatize unsolved case histories spotlighting wanted fugitives. A significant number of nationally prominent criminal investigations have been cleared as a result of televised reenactments, as the programs reach more than 60 million households. To date, as a result of the most popular of such programs, *America's Most Wanted*, 59 missing children have been recovered and more than 998 fugitives arrested, including 8 who appeared on the Federal Bureau of Investigation (FBI)'s Ten Most Wanted list.[2] For many years, the Drug Enforcement Administration (DEA) has operated a toll-free number designed to gather narcotics information. Any individual calling the number is assured absolute anonymity. There are programs offering monetary rewards in addition to guaranteed anonymity, but many highly successful ones have no monetary provisions.

Informants with Ulterior Motives

Some individuals provide the police with information for self-serving reasons. Such **informants with ulterior motives** do not demand or receive money for their information; however, serving as an informant benefits them in some fashion. Civic duty may be stated as the reason they are informing, but their true motivation may be something quite different. Revenge has always been a strong motivating factor for this type of informant. A person may seek to inflict harm on another for a real or imagined injury. Criminals who feel they have been cheated in the division of stolen property often anonymously inform on their former partners. Wives may inform on husbands whom they suspect to have been unfaithful or vice versa. Occasionally, a victim who has been swindled in a bunco scheme through greed motivations may anonymously inform for revenge.

Some arrested suspects provide information in the belief that their cooperation will result in their release or a reduced sentence. As previously mentioned, officers must never indicate that they have the authority to reduce a suspect's sentence; only the prosecuting attorney, in cooperation with the court, has this authority. Officers can indicate that a suspect's cooperation will be brought to the attention of the prosecutor, but they can go no further in attempting to elicit information.

Informing to eliminate fellow criminal competitors has traditionally benefited the investigator. Many criminals operate along typically businesslike lines of profit and loss. When one suspect is economically threatened by the competition of others, the result may be a timely phone call alerting the investigator to the competitor's illegal activity. With the increase in illegal drug sales, investigators have noted a sharp increase in this type of informant. Other common ulterior motives are guilt and the desire to receive attention.

Regardless of the true motivation involved and despite the often distasteful people with whom the officer must converse, all informants must be given equal credence and consideration.

Paid Informants

Any individual who receives monetary compensation for information is a **paid informant**. Paid informants vary in background and criminal association, but all provide information for money. In the majority of cases, the paid informant either is actively involved in crime or has close contacts with those who are. Because of public sensitivity concerning the use of informants, many police agencies reveal few details concerning the practice. Yet, the paid informant and the police have been strange working companions for many years. From the earliest organized police forces to the present day, the paid informant has been in constant demand. The failings of human nature—greed, in this case—suggest that this source of information will always be with us. Police agencies on the local, state, and federal levels spend millions of dollars annually for the informant's services. Recently, the Internal Revenue Service paid $6.6 million to 708 individuals who provided confidential information relating to income tax cheating.[3] The FBI, Treasury Department, and a host of other federal investigative agencies have sizable portions of their annual budgets earmarked for this purpose. State investigative agencies also routinely pay informants, with the majority of the money spent in cases relating to narcotics and organized crime. To date, the single largest amount paid by a government agency to an informant has been $30 million. In exchange for information leading to the location of Iraq dictator Saddam Hussein's fugitive sons, the U.S. State Department paid the sum in 2001. Wanted for numerous murders among other crimes, the subjects were located and killed in a gun battle with American military forces.

Critics of the use of paid informants point to the huge amounts of money involved and to the immorality of police paying unscrupulous individuals (frequently criminals) for information. Yet, the paid informant is a necessary, even essential, element of criminal investigation. It is perhaps unfortunate that these individuals have become so important, but the very nature of criminality demands their use. Crime is secretive and perpetrated by people who take great pains to avoid identification. Consequently, the task of criminal identification is a difficult one, demanding the use of all legal aids available to the officer, including the paid informant.

Certain investigations involving **consensual crimes**, in which complaints are rarely filed, often demand the use of paid informants. Narcotic crimes and prostitution fall into this category. Information gathered from paid informants often results in the recovery and return of substantial amounts of stolen property. For example, during one year, informants paid by the FBI accounted for 14,233 arrests and the recovery of more than $51 million in money and merchandise.[4] The DEA is another agency that is highly dependent on paid information. At any given time, the DEA maintains 4,000 informants who receive various payments totaling from $2 million to $4 million a year.[5] Although such expenditures may seem extravagant, the results they produce are significant. As former FBI director William Webster has written, "The informant is the single most important tool in law enforcement."[6]

Although the typical paid informant is a criminal type, many individuals with noncriminal backgrounds provide valuable information in exchange for money. The practice dates back nearly two centuries in this country. The offering of rewards for a suspect's identity or whereabouts was commonplace in the United States from the late 1700s to the turn of the century. In many areas of the country, cash payments were nearly the sole method of criminal apprehension because of the absence of any effective criminal investigation. A revival of interest in the cash reward appears to be gaining in popularity. Chiefly motivated by the increase in serious crime during the mid-1960s, numerous private and public agencies began to offer cash for information used in crime solution. In some cities, banks post photographs of robbery suspects on billboards and in buses. The Maryland Association for Bank Security has developed a highly successful Bank Robbery Reward Plan. Reward posters (Figure 1) are posted in all of the members' bank branches and related Web sites stating that cash rewards will be paid for information leading to convictions for bank robbery. Many newspapers and radio and television stations have also instituted programs designed to reach individuals with information for sale.

In many American communities, "Crime Stoppers" or similarly titled programs have become commonplace and highly effective in producing apprehensions. Through such programs, typically promoted in newspapers and sometimes in radio and television spots, cash rewards are paid for information leading to arrests and convictions in unsolved crimes. Reporting methods are devised that guarantee anonymity to the informant. Many such local programs are funded by private sources, such as a business community or a chamber of commerce. Police investigators typically provide the facts of an unsolved investigation for public announcement and assist in the evaluation of incoming tips.

The *Detroit News* advertised to its readers that rewards of $1,000 to $5,000 would be paid for information leading to convictions in specific crimes. In six years of operation, this program helped solve 31 murders and many more

FIGURE 1 Citizen tips through various media sources have led to the capture of thousands of dangerous felons during the past decade. Here, an FBI official, White House reporter, and the host of a television series dedicated to apprehending fugitives celebrate the 50th anniversary of the FBI's *Ten Most Wanted* program. *(Source: Dennis Cook/AP Wide World Photos.)*

felony offenses. Readers of the *Sacramento Bee*, in response to a similar program, solved 93 crimes and provided information leading to 48 major arrests during an 18-month period.[7] A trend that uses a newspaper format identifies wanted criminal suspects by name. Advertisements are purchased in local shopping-oriented papers by police or county prosecution officials, listing suspects' names and birth dates. One such program in Barron County, Wisconsin, listed 346 individuals wanted by the authorities. The advertisement quickly resulted in 12 arrests through informant information and in the voluntary surrender of 72 suspects after they became aware of the newspaper advertisement.

Reward programs are obviously of great benefit to the police; however, such programs must be closely supervised. A mutual cooperation and understanding must be established between the police and program agency. Investigators must stress to the citizens who operate such programs that criminal investigation is strictly a police responsibility. Accordingly, all information obtained through the program must be turned over to the police for proper investigation. Independent agencies other than the police should then determine the amount of reward to be paid to the informant.

The legality of an anonymous tip to the police has been upheld many times by various state supreme courts. The U.S. Supreme Court, as recently as 1990, determined that an anonymous tip, corroborated by independent investigative work, can provide reasonable grounds for suspicion and investigatory detention of a suspect. In *Alabama v. White*, the Court ruled that an anonymous informant who had access to information concerning a suspect's movements would also be likely to have access to reliable information about the suspect's illegal activities.[8]

Managing the Paid Informant

Informants who receive money for the information they supply must be managed very carefully. The paid informant is typically a career criminal or someone marginally involved in criminal activities. Obviously, this type of individual is untrustworthy—likely to take advantage of any mistake in management by the officer. One of the most important rules of informant management is that the investigator must always control the informant and never the informant the investigator. It is the investigator who must decide the details of the informant's activities, such as the manner in which evidence is gathered, meeting locations, and the amount of money paid for specific information.

Not only does the investigator manage the paid informant's activities in the field closely—all contacts involving money must be scrupulously managed. All funds paid to informants must be documented to protect the investigator and the police agency. Receipts should be obtained from the informant following payment, showing the amount paid, date, and signature of the recipient. Documentation of payment protects the officer from allegations that no payment was made or that a portion of the payment was withheld. Informants often hesitate to sign such receipts for fear of their identity being revealed. The investigator must give assurance that the receipt is for purposes of record keeping only and will remain confidential. Before any informant is paid, the investigator has an obligation to confirm the accuracy of the information. It is desirable that information be cross-checked using different sources, if at all possible. Similar information from other informants or confirmation by field surveillance will periodically serve to establish an informant's general reliability. If such checks are not made, informants may begin to supply information that is inaccurate or totally fictitious.

This type of informant is usually involved in a criminal organization, supplying information that will lead to a long investigation. All paid informants, regardless of the nature of their information, should be thoroughly identified by the police agency. This includes photographs, physical description, name, address, and fingerprints. Such information serves to identify and locate the informant for other officers and enables the background check to be made. Information gathered on the informant should be filed in a secure area. Although most state and federal investigative agencies allow open access to such files for all investigators, local agencies tend to restrict availability to the detective division. In addition, many local agencies require investigators wishing to review the files to obtain permission from the chief law-enforcement executive or command-level supervisors.[9]

A successful working relationship between investigator and informant is based on trust. The informant must have considerable trust and confidence in the ability of the officer. The informant's position is sometimes a very dangerous one; injury or even loss of life could result from an error in judgment. Consequently, the investigator must take great care to protect the informant's identity from everyone, with the exception of those who have a legitimate need to know. The investigator should never use the informant's true name in conversation or in investigative reports. Code names or number designations should be substituted. Obviously, when a meeting is required, the informant should never come to the police agency. Meetings should be held in out-of-the-way places, with a different locality selected for each meeting.

Police agencies that routinely use paid informants would do well to adhere to guidelines developed by the attorney general of the United States. Although the following guidelines were specifically developed for the FBI and DEA, they are applicable in theory to all police agencies:

1. When dealing with paid informants, a documented record of payment will be kept.
2. Supervisors will conduct frequent reviews of the activities of each informant.
3. The police agency will notify other authorities when an informant commits a crime in the jurisdiction of those authorities.
4. A background investigation will be completed for all informants.
5. Officers will be prohibited from making deals with informants who are seeking leniency in exchange of information.
6. Prosecution officials will review investigations using paid informants for legal adherence.
7. Officers will obtain the approval of a supervisor before using a paid informant
   (a) who is under 18 years of age,
   (b) who is currently on parole or probation,
   (c) who is undergoing treatment for drug addiction or who was addicted to drugs in the past, or
   (d) who has been convicted of two or more felony offenses.[10]

Informant Legal Considerations

A frequent area of difficulty arising from the use of informants in criminal investigations concerns the protection of their identities during the trial. The majority of informants, particularly the paid variety, do not wish to testify in public. Fortunately, our judicial system has historically recognized the need for informant confidentiality. State and federal courts have developed a doctrine known as the **doctrine of informer privilege**, which recognizes that an informant's identity should not be disclosed during the trial for two basic reasons, as follows: (a) Disclosure may result in retaliation and harm to the informant, and (b) confidentiality ensures a continued flow of information to the police. However, courts are also rightly concerned with providing a fair trial to the defendant. In response to these seemingly conflicting concerns, courts have developed certain "balancing" procedures to determine whether the informant should be required to testify in a particular criminal trial. Can a defendant be tried fairly without the opportunity to confront the informant? Is the informant's presence for cross-examination necessary and material to the suspect's defense? The court must weigh these factors carefully, examining the nature of the informant's involvement in the offense being considered. If the information provided by the informant merely initiated the investigation and the police subsequently established the elements of the crime through their own efforts, the informant's identity is rarely necessary. However, when the informant was physically present to witness the offense or participated in some element of the offense, an appearance in court may well be required. If the informant witnesses events between the officer and suspect, the officer's testimony will normally negate the necessity of having the informant testify. Occasionally, judges may interview informants privately to determine if their testimony would differ from the officer's and thus be important to the suspect's defense.

Certain types of investigations may involve an informant who has directly participated in an illegal transaction, for example, the purchase of narcotics. As a general principle, if an informant participates directly in the offense, either by handling evidence or otherwise engaging in the transaction, that informant becomes a material witness; that is, the informant's testimony may be important in the determination of guilt or innocence. Thus, the informant's testimony will be required by the defense, necessitating a court appearance.

A second commonly contested legal issue involving informants is **entrapment**. A common defense in cases involving informants or undercover police officers, entrapment can be asserted to challenge the legality of various investigative techniques. Often used as a criminal defense by drug defendants and other suspects charged in a variety of vice crimes, a claim of entrapment asserts that police have induced an individual to commit a crime. When defendants make such claims, the burden of proof falls on investigators to prove the defendant was, in fact, predisposed to commit the criminal offense. Inducement generally requires more than merely establishing that an officer approaches and requests a defendant to engage in criminal conduct. Government conduct is required that creates a substantial risk that an undisposed person or otherwise law-abiding citizen would commit the offense.

To ensure that undercover investigations do not give rise to successful claims of entrapment by suspects, officers should be aware of three essential points. First, investigators should be prepared to articulate to the court a legitimate law-enforcement purpose for beginning the undercover operation. Second, officers should avoid using persistent or coercive techniques and instead merely create an opportunity or provide the facilities for the suspect to commit the offense. Finally, investigators must document the factors demonstrating why a defendant was disposed to commit the criminal act prior to police contact. Such factors often include a prior arrest record, the suspect's familiarity with drug terminology, and eagerness to engage in criminal activity.

Many of the search warrants issued each year in the United States are based on information supplied by informants. Although the law varies from state to state, a search warrant will be issued if the informant is reliable and knowledgeable and has timely information.

Informant reliability is determined mainly from past associations between the informant and the authorities. If the informant has aided the police by identifying criminal suspects or locating wanted suspects or has generally supplied information that has proved to be accurate, reliability can be established. Accurate knowledge is necessary for the establishment of probable cause. The warrant can be issued only when the probable cause is sufficient to convince the judge of the warrant's worth. The investigator must determine if the informant's knowledge is firsthand and based on actual perception.

It is probable that the use of informants will continue to cause controversy and disagreement. Many defense attorneys feel that it is blatantly unconstitutional for informants to acquire information to be used in investigations. The objection centers on the lack of protection against self-incrimination when suspects are questioned by paid informants. Under the *Miranda* decision, police are required to warn a suspect of rights to silence and counsel, but an informant is free to question an unwary suspect without any such warnings.

A final legal informant consideration involves the use of *cellmate informants*. Cellmate informants are undercover police officers or, more commonly, fellow prisoners who obtain incriminating information from suspects confined in a correctional institution. Criminal investigators have found this technique to be an effective tool with certain types of suspects who are likely to boast while in jail or prison. The U.S. Supreme Court in *Illinois v. Perkins* (1990) held that the use of cellmate informants does not violate the *Miranda* rule. Undercover officers or actual cellmates need not give the warning before inquiring about a crime, as a prison cell lacks the psychologically compelling atmosphere that *Miranda* was designed to protect against. When an imprisoned suspect has previously invoked his or her right to silence during an earlier phase of the investigation, however, the legal use of cellmate informants is questionable in many circumstances.[11]

DOCUMENTARY SOURCES OF INFORMATION

Few people outside the law-enforcement profession realize the investigative importance of documentary sources of information. **Documentary information** is any type of information of a printed nature or data otherwise recorded and stored for retrieval. Such information may be obtained from within the police agency, from other criminal justice agencies, and from sources not connected with law enforcement. The media image of the criminal investigator rarely includes the paperwork aspect of the job. The investigator deals with people and crime scenes on a continual basis, but much time is spent tracking down and evaluating "paper information." It is a rare felony investigation in which an officer does not spend many hours processing reports, files, and records in an effort to document the case. Such duties require patience, knowledge, and a systematic thoroughness for proper results.

Internal Agency Sources

The first step in becoming skilled in gathering and evaluating documentary information is to be aware of the typical municipal police agency as a source. Since police departments vary considerably in size and budget, no two agencies will be identical in their information-gathering capabilities. However, all medium-sized and large departments have the same general reporting and recording systems. The majority of police agencies have some type of computerized *master file* containing the following information:

1. names and addresses of individuals who have been arrested or questioned in some manner or who have reported an offense, witnessed an offense, or who have otherwise made contact with the police agency;
2. references to crime reports by the name of the reporting party, victim, or suspect or by the assigned officer;
3. reports of all traffic accidents and other traffic contacts; and
4. name listing of all suspects having warrants for their arrest.

In addition to the master file, police agencies typically have records located in the division in which the greatest use will be made of them. The detective division often has a *modus operandi* (MO) file, cross-indexed by type of crime, name of criminal, and method of criminal operation. Investigators frequently refer to photographic files of previously arrested subjects. This type of file or book is arranged by the type of crime committed and is used to aid victims or witnesses in identifications. Printed bulletins and notifications of recent crimes are also found in the detective division. Depending on the size of the agency, files of informants and of criminal intelligence may also be available to the investigator.

The patrol division is capable of helping the investigative efforts of the entire department; it operates around the clock and has tremendous information-gathering potential. Patrol divisions that routinely use the field interview gather much important information that is ultimately recorded and filed for future reference.

The jail division routinely records the names of suspects who are currently confined, along with the offense and background information from the booking form. The booking form may be very useful in that it lists the address, date of birth, physical description, place of employment, occupation, possessions at time of arrest, and other important data on the suspect. The jail department also houses fingerprint cards and photos taken at the time of arrest.

The identification division of a police agency often is a source of files of a forensic nature. Records of latent fingerprints, crime-scene photos, tool marks and impressions, paint samples, and ballistics materials are normally stored in this area. The property room contains stolen or recovered items that are held until trial. Records of such property indicate the basic physical description of the item, serial numbers, recovering officer, and other pertinent information.

The New York City Police Department initiated an internal information system in 2008, which effectively combines many previously separate criminal databases into one high-tech operation. Termed the Real Time Crime Center, the $11 million computer complex provides 24-hour instantaneous access to all computerized records of value to criminal investigators. Uniformed field officers and detectives can instantly summon information to aid investigations in minutes rather than taking days or longer to produce similar results.

The center has instant access to various databases including surveillance images, arrest and parole histories, tattoo databases, 120 million citizen criminal complaints, warrants, 911 call records for the past ten years, satellite imaging, and computerized geographic crime mapping, among many other sources of information. As officers receive tips in the field, or seek information while at crime scenes, they communicate inquiries directly back to the center for rapid data retrieval. The quick receipt of tracing information greatly increases the probability of an arrest before a suspect can either escape or commit future offenses.

Criminal Justice Agency Sources

Cooperation is the backbone of effective criminal investigation. The long-standing tradition of sharing documentary information among the various enforcement agencies has benefited the entire criminal justice system. Criminal investigators should be aware that, in addition to their own agencies, a multitude of other agencies at the local, state, and federal levels may serve as information sources. Each level provides unique and often essential services to aid the investigative process.

Local agency sources are normally municipal police departments, county sheriff's offices, and county probation and parole bureaus. Neighboring municipal police departments provide similar information, yet, the specifics of the information are unique to each source. Because of the increased mobility of the criminal, similar crimes in several adjacent communities are occurring with greater frequency. Close communication and cooperation among local agencies may result in the recognition of such a pattern. Cooperation with a sheriff's department can also result in the acquisition of valuable intelligence information. Since the sheriff's department has an enforcement responsibility to the entire county, the documentary information found there is of a broader scope than that of a typical municipal police agency. The sheriff is also responsible for the operation of the county jail, including the collection and storage of all booking information resulting from jail procedures.

Probation, parole, and prison records have considerable information of possible value to the investigator. All convicted offenders who are placed on probation or released on parole have been investigated by these departments. The detailed background investigations on these offenders may provide insights not available elsewhere. The extent of such data can be appreciated when one considers there are currently over four million people on probation and 700,000 on parole. These figures do not include the millions of Americans who have previously been under probation and parole supervision. Prison records can provide data regarding inmate associates, gang affiliations, and DNA profiles. The coroner's or medical examiner's office is responsible for the investigation of suspicious or violent deaths. To arrive at a conclusion of the cause of death, this office conducts a postmortem examination of the deceased.

Such a procedure involves the compilation of considerable information regarding the victim, witnesses to the death, and all other pertinent areas of inquiry.

State governments provide investigative assistance through various specialized departments. They also consolidate information from local enforcement agencies. The attorney general of each state is considered its chief law-enforcement officer. The major function of the Office of the Attorney General is to review existing state statutes, supervise local prosecutors, and investigate specific criminal or civil violations. State attorney generals frequently aid local agencies by conducting training seminars or by issuing statewide bulletins of enforcement interest. *Alert*, a monthly news bulletin published by the Office of the Attorney General of Maine, interprets the latest laws and court actions affecting police officers' job execution. Many states have sizable investigative agencies, such as the California Department of Justice and the Florida Department of Law Enforcement, which provide investigative assistance to requesting local agencies or instigate investigations into multicounty crimes. State investigative bureaus can assist the local investigator by providing informants, undercover agents, and intelligence information. In addition to state investigative agencies, the majority of states have bureaus of identification.

Identification bureaus provide a central location for crime reports, DNA profiles, fingerprint cards, MO files, laboratory equipment, and personnel for all enforcement agencies within the state. The trend in recent years has been to combine the state identification bureau with the state investigation department, merging the two into a single agency. Occasionally, the state police or highway patrol of a given state also functions as an identification bureau. There are approximately 55 million criminal history records in state criminal identification repositories throughout the United States.

Within the government structure of each state, the motor vehicle bureau contains much documentary information of possible investigative value. This department is often administered by the secretary of state. Since our society is highly mobile, the automobile has become increasingly more important as a tracing clue in various crimes. Contained within the department are records of all motorized vehicles within the state and licensing information on all drivers. The licensing information can be very useful, containing a detailed physical description, date of birth, address, signature, handwriting sample, and photograph.

Federal criminal justice agencies exercise wide territorial authority and are varied in the specific enforcement assistance they can provide to local officers. The Department of Justice agencies include the FBI, the DEA, the Bureau of Prisons, and the Law Enforcement Assistance Administration. The FBI has a long history of providing valuable information to local law-enforcement agencies. Having the most massive data collection of any justice agency, the FBI has compiled records on nearly 80 million individuals and organizations since its founding in 1908, with 800,000 new names added to its files each year. Information has been gathered from routine background inquiries, national security checks, and standard criminal investigations.[12] In addition to investigating the 206 federal offenses over which it has jurisdiction, the FBI serves any requesting police agency via the following:

1. ***The National Crime Information Center (NCIC).*** On January 27, 1967, the **NCIC** computerized electronic data exchange became operational. Developed to complement computerized systems already in operation by local and state enforcement agencies, this system records

enormous amounts of criminal information in a central computer bank in Washington. The system is designed to link thousands of police agencies by remote computer terminals to the control center. Agencies using the service can instantaneously determine if a suspect is wanted in another jurisdiction or if recovered property is stolen. Participating agencies also have the capability of entering information into the system concerning locally wanted people, automobiles, and other types of property. The NCIC system contains more than 20 million records on wanted and missing persons, stolen property, and other matters. It has proved to be an extremely useful system. Nearly 60,000 authorized users conduct a million transactions daily. Among its many uses, the NCIC system has proven to be extremely helpful in apprehending wanted fugitives, as more than 300,000 entries are contained in the Wanted Persons File. Technological advances planned for the near future will allow users to receive and transmit suspect fingerprints and photographs. A wanted suspect's fingerprints will be computer transmitted, searched, and matched from the Wanted Persons File within 20 seconds.[13]

2. *The Criminalistics Laboratory Information System (CLIS).* This computerized information system collects and disseminates forensic science data for law-enforcement agencies throughout the United States. The data are collected, identified, and stored for online retrieval through NCIC terminals. Information on the latest analysis methods, crime-scene collection procedures, and the like is instantly available for any officer.

3. *The FBI Laboratory.* The largest forensic laboratory in the world, its facilities are available without cost to any U.S. enforcement agency. More than 900,000 forensic examinations are conducted yearly in all areas of criminalistics. In addition to forensic testing, the laboratory operates the National Fraudulent Check File, the Anonymous Letter File, the Bank Robbery Note File, the National Stolen Coin File, and the National Stolen Art File. The check file is a national repository for fraudulent checks that has proven very helpful in tracking fraudulent check passers moving rapidly from one community to another. When a fraudulent check is submitted, handwriting and other factors are compared against previously submitted checks. Additional descriptive data on the suspect MO, photographs, and identification records of check passers are furnished to requesting enforcement agencies. The bank note file connects robberies to individual perpetrators through analysis of holdup notes. During a recent year, 1,129 such notes were searched in the computerized files, resulting in 144 associations with other robbery notes. The art file contains more than 4,000 detailed descriptions of stolen fine art and helps establish the method of operation.[14]

4. *The FBI Identification Division.* Formed in 1924, this division receives fingerprint cards of arrested suspects and others from 7,200 contributing agencies. The sets of fingerprints submitted daily number 25,000. The identification division informs police agencies of a suspect's prior record and possible wanted status. Deceased subjects are also identified. The fingerprint collection of this division is in excess of 175 million cards.

5. *The Combined DNA Index System (CODIS).* Because of the DNA Identification Act of 1994, the FBI was authorized to establish a national DNA database for law-enforcement purposes. The CODIS system

enables public laboratories on the local, state, federal, and international levels to exchange and compare DNA profiles via computer. The system allows investigators to compare identified DNA profiles against genetic evidence secured from past unsolved crimes or recently arrested suspects and assists in establishing the identity of suspects and victims. The central FBI CODIS computer index currently contains over 2.3 million DNA profiles from all 50 states and 18 foreign countries. To date, at least 5,000 unsolved crimes have been cleared by the system, and many thousands of felons have been correctly identified who otherwise might have remained unknown.

The Federal Bureau of Prisons administers federal correctional institutions throughout the United States. Information concerning a suspect's conduct while in prison, personal acquaintances, medical and psychological data, and photographs are available to the officer from this source. The DEA was established in 1973 to control narcotics and dangerous drug abuse. The agency is additionally responsible for supervising licensing and inspection of those individuals who are legally allowed to handle and prescribe narcotics. The DEA provides numerous training seminars in narcotics investigation to local police agencies and maintains a laboratory for narcotics analysis. Local police agencies may use the record resources of the DEA, such as the known-addicts file. All suspects who have been arrested or otherwise identified as narcotics users are fully identified in this file. The DEA also routinely provides undercover agents to assist departments that lack the expertise, personnel, or budget for undercover operations.

The U.S. Department of the Treasury comprises the Internal Revenue Service (IRS) and the Bureau of Alcohol, Tobacco, Firearms and Explosives (ATF). Organized in 2003, the U.S. Department of Homeland Security (DHS) houses the Secret Service and newly combined Bureau of Immigration and Customs Enforcement (ICE). Homeland Security was primarily formed to keep America secure from terrorist attack, and is particularly focused on safeguarding the country's borders, airports, seaports, and waterways. Further responsibilities of this federal department include developing the latest security technologies, responding to natural disasters or terroristic assaults, and analyzing intelligence reports leading to publicized threat-level alerts. The Bureau of Customs prevents smuggling and regulates the transfer of people and property into and out of the country. This agency additionally maintains files on suspects who have engaged in smuggling activities, including the method of operation used by such suspects. The IRS oversees and enforces the internal revenue statutes. The Intelligence Division of the IRS maintains information on tax evaders, including many organized crime and narcotics suspects. The Secret Service has considerable information on counterfeiting suspects and those suspected of threatening persons protected by this agency. The Secret Service also maintains a forensic section to analyze forged or counterfeited currency and securities.

The ATF operates as a separate bureau of the Treasury Department. Information on suspects who have been investigated or convicted of crimes in these areas is available in this bureau. A national office laboratory in Washington, D.C., offers a wide variety of services to enforcement officers. These include firearm and toolmark examination, chemical and instrumental analysis, and questioned document examination. Local investigators who encounter cases involving explosive devices almost always consult with ATF investigators; the latter are experts on the handling and field practices that are called for in such cases.

The U.S. Department of Defense includes the Army, Navy, Marines, and Air Force, in addition to civilian intelligence-gathering agencies. Each branch of the armed forces has specific internal enforcement agencies. Records are maintained on individuals who have been members of the armed forces and civilian individuals who have been the subject of criminal or intelligence investigations.

Other law-enforcement agencies of the federal government can assist the investigator in various ways. For example, the U.S. Postal Service can provide a change of address and record information that appears on the outside surface of an envelope. Or the Federal Aviation Administration (FAA) can provide detailed information regarding aircraft and data concerning suspects who are licensed pilots. With the rapid increase in narcotics cases involving aircraft, the FAA has been consulted with considerable frequency. ICE can provide fingerprints, photos, and other data on suspects who are aliens or naturalized Americans. Because of the sizable number of federal agencies and their specialized areas of inquiry, it is advisable for every local police agency to obtain a directory of the federal government. Directories listing the name, address, and function of each federal agency are available online or from the Government Printing Office in Washington, D.C.

A relatively new but very helpful agency is the **National Criminal Justice Reference Service** (NCJRS). This federal department has become the largest criminal justice information network in the world. The NCJRS was created to furnish research findings to criminal justice professionals and operates five clearinghouses that provide free information to criminal investigators and other justice practitioners.

Outside Sources

Sources not connected with law enforcement vary substantially in quality and accessibility. Many publishing companies issue annual directories of individuals with common interests or backgrounds. Various *Who's Who*–type publications or Web sites can supply the investigator with biographical data on certain prominent individuals. There are a number of financial listings of varying usefulness. Dun & Bradstreet has financial data on businesses. Standard and Poor's *Register of Corporations, Directors and Executives* and Moody's *Bank and Finance Manual* also list business and corporation information. The annual *Physician's Desk Reference* lists more than 2,500 drug and narcotic products. Although this publication is intended for physicians, the compound analysis of the various drugs and the physical side-effect information that is given can help an officer who is working narcotics. The book also contains a visual products section in which the color, size, and product markings of many dangerous drugs are illustrated. Other directories are available that list subscribing professional people, such as physicians, engineers, and educators. Names, addresses, and phone numbers, and sometimes background data are given.

Private industry has given rise to numerous credit-reporting agencies for investigating the financial background of potential customers. Hundreds of major businesses make use of such agencies. Many retailers deal with local credit bureaus that compile and exchange information on the local level only. The national computer-based services and local credit bureaus have similar types of documentary information. Such information is limited because it is normally obtained from an individual during application for credit. Full name, address, previous places of residence, past and current employment, and various indicators of financial worth are normally listed. The three largest nationwide consumer credit-reporting companies in the United States (and their respective toll-free phone numbers) are Equifax 1-800-525-6285, Experian 1-800-397-3742, and TransUnion 1-800-680-7289. Web sites for these organizations are listed at the end of this chapter in the Relevant Web sites section. Similar information is documented in central depositories that are operated by banks and finance companies; however, because of the greater risk involved, this information is generally more extensive and detailed. Employee records, phone company information, medical files, and student records may additionally assist the officer.

The availability of private information sources is as great or as limited as the resourcefulness of the investigator. In today's computer-driven society, it is a rare individual indeed who has not deposited documentary information somewhere. If the investigator has procured some general information concerning a suspect, such as a name or place of employment, few private sources of information will remain untouched.

PHYSICAL SOURCES OF INFORMATION

The Crime Scene

The scene of the criminal offense is the source of most of the physical information pertinent to the investigation. All evidence secured from the crime scene is reviewed as to its information potential. It may be determined that additional examinations by others are required. Crime-scene evidence often has significant value in providing the officer with suspect-tracing information. Latent fingerprints, clothing, and bodily fluids are only a few of the hundreds of tracing clues that may result from a thorough search of the scene.

It is important for the investigator to realize that the informational value of physical evidence may best be judged by specialists with the necessary expertise. Although an officer may be very experienced and have considerable knowledge of forensic science, evidence should be submitted to the police laboratory for all value judgments. Criminalistics is a relatively young and rapidly expanding science. Consequently, evidence that was valueless in past investigations may be very useful to the present case as a result of new forensic discoveries.

PRIVACY CONSIDERATIONS

Public concern with the right to privacy can be attributed in part to the tremendous growth of computerization. Never before in U.S. history has government and industry had so great a capability to gather and use information. In a modern-day sense, privacy is often a legal right; however, the legal right of an individual to remain publicly anonymous is far from absolute. U.S. courts are often faced with a true dilemma when confronted with privacy considerations.

On the one hand, there is the need of government and industry to store and disseminate information; on the other, there is the right of individual protection against the storage and dissemination of incorrect or damaging data.

Philosophical Objections to Information Gathering

Many Americans feel threatened by the information-gathering capacity of private and public sectors of the population. A feeling that individuality has been sacrificed to "the right to know" is commonly expressed by some opponents of data-collection systems. Other opponents argue that the personal development of an individual can be seriously damaged by computer files. They fear that individuals may become overly concerned with how they are presented in a file and attempt to structure their lives to conform with the computer's expectations. Philosophical objections range from situational opposition to the rejection of all information gathering in any format. Additionally, many citizens feel that secretive data systems hamper effective government. The objections to information gathering are not groundless, for large computerized systems do make mistakes. Individuals can suffer financially or otherwise from false information routinely released by an impersonal data center.

The historical and philosophical development of our country has been rooted in the right to individuality and privacy. Thus, the investigator may be in a difficult position. Criminal investigation in a large, mobile society is inherently difficult, demanding the development and use of modern information systems. Yet, despite the difficulties and the need to overcome them, right of individual privacy must be observed.

Private Information Gathering

Information is collected, stored, and released by thousands of private agencies. Business concerns, data-processing bureaus, and many other nongovernment sources annually gather a tremendous amount of information on thousands of individuals. It is estimated that more than 100 million people are the subject of detailed computerized files in one or more private-industry computers.[15] The development of computer processing has been of great benefit to commercial business. Private industry has the capacity to check financial stability, past credit ratings, and other financial risk factors with computer assistance. Masses of paper that at one time were difficult to store and utilize can be stored in data banks at a greatly reduced size. A matchbox can hold computer record information that, in print, would fill a cathedral.

Credit bureaus have traditionally been an aid to the investigator; the information they record frequently helps to identify or trace a suspect. Credit investigators gather much useful information on people who apply for credit, loans, or life or automobile insurance, and on those who apply for certain types of employment. For example, the Medical Information Bureau of Boston collects and stores medical history forms from 90 percent of all life-insurance companies. Any person applying for life insurance with a subscriber company has a completed medical history form stored in the bureau's computer banks if one or more of 250 specified medical or psychiatric illnesses is cited.[16] The bureau's files currently number more than 11 million. Many other data-reporting agencies operate in a similar manner, storing information received during the application procedure for credit, loans, or other services.

The capacity to store and evaluate information automatically has produced correspondence privacy difficulties. Widespread reports of misuse of information by private industry led to the passage of the Fair Credit Reporting Act of 1970. The act gave an individual the authority to obtain, on demand, a report of what was in his or her credit file and to challenge any information found to be untrue. This had the impact of making it more difficult for the officer to gain access to private information files. Criminal investigators who, in the past, obtained such information through personal contact now find private sources reluctant to release information. In many situations, a court order is necessary to obtain the requested information, as is the case with telephone records.

Criminal Justice Information Gathering

Law-enforcement agencies on the local, state, and federal level have developed effective record-keeping data systems. Most police departments have totally computerized record divisions. It has been estimated that the federal government operates more than 8,000 record systems containing information that would total 92 billion pages.[17] Public suspicion and mistrust of private industry data gathering extends also to government record keeping. To counteract fears that false information was being filed against individuals or that U.S. citizens had no access to tax-supported record systems, Congress passed the **Freedom of Information Act** (FOIA) in 1966. This act recognized the "people's right to know" by setting up a formal request procedure for public access to government records. Prior to the FOIA, an individual had to prove a direct interest in the information requested. The 1966 act did away with that stipulation—if an individual took legal action to demand information, the burden of proving a legitimate reason for denial rested with the government. Because of various complaints (mainly from the news media) that the act was cumbersome, new legislation was proposed to amend it. On December 31, 1974, the **Privacy Act** was enacted by Congress. The Privacy Act has had a major impact on all federal agencies and particularly federal law-enforcement agencies.

Essentially, the Privacy Act and FOIA opened federal records to the individuals to whom they pertain. The individual has the right to review and amend incorrect information and to subject the report to judicial review if the agency refuses to amend the data. Additionally, the Privacy Act prescribed information-collection procedures designed to improve the accuracy of the data. The Privacy Act does contain specific exemptions, prohibiting the review and release of information that falls into the following categories:

1. information classified as necessary for the national security;
2. information relating to the internal personnel rules and practices of an agency;
3. privileged trade-secret information; and
4. information concerning personnel, medical files, or investigative records that, if disclosed, might jeopardize the right to fair trial, invade personal privacy, or expose confidential sources.

Each federal agency must determine the investigative effects of data disclosure. It is fortunate for law enforcement that such exemptions are stipulated in the act; otherwise, criminal suspects undergoing a current investigation could keep abreast of each investigative development and learn the identity of all sources, obviously undermining the investigative effort.

Although the Privacy Act was directed toward all federal agencies, it has greatly influenced record keeping on the state and local levels. Many state legislatures have enacted state laws based on the Privacy Act. The majority of the states specify that information may be reviewed only by law-enforcement personnel. For example, the Illinois statute states, "No file or record . . . hall be made public, except as may be necessary in the identification of persons suspected or accused of crime . . . and no information . . . hall be given or furnished by said Department to any such person."[18]

Accordingly, the Crime Control Act gives the subject of a specific criminal-history record file the right to inspect and challenge inaccuracies. It is important to note that investigative records and criminal intelligence files are not classified as criminal-history record information; thus, a subject may not review and correct such files. To prevent access to these files, all information pertaining to the five points previously listed must be maintained in separate files.

It is probable that additional legislation will be proposed governing the accessibility of police information. Although some individuals welcome continued efforts to "open up government," the necessity of restricted access to police records must be appreciated. This concern is particularly true given the investigating demand of the war on terror. Without the assumption of confidentiality, informational sources will be more difficult to locate. Many investigators report a current trend toward reluctance to be interviewed on the part of subjects. Such informants fear their identities will be disclosed under the FOIA. Other problems relate to the time and money necessary to implement accessibility. Since the FOIA amendments in 1974, many federal agencies have been overwhelmed by requests for information. The FBI alone has a backlog of more than 5,000 such requests that cannot be acted upon because of staff limitations. Since the Privacy Act, federal requests have averaged more than 12,500 a month, with resulting monthly processing costs of $8.2 million.[19] Since so many requests for FBI files are repeated for similar notorious cases, the agency decided in 1998 to place a large number of commonly requested files online so they would be available through open Internet access. Many famous investigations are now readily available via Internet, totaling an extraordinary 1.3 million pages of information.

Electronic Surveillance

The use of electronic devices to gather information continues to be highly controversial. Government officials and some segments of the general public are sharply split on the issue. Many Americans are generally confused. Listening surreptitiously to private conversations of others has been practiced for many centuries. Historical accounts are filled with descriptions of individuals (both public and private) attempting to gather information by eavesdropping.

In the United States, *wiretapping* was not practiced with any degree of frequency until the outbreak of the Civil War. From 1861 to 1865, surreptitious "tapping" of telegraphic lines became a standard military practice. Confederate cavalry leaders became particularly adept, with General John Morgan employing the services of a tapping expert to accompany his troops and gather information.[20] The interception of telephone calls did not come until the turn of the century, when telephone usage became commonplace.

Electronic surveillance, or *eavesdropping*, normally refers to the listening in on spoken interactions via devices that gather and amplify sound. Unlike wiretapping, this technique does not depend on a physical entry into a circuit. Wiretapping and electronic surveillance techniques were greatly improved during World War II and are currently in a highly sophisticated state of electronic development. Prior to 1968, electronic information gathering was practiced by public and private individuals but not on a consistent basis. Although many states prohibited the practice, the statutes were unclear about what specifically constituted the practice. In June 1968, Congress passed the Omnibus Crime Control and Safe Streets Act, which legalized electronic surveillance by law-enforcement officers. The act was the first federal legislation in history to allow federal, state, and local officers to intercept wire and oral communications—with certain specified safeguards. Congress was prompted to pass the act to control organized crime and certain other serious criminal offenses.

The Omnibus Crime Control Act specified that electronic surveillance of a judicially unauthorized nature was illegal. It additionally specified punishments for violations and banned the manufacture, distribution, possession, and advertising of devices used to eavesdrop. The act also set forth procedures by which to apply for authorization to practice electronic surveillance and specified certain criminal cases in which the practice would be permitted. Certainly, the prohibition of private eavesdropping is one of the act's strong points. Private eavesdropping was common prior to 1968, with private investigators and other unauthorized individuals frequently engaging such means in investigations involving divorce and other domestic situations.

The thrust of the Omnibus Crime Control Act was to provide law enforcement with a modern, effective tool with which to combat organized crime and other serious offenses. Since the passage of the act, it has been documented that many law-enforcement agencies have made use of electronic surveillance. Figures published by the federal government for 2004 are typical of recent usage patterns. They indicate that 1,710 wiretap requests were approved by the federal and state judges. Each wiretap averaged nearly 2,000 conversations. The majority of court-authorized electronic surveillances are requested by state and local law-enforcement agencies. In a recent year, nearly 60 percent of all requests were made by local rather than federal authorities. Of the total warrants issued, 73 percent were sought in drug investigations, with most of the other warrants being used for gambling and organized crime cases. As cell phones, pagers, e-mail, and fax machines have become more common, a growing number of court-authorized wiretaps have been used in cases that involve this expanding wireless electronic technology. Nearly nine of every ten wiretaps targeted portable devices, such as cell phones and pagers.

Although the majority of the states have statutes sanctioning court-ordered electronic surveillance, it is far from a common police practice. Annual reports submitted to Congress indicate that only a minority of the states having the power to use electronic surveillance actually use such means. Overall, the use of electronic surveillance has been greatly exaggerated in media accounts and other popular outlets. In reality, only slightly more than 8,000 criminal wiretaps have been authorized by courts in the past ten years. Yet, the effectiveness of this selective method of investigation is well illustrated by the 22,000 convictions that resulted from the 8,000 surveillances.[21] In 2004 alone, wiretaps resulted in 4,506 arrests, which concluded in 634 convictions.

Wiretapping and electronic surveillance should not be confused with recording conversations in which the officer is one of the parties. The federal statute applies to the surveillance of those conversations that do not include the officer as a participant. In undercover fieldwork, recording devices concealed on the officer's body are frequently used. Since the undercover officer, or informant, is one of the parties to the conversation, court authorization is not normally necessary. Some states have enacted statutes demanding that such recordings be authorized by a local state's attorney or district prosecutor. For example, Illinois requires that an investigator secure the consent of a state's attorney to record conversations, even in cases in which the investigator is one of the parties. To date, 40 states and the federal government allow the taping of conversations if one party agrees to the recording.

Summary

In addition to obtaining information through interviewing, investigators must be skilled at gathering data from other sources. Information can be obtained from human, documentary, and physical sources. Human sources include citizens providing information as a result of civic duty, suspicion, or other natural motivations. Some provide information purely for monetary gain; others have ulterior motives. All human-oriented information must be evaluated objectively, and efforts must be made to corroborate the data through supporting sources. The paid informant often needs strict supervision and control, for such individuals typically have been or currently are involved in criminal activities.

The use of documentary sources of information necessitates a complete understanding of the location and type of data within the investigator's agency. A multitude of other criminal justice organizations also have informational sources of frequent benefit to the investigative process. Many federal data-gathering services are available to the investigator, including vast criminal history files and the National Crime Information Center. Sources of data not connected with law enforcement vary from privately published directories to information gathered by the credit and banking industries. Most physical evidence, however, is obtained from actual crime scenes. This form of evidence is often evaluated by experts trained in the science of criminalistics.

As technology devises newer and better methods to obtain investigative information, a corresponding concern with privacy arises. Privacy concerns are often difficult to resolve in a completely satisfactory fashion, for the rights of individuals must be balanced with the need of government to serve and protect effectively.

Exercises

1. Complete a research paper on the use of police informants from a historical and present-day perspective.
2. Interview a local police official as to departmental policy regarding the use of paid informants.
3. Research the degree and type of court-authorized electronic surveillance conducted by police in your city, county, or state.

Relevant Web Sites

http://www.icje.org/id114.htm
   Extensive essay details entrapment problems in handling informants. Links to essays on informant liability issues.
http://www.fas.org/irp/agency/doj/fbi/is/ncic.htm
   Site of National Crime Information Center operated by the FBI. Details the various categories of individuals covered by the system. Links to sites dealing with the Privacy Act.
http://www.equifax.com
http://www.experian.com
http://www.transunion.com
   Sites of the three largest consumer credit–reporting agencies in the United States.

Notes

1. James H. Morton, "'Robby' the Informer," *Police Chief*, **40**, no. 8 (August 1973), pp. 42–43.

2. *Kearney Hub* (Nebraska), 1 June 1996, p. 7A.

3. "The Big Prize," *U.S. News & World Report*, 7 May 1990, p. 21.

4. "Informers under Fire," *Time*, 17 April 1972, pp. 77–88.

5. Gary S. Katzmann, *Inside the Criminal Process* (New York: W. W. Norton, 1991), pp. 40–41.

6. William Webster, "Sophisticated Surveillance— Intolerable Intrusion or Prudent Protection?" *Washington Law Review*, **63**, 1985, p. 351.

7. "How You Can Join the War against Crime and Drug Pushers" (Pleasantville, N.Y.: The Reader's Digest Association, 1973), p. 5.

8. "Selected Supreme Court Cases," *FBI Law Enforcement Bulletin*, **59**, no. 11 (November 1990), p. 29.

9. "Models for Management," *Police Chief*, **57**, no. 1 (January 1990), pp. 56–57.

10. Publicity Release, Office of the United States Attorney General, December 28, 1977.

11. Kimberly A. Crawford, "A Constitutional Guide to the Use of Cellmate Informants," *FBI Law Enforcement Bulletin*, **64**, no. 12 (December 1995), pp. 18–23.

12. *Omaha World Herald*, 8 July 1996, p. 5.

13. David F. Nemecek, "NCIC 2000 Technology Adds a New Weapon to Law Enforcement Arsenal," *Police Chief*, **57**, no. 4 (April 1990), pp. 30–33.

14. William Y. Doran, "The FBI Laboratory: Fifty Years," *Journal of Forensic Sciences*, **27**, no. 4 (October 1982), p. 743.

15. "The Brave World of Data Surveillance," *Unesco Courier*, July 1973, p. 17.

16. *Baltimore Sunday Sun*, 13 July 1975, p. 1.

17. *Champaign-Urbana* (Illinois) *News Gazette*, 24 December 1976, p. 24C.

18. *Illinois Revised Statutes*, Chap. 38, pp. 206–207.

19. "Freedom of Information," *U.S. News & World Report*, 9 August 1976, p. 55.

20. Howard Swiggett, *The Rebel Raider: The Life of John Hunt Morgan* (Indianapolis: Bobbs-Merrill, 1934), p. 61.

21. "Keeping the Cybercops Out of Cyberspace," *Newsweek*, 14 March 1994, p. 38.

Information Technology

Information Technology

Tools for the Task

Key Terms and Concepts

CompStat
Computer-aided dispatch (CAD)
Crime analysis
Geographic information system (GIS)
Geomapping

Geographic profiling
Global Positioning System (GPS)
Hot spot
Mobile computing
Records management system (RMS)
Street-level criminology

Learning Objectives

As a result of reading this chapter, the student will:

- Understand the function of the three basic aids for crime analysis: computer-aided dispatch (CAD), mobile computing, and records management systems (RMS)
- Know the difference between strategic and tactical crime analysis
- Comprehend how crime patterns can be geomapped
- Be able to trace the development, purposes, and methods of CompStat, and understand how it can function today in agencies of all sizes
- Understand geographic profiling and hot spots
- Be able to explain Global Positioning Systems (GPS) with regard to using police resources
- Know how the Internet and an intranet apply to policing and crime analysis
- Understand the kinds of knowledge, skills, and abilities needed to be a crime analyst

God hath made man upright; but they have sought out many inventions.

–Ecclesiastes 7:29

INTRODUCTION

According to the National Commission of Law Observance and Enforcement in 1931 (best known as the Wickersham Commission), the advent of the radio-equipped patrol car brought a new era where "the roving patrol car, fast, efficient, stealthy . . . [was] just as liable to be within 60 feet as 3 miles of the crook plying his trade . . . who is coming to realize that a few moments may bring them down about him like a swarm of bees—this lightning swift angel of death."[1] And thus was police technology born, with the introduction of the radio-controlled patrol car hailed as the technological innovation that would turn the tide against criminals.

For more than four decades, the police have been employing myriad technologies to gather, store, and share information. In addition, today's police officers are on a cell phone, deploy a TASER instead of a six-shot revolver, use a defibrillator from the patrol car trunk to resuscitate heart attack victims, send latent fingerprints to an automated database for matching, use digital photographs and other identification means to see if someone is telling the truth, and utilize many other kinds of databases and tools of the trade (many of which are discussed later in this chapter) that would boggle the minds of such pioneers as August Vollmer and O. W. Wilson. Today technology can help the police to better serve their communities by automating time-consuming tasks, dispatching personnel more efficiently, and improving an agency's ability to collect and analyze data as well as disseminate it to both internal and external audiences.

This chapter examines the current use of technology as it can be applied to community oriented policing and problem solving (COPPS); specifically, we look at how it can generally assist with analyzing crime information. We begin with a consideration of the function of crime analysis in the problem-solving concept and list several criteria that must be met for analysis to succeed. Then we consider what we call the basic systems of analysis: computer-aided dispatch, mobile computing, and records management. Next is a section where we briefly distinguish between strategic and tactical crime analysis. Following that is a look at how geomapping is used to reveal crime patterns.

Then we turn to a concept that often represents a higher level of accountability for crime analysis: CompStat. This involves the collection and analysis of a number of types of data, and we provide examples of how CompStat evolved and what its functions are. Then we look at applications of geographic profiling, the mapping of hot spots, and Global Positioning Systems. Next we review how use of both the Internet and an intranet can assist the police in engaging the community as well as in doing analysis, and then we briefly consider how surveys are used in this same regard. After a brief look at counterterrorism, the chapter concludes with a discussion of the kinds of knowledge, skills, and abilities that should be possessed by today's professional crime analyst.

CRIME ANALYSIS

Street-Level Criminology

Integral to the process of problem solving is **crime analysis,** which may be simply defined as "the collection and analysis of data pertaining to a criminal incident, offender, and target."[2]

The importance of analysis in this era of COPPS can be summed up in the following statement: "Community policing can be distinguished from professional policing because it calls for information from domains that had previously been neglected and for more complex analysis of that information."[3] Indeed, the more that important data is collected, analyzed, and related to all components of the crime triangle (victim, offender, and location), the better equipped police will be to develop innovative solutions that include the full spectrum of suppression, intervention, and prevention options.[4]

It is very important for officers who are engaged in problem solving to understand how, when, where, and why criminal events occur rather than merely responding to them. In this vein we do not mean to say that patrol officers should develop expertise in understanding the mental processes and theories that are involved in a person's choosing to commit crimes (although criminology or psychology courses at a college or university would certainly benefit the problem-solving officer); rather, we are referring to what might be termed **street-level criminology.** This matter is relatively new to policing at the street level, and it requires that we learn more about crime occurrences through analysis and experimentation with the problem-solving process.

An important note of caution must be stressed, however. Crime analysis will only be as good as the data or information that is collected. There are three essential criteria for crime analysis that police agencies should use when designing data collection processes and interpreting the meaning of information gleaned from crime analysis[5]:

1. *Timeliness.* Does the pattern or trend presented reflect a current problem or issue, or does it represent a previous situation? Deployment decisions with respect to both prevention and offender apprehension efforts must be based on current information to the extent that is possible.

2. *Relevancy.* Do the measures used in the analysis accurately reflect what is intended? For example, whether a pattern is based on calls for service data or incident data can be a very important determination depending on what the police manager is trying to understand.

3. *Reliability.* Would the same data, interpreted by different people at different times, lead to the same conclusions?

The Basics: Computer-Aided Dispatch, Mobile Computing, and Records Management

Here we briefly describe the computer-aided dispatch system, mobile computing, and records management system. While there are other police information technologies (several of which are discussed below), these are described in detail because they are the primary technologies for offering *core* data management capabilities for COPPS, such as data capture and entry; search, retrieval, and display; messaging; and linkages between data elements.[6]

Computer-Aided Dispatch (CAD). Computer-aided dispatch (CAD) has become an indispensable technology in policing, designed to handle all information related to receiving and dispatching emergency calls for service (CFS). CAD is often the first point of data entry, whether processing an emergency 911 CFS or managing an officer-initiated car stop. CAD fully automates the call-taking and dispatching functions; used with automated vehicle location (AVL) systems that track patrol vehicle status, CAD can help to prioritize CFS and make recommendations for unit and resource dispatching based on beats, zones, closest resources, and/or current unit activities. Some CAD systems can also provide the number and type of prior calls that were made at the location, whether there are existing warrants for residents, or if there are specific hazards related to the location.[7] Exhibit 1 provides an example of how CAD works.

Mobile Computing. Mobile computing has become the catchall phrase for outfitting an officer's vehicle or person with the technology that, in effect, allows him or her to be a "mobile office." Mobile computing is actually composed of several law enforcement hardware and software technologies working together to allow officers to access, receive, create, and exchange information wirelessly in the field. Officers can proactively query local, state, and national databases; receive and initiate CAD events; view unit

EXHIBIT 1

Computer-Aided Dispatch: How It Works

Assume a 911 call for service (CFS) is received by a police dispatcher. The automatic name index (ANI) and automatic location information (ALI) come on the CAD screen, and the dispatcher adds additional call details to CAD. The computer assigns a priority rating to the call based on the information entered, checks the validity of the address using the geofile, and searches for historical location information (previous CFS, hazardous conditions, weapons, warrants); it then makes recommendations about dispatching available officers and units (cars, foot/bike patrol, etc.) to the scene based on unit proximity and availability. The dispatcher can use a radio or silently dispatch the call to officers via mobile computers (laptops) in their patrol cars. The system constantly updates unit and call status for the dispatcher and officers to view. The computer automatically maintains status information, listing all vehicles that work on a specific tour of duty, their status and their current assignment. Response times are documented and reports are captured.

Source: U.S. Department of Justice, Office of Community Oriented Policing Services, *Law Enforcement Tech Guide: How to Plan, Purchase, and Manage Technology (Successfully!)* (Washington, D.C.: Author, 2002), p. 248.

EXHIBIT 2

Mobile Computing: How It Works

After receiving dispatch information via the mobile laptop computer, the officer responds to the incident, running queries and other inquiries against databases remotely. When the incident is closed, the officer completes a required report via laptop or handheld unit. The report information is electronically forwarded to a supervisor for approval via a wireless communications network. The supervisor decides whether to approve the report. If not approved, the report is sent back to the officer for corrections; if approved, the report is electronically submitted to the records unit. Once it is received by the records unit, records staff performs quality assurance on the report prior to submitting it electronically to the records management system.

Source: U.S. Department of Justice, Office of Community Oriented Policing Services, *Law Enforcement Tech Guide: How to Plan, Purchase, and Manage Technology (Successfully!)* (Washington, D.C.: Author, 2002), p. 248.

status; send e-mail; prepare and file incident reports; issue citations; capture field interview information; access department policies and procedures; research penal codes; and perform many other functions. In sum, they are able to do nearly everything they could do in the station house.[8] Exhibit 2 discusses how mobile computing works in the field.

Records Management System (RMS).   Today a **records management system (RMS)** is a key asset to effective policing, offering robust analytical tools and the ability to seamlessly share information, developing complex linkages between myriad data and information, and assisting in effective management strategies. In its simplest form, an RMS captures, maintains, and analyzes all police agency and incident-related information and is vital for tracking and managing criminal and noncriminal events, investigations, and personnel information. An RMS automates the daily practice of entering, storing, retrieving, retaining, archiving, viewing, and exchanging records, documents, data, information, or files related to persons, vehicles, incidents, arrests, warrants, traffic accidents, citations, pawn tickets, civil process papers, gun registration investigations, property, and evidence.[9] Exhibit 3 provides an example of how an RMS works.

Together, CAD and RMS can produce most of the data in CompStat (discussed below) with a touch of a button. Otherwise, a data entry clerk or crime analyst must enter the details of *every* incident reported, arrest effected, summons issued, case cleared, and other such information into a spreadsheet or database to produce the reports.[10]

Strategic and Tactical Crime Analysis

The collection and analysis of data spanning a long period of time result in strategic crime analysis. This type of analysis is research focused because

EXHIBIT 3

Records Management System: How It Works

Officers prepare reports via desktop or mobile computer and submit them electronically to a supervisor, who reviews them. Once the supervisor's approval is given, a report is automatically added to the RMS. If property or evidence has been received, it can be bar coded and linked directly to the recorded data in the RMS. Information stored in the RMS becomes available to agency users, such as detectives, crime analysis and COPPS divisions, command staff, and others. A public interface is built into most RMS systems to provide information to the community, and appropriate RMS data and information can be shared and exchanged with other justice systems.

Source: U.S. Department of Justice, Office of Community Oriented Policing Services, *Law Enforcement Tech Guide: How to Plan, Purchase, and Manage Technology (Successfully!)* (Washington, D.C.: Author, 2002), p. 248.

it includes the use of statistics to make conclusions. This analysis can be useful to departments in terms of forecasting crime trends or estimating future crime based on past trends. (*Note:* Although we will not delve into it at this point, it should be mentioned that the Microsoft Word Excel function is very useful for making forecasts of crime trends; this task can be accomplished fairly easily.)

While strategic crime analysis involves the review of data spanning generally a year or more, tactical crime analysis uses real-time data spanning several days. One of its principal uses involves problem identification, or the pattern detection of multiple offenses over a short period of time that have common characteristics, such as the type of crime, modus operandi, and type of weapon used.[11] One example of tactical crime analysis that is discussed later in this chapter is geographic profiling, which can be used to suggest the likelihood of where an offender resides based on the pattern of where victims and offenses occur. Linkage analysis involves connecting a suspect to a series of incidents based on commonalities in modus operandi and suspect descriptions as well as known offenders who live in close proximity to a given area. For example, many states search their databases of registered sex offenders when a series of sexual offenses is identified.[12]

Crime Pattern Geomapping

Mapping crime patterns has become increasingly popular among law enforcement agencies and is given high visibility at the federal level, in the media, and among the largest police departments in the nation. A **geographic information system (GIS)** is an automated system for the capture, storage, retrieval, analysis, and display of spatial data. It has been said that "GIS technology is to geographical analysis what the microscope, the telescope, and computers have been to other sciences."[13]

Replacement for Pin Maps. The traditional crime map was a jumbo representation of a jurisdiction with pins stuck in it. These maps were useful for showing where crimes occurred, but they had several limitations as well: As they were updated, the prior crime patterns were lost; the maps were static, unable to be manipulated or queried; they could be quite difficult to read when several types of crime were mixed together.[14] Consequently, during the 1990s pin maps largely gave way to desktop computer mapping, which has now become commonplace and fast, aided by the availability of cheap color printers.[15]

The importance of **geomapping** is evidenced by the fact that the National Institute of Justice has established a Crime Mapping Research Center (CMRC) to promote research, evaluation, development, and dissemination of GIS technology for criminal justice research and practice. The CMRC holds annual conferences on geomapping to provide researchers and practitioners an opportunity to gain both practical and state-of-the-art information on the use and utility of computerized geomapping. The CMRC Web site address is http://www.ojp.usdoj.gov/cmrc.[16]

GIS for COPPS. GIS has revolutionized the way in which COPPS is conducted internationally. This is largely due to the ability of the police to now overlay seemingly diverse types of data that all contribute to a true understanding of a particular problem.

For example, a series of burglaries taking place between the hours of 1 A.M. and 3 A.M. might be the first thing visually displayed on a crime map. However, getting at the underlying causes of the burglary problem requires deeper probing and innovative thinking. In this case, the crime analyst might overlay the burglary incident data with available data about land usage in the area and might then learn that the burglaries are occurring within walking distance of an area high school.[17]

Although this might seem to be an obvious linkage to many, individuals often overlook such connections. By visually displaying overlays of various potential data combinations, GIS can play a critical role in jump-starting the analysis process. With the above burglary example, the police manager might begin to develop a theory related to the fact that the burglaries might be caused by youths who are truant from school. Looking forward, in addition to now having a large pool of individuals from which investigators might begin seeking information about the incidents, analysts may eventually be led to a collaborative project with the school to develop responses that increase truancy enforcement.[18]

GIS pattern analysis can also indicate a broader understanding of a problem. For example, assume that a pattern is indicated of disorderly conduct and assaults in an area. An overlay with available liquor stores and bars in the area may present the analyst with some ideas as to what factors might be driving the problem. An additional benefit of GIS is that it

The Crime Mapping Research Center (CMRC) is a national clearinghouse for information about crime analysis and mapping.

U.S. Department of Justice, National Institute of Justice, Crime Mapping Research Center (Washington, D.C.: Author, 1999).

is compatible with statistical analyses to further refine an analyst's examination of a problem; for example, simple statistical analyses may link disorderly conduct and assaults in a city to the overall density of alcohol availability or other possibilities.[19]

Exhibit 4 discusses interactive geomapping on the Internet. In a related vein, Figure 1 is the initial screen that appears when the user chooses "vehicle and traffic incidents" from the San Diego County Web site, providing information about auto thefts and burglaries as well as traffic accidents. Figure 2 shows the Austin, Texas, map viewer; Figure 3 provides an example of geomapping of street gang–motivated homicide in Chicago.

Geomapping can greatly increase the accountability of a police agency by visually demonstrating incident patterns for which the agency's administrators can hold commanding officers accountable over time. A proactive police manager should use GIS and other problem-solving tools described in this chapter to create sound strategic and tactical decisions related to such things as officer deployment, resource allocation, and partnerships with other agencies for sustained crime reductions.[20]

The CompStat model of the New York Police Department (NYPD), discussed below, institutionalized the use of GIS for departmental planning purposes. The program was such a success that similar versions of CompStat have been implemented in departments across the country.

EXHIBIT 4

Interactive Geomapping on the Internet

Following are two examples of interactive geomapping efforts on the Internet in San Diego County, California, and Austin, Texas. Use of such systems not only enables citizens to obtain much more information than was previously available, but it precludes their having to make formal requests for information while freeing crime analysts to devote more time to analyzing crime instead of providing reports to the public.

In 1970, San Diego County's Automated Regional Justice Information System (ARJIS) began allowing all law enforcement agencies in the county to maintain and access crime and arrest information. Recently, however, ARJIS developed the first multiagency interactive geomapping Web site in the nation. Now anyone in the world can query and view certain crime, arrest, call, and traffic data for the county. Searches can be by geographic location (street, neighborhood, police beat, or city) as well as by time of day or day of week. ARJIS serves as a model for making interactive crime maps available to the public on the Internet. People access ARJIS for a variety of purposes: data on crime in their area, a grant proposal, support for a debate on an issue, citizen patrol data and real estate agent information.

Austin, Texas, unveiled a similarly unique approach to geomapping on the Web, tripling the amount of information that was previously available and providing aggregated data by patrol areas, ZIP codes, census tracts, and neighborhood associations. Citizens can also see crime totals within 500 feet of any user-inputted address.

Source: Adapted from *Crime Mapping News* [a Police Foundation newsletter] 3 (Summer 2001):1–6.

CompStat

Key Elements of CompStat. Unfortunately, today it seems the NYPD crime control model **CompStat** (computer-driven crime statistics) is often oversimplified to refer to aggressive or data-driven policing, where police commanders are frequently grilled about crimes in their areas of responsibility—and they are even castigated, transferred, or demoted after a lifetime of service if they failed to do something about it. According to police scholar Phyllis McDonald, this perception of CompStat "does a disservice to its management principles and its potential for other jurisdictions."[21]

The key elements of CompStat are as follows[22]:

- Specific objectives
- Accurate and timely intelligence
- Effective tactics
- Rapid deployment of personnel and resources
- Relentless follow-up and assessment

Prior to CompStat, NYPD generally had a reporting lag of three to six months for crime statistics—and even then, any meaningful analysis was impossible. Headquarters was not systematically tracking crime activity

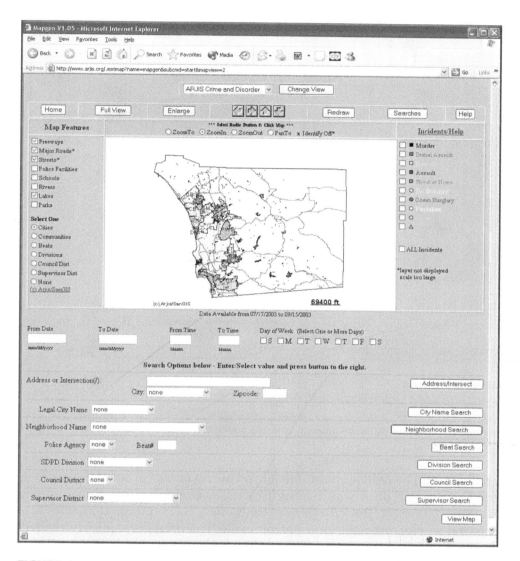

FIGURE 1

San Diego County's Interactive Crime Map

Source: http://www.arjis.org/esrimap?name=mapgen&subcmd=start&mapview=2.

in the precincts, let alone using such information to evaluate the performance of its commanding officers. As a result, the commanders did not view crime reduction as a primary job responsibility. As was common to departments across the country, reactive, incident-driven patrol was seen as more important, and detective and patrol bureaus rarely collaborated and even directly clashed over territorial concerns.[23]

CompStat was devised as a means of reforming these organizational issues by pushing all precincts to generate weekly crime activity reports so

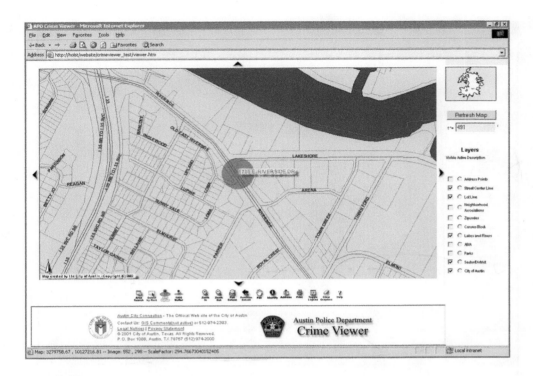

FIGURE 2

The Austin, Texas, Crime Mapping Viewer

Source: Al Johnson, "The Austin Police Department's Crime Mapping Viewer," *Crime Mapping News* (Washington, D.C.: Police Foundation, Summer 2001), p. 5.

that they could be held accountable for the achievement of several objectives. Over time, crime data was readily available, computerized, and compiled into the "CompStat Book," offering up-to-date information that was then compared at city, precinct, and patrol levels. Commanders quickly realized that their role had changed and that they had to stop simply responding to crime and start proactively thinking about ways to deal with it in terms of suppression, intervention, and prevention. To solidify this message, NYPD headquarters began to hold regularly scheduled meetings in which the commanders and their staff meet with top brass to discuss crime trends and issues. In a very intimidating environment, commanders stand before a lectern in front of three large video screens that flash GIS-generated maps of recent crime patterns. The commanders are then asked what tactics they have tried to address the patterns, what resources they have and need, and with whom they have collaborated. Brainstorming problem-solving sessions ensue about proactively responding to the crime problems, and suggestions for strategies are made at subsequent meetings, with relentless follow-up by top brass to further ensure accountability.[24]

Over time, CompStat has evolved to include other data: census demographics, arrest and summons activity, average response time, domestic violence incidents, unfounded radio runs, personnel absences, and even

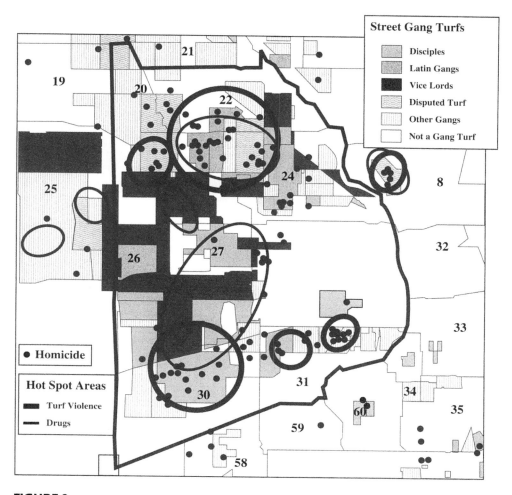

FIGURE 3

A Crime Map of Street Gang–Motivated Homicide, Chicago

Source: Carolyn Rebecca Block and Richard Block, *Street Gang Crime in Chicago* (Washington, D.C.: National Institute of Justice, 1993), p. 5.

citizen complaints and charges of officer misconduct. Scholars and practitioners have argued that CompStat has played a prominent role in the significant crime reductions in New York City following its implementation. True or not, the impact CompStat has had on police management practices cannot be denied. Certainly another benefit has been the significant increases in job satisfaction found by those who feel empowered by the problem-solving process (see Figure 4).[25]

Use of CompStat Data: An Example. Next we provide some fundamentals about how to present, compare, and map data. Although some of this information may well be beyond the training of some readers (e.g., the section that discusses descriptive statistics), we feel it is important to at least

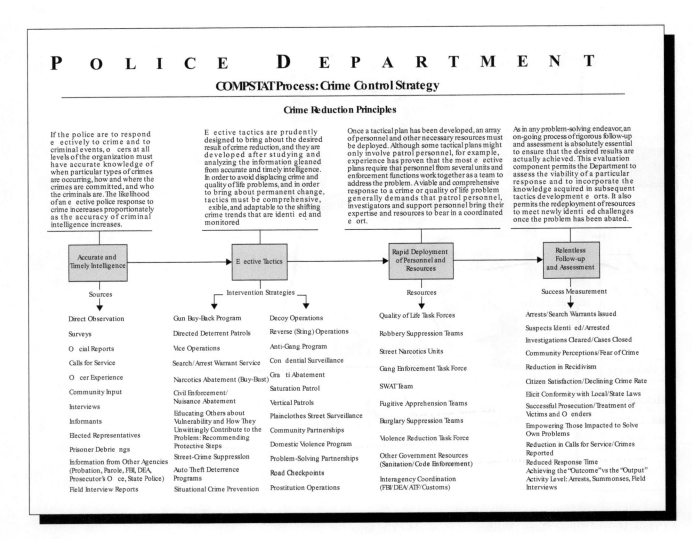

FIGURE 4
CompStat Crime Control Strategy

Source: Jon M. Shane, "The Compstat Process," *FBI Law Enforcement Bulletin,* (April 2004), p. 19.

present the process, as well as an overview of what is available with CompStat analyses. Here are the three steps[26]:

1. The first step involves descriptive statistics, or presenting the data so that everyone, from commanders down to patrol officers, can readily understand the relevant information. Data may be presented and described in a number of ways: aggregate increase or decrease; simple percentages (including increase or decrease over previous time frames); ratio and rates; incidents compared to population; mean, median, and mode; pie charts, line charts, bar charts, histograms; and so on. Figure 5 shows the means by which data may be presented.

2. The second step in presenting data, comparing, is designed to reveal the relationship between two or more crimes. These statistics are called measures of association, and

Appropriate Statistics					
Descriptive Analysis	Maximum	Minimum	Mean	Median	Mode
	Violent and nonviolent crime summary		Aggregate increase or decrease		Standard deviation
Frequency Distribution	Percentage increase or decrease	Proportion across categories	Ratio and rates Incidents to population Performance to police officers		
Organization and Presentation of Data	Pie charts (for percentage of total)		Bar charts (for aggregate data or rate; e.g., incidents per 100,000 people)		
	Line charts (frequency polygon); add trend lines to establish direction		Histograms with a normal curve (e.g., response time analysis)		Cross-tab charts

FIGURE 5
Means of Data Presentation

Source: Jon M. Shane, "Compstat Design," *FBI Law Enforcement Bulletin,* (May 2004), p. 14.

they enable crime analysts to quantify the strength and direction of a relationship—to uncover the connections between crimes and to make predictions. For example, suppose a crime analyst was interested in seeing if a relationship existed between calls for service (CFS) pertaining to drug sales and shootings. After gathering the appropriate data, by calculating the measure of association (such as a Pearson's r), the analyst can determine the strength of the relationship and its direction. Suppose a strong positive relationship was found between these two variables (i.e., the two crimes of drug sales and shootings); one might infer that the two crimes were closely related, so as one of the crimes increased, the other would also. A prediction could then be made that as there are more CFS for drug sales, a higher number of shootings might be expected as well. The analyst would do well to remember, however, that this strong positive relationship does not automatically prove such a connection exists, but this association would serve as an important clue about causation. Comparing the data allows analysts and commanders to consider adjusting or compensating for shifts in trends or patterns. Appropriate charts should display the information for each beat, zone, or precinct, as well as city- or county-wide areas, including the aggregate difference and percentage change in reported incidents (see Figure 6). The data should also be depicted in temporal (time) distribution so that commanders can see when crimes occur.

3. The final step, mapping data (called spatial analysis), can detect where criminals travel. Officers can create overlays of CFS with arrests effected, unsolved burglaries with known burglars' residences, or CFS with abandoned buildings. Analysis can create specialty maps, such as sex offenders' residences, recovered guns, recovered stolen autos, and thefts of auto parts. Most important, maps can display data to show hot spots, or areas of concentrated crime (discussed more fully below); then the police can develop appropriate intervention strategies.

Data Comparison

				Diff.	% +/–
Day to day	One chart for each week of the CompStat period				
Week to week	Current week	vs.	Previous week	+5	+3%
Month to month	March 2007	vs.	April 2007	–18	–27%
Quarter to quarter	Jan, Feb, Mar	vs.	Apr, May, Jun	+32	+44%
Half year to half year	1st 6 months	vs.	2nd 6 months	–63	–40%
Year to year	2006	vs.	2007	–27	–2%
Year to date	January 1, 2007, to present date			Aggregate	
Last 12 months	March 15, 2006, to March 14, 2007			Aggregate	
Custom date	Any time period (days, weeks, months, quarters, years, decades)				

Comparisons for each period against the prior period

Week	Current week 2007	vs.	Same week 2006
Month	Current month 2007	vs.	Same month 2006
Quarter	Jan, Feb, Mar 2007	vs.	Jan, Feb, Mar 2006
Half year	1st 6 months 2007	vs.	1st 6 months 2006
Year	Jan 1, 2007, to present	vs.	Jan 1, 2006, to present
12 months	Jan 18, 2006, to Jan 17, 2007	vs.	Jan 18, 2005, to Jan 17, 2006
Custom	Any custom date period compared with the prior date period		

FIGURE 6
Data Comparison Chart

Source: Jon M. Shane, "Compstat Design," *FBI Law Enforcement Bulletin,* (May 2004), p. 16.

Figure 7 is a matrix showing the kinds of intervention strategies that might be used to address crime that is experiencing different temporal (time) and spatial (space) occurrences. For example, in the lower-left corner of the matrix, it shows where crimes are being committed and when they are heavily concentrated in terms of time of day/week at a particular hot spot, so the police would want to use surveillance, arrest squads, CCTV, and unmarked police cars.

Future of CompStat. The future of CompStat does not lie in its survival as a tool of upper management but as a tool of the street officer. All of the principal reform movements in policing—from the now-antiquated management by objectives (MBO) through today's community policing era—have relied on line-level officers and investigators having current, ongoing knowledge of the criminal activity in their beat. Agencies have been improving their internal information management and communications infrastructure for this purpose, making it possible for any member of any police agency to create CompStat-like analyses at their discretion. CompStat belongs at the line level and has evolved from a simple file name to a technique and a belief system. It must therefore be understood by management and then pushed down to both supervisors and rank-and-file police officers.[27]

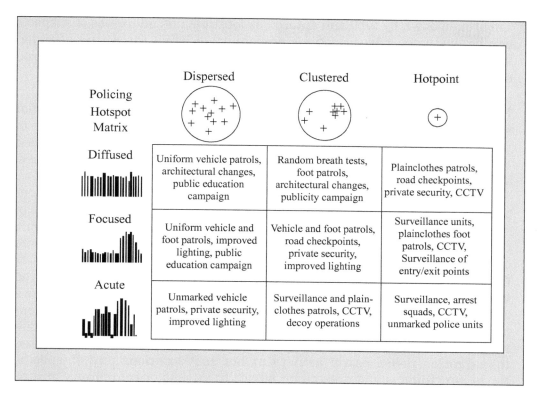

FIGURE 7
Intervention Strategies Matrix

Source: Jon M. Shane, "Compstat Design," *FBI Law Enforcement Bulletin,* (May 2004), p. 18.

Other Applications: Geographic Profiling and Hot Spots

Geographic Profiling. Geographic profiling, or the combined use of geography, psychology, and mathematics to identify the location of an offender, is most commonly associated with tracking down serial killers, rapists, and arsonists. However, it is a useful investigative tool in any case in which an individual offender has committed criminal activity across a series of locations. Geographic profiling suggests investigative alternatives based on the "hunting behavior" of the offender. Leading geographic profiler Kim Rossmo argues that criminals are no different in their pattern of carrying out their offenses than ordinary citizens are in going about their day-to-day activities.[28]

Following this principle, geographic profiling uses the nearness principle as a key rule. The nearness principle argues that offenders will remain within a limited range that is comfortable to them when committing their offenses, just as animals will forage within a limited range from their base. This principle has led to the creation of a computerized geographic profiling workstation that includes statistical analyses, GIS features, and database management to aid in calculating investigative suggestions. Crime scenes are broken down by type and entered by location, and addresses of suspects can be evaluated based on their probability of being the actual offender. This can help investigators sort through existing records, such as registered sex offenders, and other information.[29]

Hot Spots. The term **hot spot** refers to the theory that crime is not spread randomly but tends to cluster in certain places. The significance of place in relation to crime has long been the subject of research, is described as "a discrete location in space and time," and can include "stores, homes, apartment buildings, street corners, addresses, and subway stations."[30]

Generally described as areas or places with a relatively high concentration of crimes, hot spots can be readily identified through the use of spatial statistical software. This software can provide a colored electronic overlay, resembling a thermal image, with the colors indicating the degree of intensity. Hot spot identification has become increasingly popular under COPPS and is now generally considered an essential GIS tool. Coupled with the other kinds of analyses that the police can perform, this provides a more holistic approach to crime prevention, whereby social, environmental, and demographic factors are all considered before an appropriate response is developed. These responses might include (but are not limited to) targeting police patrol activity at hot spot locations and at specific times, providing crime prevention advice to victims or community groups on crime reduction strategies (target hardening), advising on the placement of closed-circuit televisions in public places, or a myriad of other situational crime prevention techniques. The identification of hot spots can also provide valuable insight into emerging crime trends and predictive patterns of behavior by looking at the modus operandi of the offenders.[31]

Global Positioning System (GPS)

Global Positioning Systems (GPS) have been used to enhance the tracking of offenders and officer deployments. GPS use satellite-based technologies for the purpose of tracking the movement of patrol cars or specially equipped stolen vehicles. In some cases, an officer's cell phone can be equipped with GPS technology, providing an alternative to conventional address matching for an officer responding to a call. GPS technology has also proven to significantly enhance aerial photography of crime incident locations, allowing for greater visualization of the complete context of a situation. Some states have capitalized on the surveillance capacity of GPS to monitor the real-time location of high-risk offenders released from prison.[32]

Internet/Intranet and COPPS

The Internet has also proven to be an important mechanism for furthering police agencies' COPPS objectives. Important features that are used by many departmental Web sites in reaching their citizens include the following[33]:

- Libraries devoted to crime prevention and safety tips (including information about known scam cases operating within the jurisdiction)
- Virtual tours of the department
- Recent jurisdictional and neighborhood crime statistics (including crime maps)
- Departmental wanted lists and upcoming court cases
- Capability for citizens to anonymously report crime or complaints about officer conduct

Many agencies are also establishing an intranet for their employees. Through the intranet, a department is able to supply a number of important informational needs through access to the following[34]:

- *Problem-solving system.* A searchable database of problems that officers have worked on over the past few years can be accessed.
- *Property evidence system.* A searchable database on property and evidence in the department's custody can be used.
- *Calls for service.* A searchable database on CFS by several categories would be accessible.
- *Records management system.* There would be online access to RMS and a wide range of search capabilities for offense reports.
- *Computer-aided dispatch system.* Online access to CAD system records, including active call information, would be available.
- *Gang database.* There would be online access to the agency's gang information.

Surveys

Not to be overlooked in crime analysis is the use of community surveys to identify or clarify problems. For example, an officer may canvass all the business proprietors in shopping centers on his or her beat. One variation on this theme occurred in Baltimore when an officer telephoned business owners to update the police department's after-hours business contact files. Although the officer did not conduct a formal survey, he used this task to also inquire about problems the owners might want to bring to police attention.

On a larger scale, a team of officers may survey residents of a housing complex or neighborhood known to have particular crime problems. The survey could assist in determining residents' priority concerns, acquiring information about hot spots, and learning more about residents' expectations of police.[35] Residents will also be more likely to keep the police abreast of future problems when officers leave their cards and encourage residents to contact them directly.

Another approach to the survey process involves developing a beat profile. In Tempe, Arizona, COPPS officers began by conducting a detailed profile of a target beat. This involved both door-to-door surveys of residents and businesses and detailed observations of the environment. A survey instrument was developed and pilot-tested, and all survey team members were trained and given a uniform protocol to follow. The instrument contained questions about sociodemographic characteristics of residents, observed crime and drug problems, fear of crime, perception of city and police services, willingness to participate in and support community policing objectives, and other information. Survey team members also recorded information about the surroundings—condition of buildings, homes, streets, and yards; presence of abandoned vehicles; possible zoning and other code violations; and existence of graffiti, trash, loiterers, gang members, and other signs of disorder.[36]

Counterterrorism Analysis

 In the wake of attacks by terrorists on U.S. soil, the role and function of crime analysts have become even more crucial. Crime analysts' approach to counterterrorism involves two major areas—investigation and prevention[37]:

- *Investigation*. Terrorists operate according to rules and principles that can be identified, analyzed, and predicted. Although they can be fanatical and fiendish, they behave in a logical fashion, picking their targets with precision. This makes them more vulnerable in the sense that analysts can predict their behavior and disrupt their efforts. Analysts must never work alone, however; they must coordinate with the appropriate federal agency, most often the Federal Bureau of Investigation (FBI).

- *Prevention*. Prevention is accomplished by denying the terrorist the opportunity to attack in the first place. The process begins with a threat assessment of the jurisdiction: identifying and evaluating the risk of targets, and constructing countermeasures by using the S.A.R.A. process. Analysts can *scan* for vulnerabilities, *analyze* these methods of attack to determine countermeasures, *respond* by allocating the necessary police resources to try to thwart an attack, and *assess* by performing periodic readiness tests and exercises to determine effectiveness.

WANTED: THE "RIGHT STUFF" TO BE A CRIME ANALYST

This chapter has certainly proved that certain kinds of knowledge, skills, and abilities are essential in order for one to become a crime analyst. The mere possession of a badge and police experience will likely not suffice, at least not without prior specialized training and education. The items in the following list have been shown in this chapter to be important for conducting crime and problem analyses; ideally, an analyst would possess all of them, but that is nearly impossible. Therefore the following is more of a job description for an analyst's position[38]:

- *Criminological theory*. We noted earlier in this chapter that one must be a "street-level criminologist"; one does not need to know all of the criminological theories in depth but should possess a working knowledge of theories that contribute the most to understanding the local crime and disorder problems (e.g., situational crime prevention, repeat victimization, rational choice theory, and routine activities theory).

- *Literature.* The crime analyst should be aware of both classic and current research literature related to community policing and problem solving and the aforementioned theories, as well as statistics and research methods. Goldstein's concepts of problem oriented policing and problem solving—both in theory and in practice—are essential, as is the history of policing and how it has evolved.
- *Research methods.* Basic research design, sampling methods, modes of observation (experiment, field research, surveying, evaluation), data collection, process and impact evaluation, and ethics are important here.
- *Statistics.* Knowledge of measures of descriptive and inferential statistics, as well as forecasting, is important.
- *Geographic information systems (GIS) and spatial analysis.* These are important because of the influence of geography on crime, on problem solving, and on crime prevention.
- *Technology.* A crime analyst should know the advantages and limits of technology for both data collection and analysis.

 ## SUMMARY

This chapter has examined what might be fairly said to be the heart of the COPPS strategy: analysis of crime data. This discussion included the kinds of methods and technologies—including various forms of computer hardware and software—that are now in the analyst's quiver and are being applied to COPPS.

It should be abundantly clear now, after reading this chapter, that these are most certainly challenging times for those persons who are charged with trying to determine the who, what, when, where, why, and how of crime; for example, the traditional reliance on a giant pin map that showed criminal locations would provide little in the way of sufficiency for addressing today's criminal element. Indeed, compared to today's computer-generated analytical tools, the pin map of not too long ago (which, by the way, is probably hanging on the walls and in use by some law enforcement agencies today) seems about as high tech as the tube-type patrol car radios of yore. It has also made clear that the attributes needed for today's crime analyst are probably much different and more sophisticated than they were even a decade ago.

 ## ITEMS FOR REVIEW

1. What is the function of the three basic aids for crime analysis (computer-aided dispatch, mobile computing, and records management systems)?
2. What is the difference between strategic and tactical crime analysis?
3. Describe how crime patterns can be geomapped.

4. Trace the development, purposes, and methods of CompStat, and discuss how it can function today in all sizes of agencies.
5. Describe geographic profiling and mapping of hot spots.
6. Distinguish between the Internet and an intranet in terms of how they apply to policing and crime analysis.
7. List and explain some of the knowledge, skills, and abilities that are needed to be a crime analyst.

◆ NOTES

1. National Commission of Law Observance and Enforcement, *Report on Police* (Washington, D.C.: Government Printing Office, 1931), p. 140.
2. Philip Canter, "Using a Geographic Information System for Tactical Crime Analysis," in Victor Goldsmith, Philip G. McGuire, John H. Mollenkopf, and Timothy A. Ross (eds.), *Analyzing Crime Patterns: Frontiers of Practice* (Thousand Oaks, Calif.: Sage, 2000), pp. 3–10.
3. Timothy C. O'Shea and Keith Nicholls, *Crime Analysis in America: Findings and Recommendations* (Washington, D.C.: U.S. Department of Justice, Office of Community Oriented Policing Services, March 2003), p. 7.
4. Heath J. Grant and Karen J. Terry, *Law Enforcement in the 21st Century* (Boston, Mass.: Allyn & Bacon, 2005), pp. 329–330.
5. *Ibid.,* p. 330.
6. U.S. Department of Justice, Office of Community Oriented Policing Services, *Law Enforcement Tech Guide: How to Plan, Purchase, and Manage Technology (Successfully!)* (Washington, D.C.: Author, 2002), p. 247.
7. *Ibid.,* p. 248.
8. *Ibid.,* p. 250.
9. *Ibid.,* p. 252.
10. Jon M. Shane, "CompStat Design," *FBI Law Enforcement Bulletin* (May 2004), p. 17.
11. Canter, "Using a Geographic Information System for Tactical Crime Analysis," p. 5.
12. Grant and Terry, *Law Enforcement in the 21st Century,* p. 331.
13. D. Cowen, "Why Is GIS Important?" http://www.env.duke.edu/lel/enn351/images/uoi.txt/ (Accessed May 4, 2006).
14. U.S. Department of Justice, National Institute of Justice, Crime Mapping Research Center, *Mapping Crime: Principle and Practice* (Washington, D.C.: Author, 1999), p. 1.
15. *Ibid.,* p. 2.
16. U.S. Department of Justice, National Institute of Justice, *Crime Mapping Research Center* (Washington, D.C.: Author, 2000), pp. 1–3.
17. Grant and Terry, *Law Enforcement in the 21st Century,* p. 332.
18. *Ibid.,* pp. 332–333.
19. *Ibid.,* p. 333.

20. *Ibid.*, p. 335.

21. Phyllis McDonald, *Managing Police Operations: Implementing the New York Crime Control Model—CompStat* (Belmont, Calif.: Wadsworth, 2002), p. 1.

22. Grant and Terry, *Law Enforcement in the 21st Century,* p. 336.

23. *Ibid.*, p. 337.

24. *Ibid.*

25. *Ibid.*, p. 339.

26. Jon M. Shane, "CompStat Design," *FBI Law Enforcement Bulletin* (May 2004), pp. 17–18.

27. Michael E. Buerger, "COMPSTAT: A Strategic Vision," *The Associate* (January-February 2005), pp. 18–23.

28. A. Onion, "Coordinates of a Killer: A Mathematical Method Can Help Investigators Locate Killers," http://www.abcnews.com (Accessed October 8, 2002).

29. Grant and Terry, *Law Enforcement in the 21st Century,* p. 340.

30. John Eck, Jeffrey Gersh, and Charlene Taylor, *Mapping Hotspots of Crime and Related Events* (New York: New York Police Department, Spatial Analysis of Crime Conference, City University of New York Centre for Applied Studies of Environment and Centre for Urban Research, 1997).

31. Peter Branca, "Police News: Mapping Crime Hotspots," http://www.wapolun .org.au/010236.htm (Accessed May 4, 2006).

32. Grant and Terry, *Law Enforcement in the 21st Century,* p. 343.

33. *Ibid.*, pp. 346–347.

34. Darrel W. Stephens, "IT Changes in Law Enforcement," in Ronald W. Glensor and Gerard R. Murphy (eds.), *Issues in IT: A Reader for the Busy Police Chief Executive* (Washington, D.C.: Police Executive Research Forum, 2005), pp. 7–29.

35. For an example of this type of survey process, see William H. Lindsey and Bruce Quint, *The Oasis Technique* (Fort Lauderdale, Fla.: Florida Atlantic University/Florida International University Joint Center).

36. Barbara Webster and Edward F. Connors, "Community Policing: Identifying Problems" (Alexandria, Va.: Institute for Law and Justice, March 1991), pp. 14–15.

37. Dan Helms, "Closing the Barn Door: Police Counterterrorism After 9-11 from the Analyst's Perspective," *Crime Mapping News* 4 (Winter 2002):1–5.

38. Rachel Boba, "Problem Analysis in Policing: An Executive Summary," *Crime Mapping News* 5 (1) (Winter 2003):4.

Advances in Policing—New Technologies for Crime Analysis

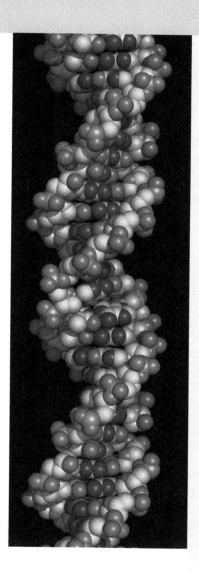

CHAPTER OBJECTIVES

- Identify the stages of technological advancement in policing and the implications of technological utilization in the field.

- Understand the different types of crime analysis and the technologies available for them, such as GIS.

- Know the variety of applications of GIS technology.

- Appreciate the many types of technologies available to modern law enforcement.

INTRODUCTION

Throughout its history, the U.S. Border Patrol has faced the seemingly insurmountable task of detecting and apprehending the ever-present stream of drug traffickers and illegal immigrants. The 60-mile area around the U.S.–Mexico border in the San Diego area alone requires the management of more than 2,000 agents and 900 seismic sensors (DeAngelis 2000). To aid them in their efforts, the U.S. Border Patrol San Diego Sector has many high-tech tools at their fingertips, such as geographic information systems (GIS), seismic sensors (more than 900), and infrared night-vision equipment.

The agents use the GIS technology to map the locations of alien apprehensions as a means of determining why certain areas are higher in illegal migration and drug trafficking than others. Using real-time sensor feeds from the intelligent computer-aided detection (ICAD) system, agents monitor "hits" corresponding to potential illegal migrant entry into the country. After identifying a possible entry point, agents are able to map out the travel route that has the highest probability of leading to the apprehension of the illegal border crossers.

In addition to the tremendous challenges presented by the region's mountainous terrain, illegal traffic has also found underground avenues of escaping detection. To combat this eventuality, the Border Patrol has used Global Positioning System (GPS) receivers and GIS to plot storm drain and sewer system routes that are facilitating traffic from Mexico into the United States.

The application of such technologies to the practice of law enforcement has revolutionized the capacity of police to both *respond* to crime that is taking place in real time and proactively identify problems, analyze their causes, and develop strategic plans that truly enhance an agency's *crime prevention* capabilities. For example, the U.S. Border Patrol also targets high-risk areas with warning signs in Spanish regarding the dangers of crossing the border illegally.

In this technological era, law enforcement has had to evolve to be better equipped to fulfill its mandate of contributing to public safety. Technology has proven invaluable in responding to the problem of linkage blindness across jurisdictions, as well as with other criminal justice agencies and sectors of the community. In an age faced with continuing threats of transnational crime and terrorism, the importance of continued technological advances cannot be overstated.

However, the increasing reliance on and availability of technology to law enforcement can be intimidating. This technology brings with it new legal challenges, particularly in relation to the balance between crime control and the private interests of citizens. This chapter will begin with a brief overview of the technological advances related to law enforcement, followed by a descriptive coverage of key technological applications in policing. Particular attention will be paid to the use of GIS in facilitating proactive police management in the twenty-first century.

THE STAGES OF TECHNOLOGICAL ADVANCEMENT IN POLICING

Soulliere (1999) provides a useful conceptual framework for describing the advancement of technology in policing since its early professional origins. Although there is significant overlap with Kelling and Moore's (1987) three eras of policing, she offers four useful stages to help conceptualize technological development in policing. Table 1 summarizes **Soulliere's stages of technological advancement**.

TABLE 1	Soulliere's Stages of Technological Advancement in Policing		
Stage 1 (1881–1945)	**Stage 2 (1946–1959)**	**Stage 3 (1960–1979)**	**Stage 4 (1980–present)**
Mobile patrol Radio communications Telephone communications	Traffic violation detection instruments	911 Centralized dispatch Civilian specialists Research and development organizations Computer age begins	Telecommunications advances Mobile data communications Expert systems Imaging Biometrics GIS

Source: N. Soulliere. 1999. *Police and Technology: Historical Review and Current Status.* Ottawa, ON: Canadian Police College.

The First Stage (1881–1945)

Much of policing's initial technological advances can be attributed to the work of August Vollmer, who headed the early twentieth-century police department in Berkeley, California. Under his guidance, law enforcement increased its mobility through motor vehicle patrol and enhanced officer–precinct communications through telephone and radio. With his establishment of the first forensic laboratory, criminal investigators had access to an increasing array of technological expertise that would continue to increase exponentially throughout the development of law enforcement. For example, Vollmer's crime laboratory pioneered the use of polygraph, as well as fingerprint and handwriting classification systems (Seaskate 1998).

Soulliere (1999) cites several ways in which these early technological advances impacted the police organization, including the following:

- The development of increasingly complex police organizations through the creation of specialized sections within large police organizations to handle the new technology, such as radio communications and forensic labs
- Increased mobility for patrol activities offered by the use of automobiles
- Increased officer safety made possible with enhanced communications and the use of automobiles

The Second Stage (1946–1959)

Roughly corresponding with the beginnings of Kelling and Moore's Reform Era of policing, Soulliere (1999) claims that the second stage of technological advancement facilitated a major portion of the bureaucratization of policing organizations. During this stage, traffic police received a significant boost with the advent of the first instruments to measure both speeding violations and the condition of the driver. Although early instruments were rather crude indicators, they would grow over time to include the significant automobile surveillance mechanisms and blood alcohol measures.

The Third Stage (1960–1979)

As society entered the computer age, Soulliere (1999) claims that police technology began to truly emerge. During this stage, call distribution centers, computerized databanks, and computer sections became commonplace in police agencies. Some of the significant technological advancements in this stage can be attributed to President Lyndon B. Johnson. In 1967, he created the President's

Commission on Law Enforcement and the Administration of Justice to analyze crime patterns in the country, as well as the resources available to combat them. The commission's report highlighted the slow infusion of technological advances into the criminal justice system, with particular attention paid to policing. To this end, the report stated (President's Commission on Law Enforcement and the Administration of Justice 1967):

> The police, with crime laboratories and radio networks, made early use of technology, but most police departments could have been equipped 30 or 40 years ago as well as they are today. . . . Of all criminal justice agencies, the police have had the closest ties to science and technology, but they have called on scientific resources primarily to help in the solution of specific serious crimes, rather than for assistance in solving general problems of policing. (p. 125)

A notable gap existed between the technologies that were currently available that had potential law enforcement applications and what police agencies were actually using. In response to this gap, the Johnson administration began "the flow, a trickle at first, of what eventually became billions of dollars in direct and indirect assistance to local and state law enforcement" (Seaskate 1998, p. 2).

The commission argued for the establishment of a single telephone number that citizens across the country could use to contact the police in the case of an emergency. In only a matter of years following AT&T's announcement of the first **911 system** in 1968, 911 became a driving force for police departments across the country (Seaskate 1998). This increasing emphasis on calls-for-service would have both benefits (the seeming ease of access to the police in times of emergency) and detriments (this became the principal means of determining police resource deployment and performance evaluation). Skolnick and Bayley (1986) point out that patrol officers can become exhausted by rushing between calls for service, rather than taking the time needed to truly digest and understand the human situations in which they are regularly thrown.

During this third stage of development, large municipalities began the process of centralizing the dispatch of all fire, police, and medical services (Seaskate 1998). The overreliance of the average citizen on the use of 911, regardless of the nature or seriousness of the problem, has led to the establishment of **311 systems** in many metropolitan areas to try and decrease the significant burden 911 has had on city emergency resources. The 311 system is available for all calls to police and fire personnel that are not emergencies. Other recent strategies for handling the call volume brought about by 911 include the differential response approaches described in Chapter 6.

Increased research on law enforcement applications and technological development was also a key characteristic of the third stage. The National Institute of Justice (NIJ) was created in 1968, and it continues to play a leading role in enhancing the field of law enforcement internationally (Soulliere 1999). An increasing reliance on civilian specialists within large police organizations also continued throughout this stage with developments in the areas of forensics and communications technologies.

The Fourth Stage (1980–present)

Information access and use characterize Soulliere's (1999) fourth stage of technological development. In addition to simply amassing a large volume of information—a task that law enforcement agencies have been successful at since their creation—technology now focuses on the speed and ease of information use. Moreover, technology developed throughout the fourth stage now provides law enforcement with access to data that would be unavailable to them without these tools. Collaboration in the research and development activities of traditional law enforcement and the military has resulted in many of the technologies introduced in this stage. Examples of such new tools include telecommunications, mobile data computers, expert systems, imaging, and biometric technologies (Soulliere 1999). Each of these areas will be described further throughout the chapter.

The importance of law enforcement access to such technological advancements is in many ways a balancing act between concerns for personal liberties and public security, as illustrated by Cowper (2003) (see Figure 1).

Kurzweil (2001) discusses the significant rate of technological development in modern society. He notes that although technology has always increased exponentially, earlier generations were at such an early stage of development that the trends appear flat due to the low baseline. Kurzweil argues that although everyone in society generally expects technological progress to continue at the same pace, the rate of change is accelerating. Rather than just being increased incrementally every year, technological advancement is characterized by exponential growth, doubling every year. He organizes these observations into the **law of accelerating returns**:

- The enhanced methods resulting from one stage of progress are used to create the next stage.
- Consequently, the rate of progress of an evolutionary process increases exponentially over time.
- In addition, the speed and cost-effectiveness of a technological advancement will also increase exponentially over time.
- Finally, current methods of solving a problem in technology (such as shrinking transistors on an integrated circuit as an approach to making more powerful computers) will provide exponential growth until the method exhausts its potential. At that time, a fundamental change will result that will allow the exponential growth to continue.

Cowper (2003) summarizes the law of accelerating returns by stating that we will have 100 years' progress in the next 25 years and 20,000 years' progress in the next 100 years. Applications available to policing now or in the near future might have once seemed the work of science fiction rather than reality.

Certainly the applications of technology to policing have greatly enhanced the ability of law enforcement organizations to meaningfully engage in the problem-solving process. Although many police departments continue to be behind the curve in terms of integrating new technologies into day-to-day operations, the success of many applications to sound policing will make ignoring progress increasingly difficult over time.

CRIME ANALYSIS

Integral to the process of problem solving discussed in the previous chapter is crime analysis. **Crime analysis** has been defined as involving "the collection and analysis of data pertaining to a criminal incident, offender, and target" (Canter 2000, p. 4). Ideally, crime analysis will guide police managers in making deployment and resource allocation decisions that are linked to a true understanding of the nature of the problem. The more important data bearing on all components of the crime triangle, the better equipped police organizations will be to develop innovative, "out of the box" solutions that include the full spectrum of suppression, intervention, and prevention options.

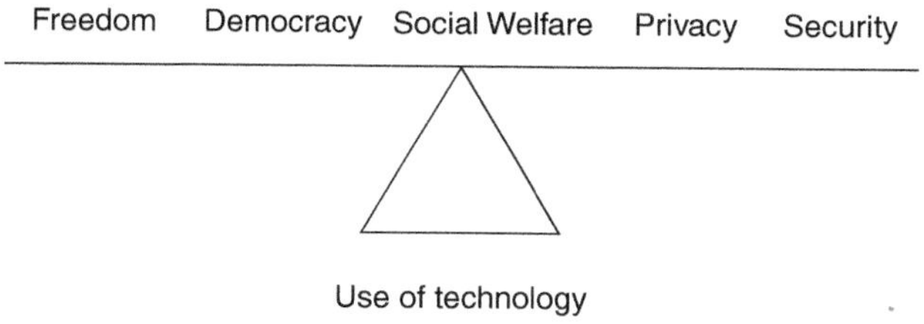

Freedom   Democracy   Social Welfare   Privacy   Security

Use of technology

FIGURE 1 The Balancing Act for Law Enforcement Technology Use. *Source:* Modified from Thomas Cowper. 2003. "Emerging Technology and the Future of Policing," paper presented at the International Police Studies Conference, June 12–15, Eastern Kentucky University, Richmond, KY.

An important caution must be stressed here. Crime analysis will only be as good as the data or information that is collected. Three **essential criteria for crime analysis** should be used by departments in designing data collection processes and in interpreting the meaning of information resulting from crime analysis:

1. **Timeliness.** Does the pattern or trend presented reflect a current problem or issue or is it more representative of a previous situation? Deployment decisions with respect to both prevention and offender apprehension efforts must be based on information that is as current as possible.
2. **Relevancy.** Do the measures used in the analysis accurately reflect what is intended? For example, whether a pattern is based on **calls-for-service data** or **incident data** can be a very important determination depending on what the police manager is trying to understand.
3. **Reliability.** Would the same data, interpreted by different people at different times, lead to the same conclusions?

Canter (2000) categorizes crime analysis into strategic and tactical functions.

Strategic Crime Analysis

The collection and analysis of data spanning a long period of time is **strategic crime analysis**. It is said to be research focused as it includes the use of statistics to make conclusions (Canter 2000). This form of analysis can be useful to departments in terms of **crime trend forecasting**, or using data to estimate future crime based on past trends (Canter 2000). With crime trend forecasting, important decisions can be made with respect to the deployment of patrol allocation as a reflection of the changing volume of criminal activity.

Another important benefit of strategic crime analysis is the analysis of changing community dynamics and risk factors that might be contributing to the particular crime trends of a specific area (Canter 2000). Once again, this type of analysis over time can result in more informed decision making that is more likely to lead to police partnership with other city and community agencies that can help create more long-term, sustainable reductions in criminal activity.

Tactical Crime Analysis

Whereas strategic crime analysis involves the review of data spanning generally a year or more, **tactical crime analysis** uses real-time data spanning several days. One of the principal uses of this type of analysis involves problem identification, or the **pattern detection** of multiple offenses over a short period of time that have common characteristics, such as type of crime, modus operandi, and type of weapon used (Canter 2000). One example of tactical crime analysis that will be discussed later in this chapter is geographic profiling, which can be used to suggest the likelihood of where an offender lives based on the pattern of where offenses occur. Tactical crime analysis can occur on as large an area as a department's entire jurisdiction or as small as the few-block radius of a hot spot.

Linkage analysis involves connecting a suspect to a series of incidents based on commonalities in modus operandi and suspect description, as well as known offenders who live in close proximity to a given area (Canter 2000). Following a nationwide effort by state legislatures to implement sex offender registration laws (Terry and Furlong 2004), many police departments regularly search their databases of registered sex offenders when a known series of sexual offenses is identified.

Finally, **target profiling** involves the use of data to determine the potential risks certain areas may have for criminal victimization based on known offense patterns in the area. Following the previous example, some departments have experimented with community risk profiles (i.e., day-care centers, presence of parks, etc.) as a means of guiding the community notification process for the presence of registered sex offenders.

GEOMAPPING CRIME PATTERNS: MOVING BEYOND PUSHPINS

Based on the previous discussion of the applications of crime analysis to policing, the integral role that **geographic information systems (GIS)** play in the process is readily apparent. A GIS is an automated system for the capture, storage, retrieval, analysis, and display of spatial data (Clarke 1990). Others have noted that GIS technology is as important to geographical analysis as equipments such as the microscope, the telescope, and computers are to other sciences (Abler, 1987). By visually representing diverse data sources that can be geographically located, such as crime events, land usage, property values, and racial ethnic composition, GIS enables planners to display geographical information in new ways (Abler, 1987). Despite its diverse applications across various fields, the common focus of GIS is the enhancement of decision making.

In law enforcement, GIS has revolutionized the practice of electronic **crime mapping**, or visually displaying crime incidents on a mapped surface of a particular jurisdiction. However, the use of crime maps has a long history within policing. For example, the NYPD used pin maps to represent crime patterns at least as far back as 1900 (Harries 1999). Moreover, criminologists and sociologists have examined the spatial trends of crime and delinquency since as far back as mid-nineteenth century France's Quetelet (Phillips 1972) and the Chicago school's **social ecology of crime** efforts pioneered by Shaw and McKay (1942). The difference is, of course, that until the use of GIS became more commonplace in policing practice during the 1990s, crime patterns were literally represented by inserting pushpins into the map of a jurisdiction that was usually mounted on the wall.

Although these early crime maps proved to be useful in visually showing where crimes occurred, patterns would be lost over time as more and more pins were added to the map. Additionally, these maps were very difficult to archive for later retrieval and analysis unless they were photographed (Shaw and McKay 1942).

What Crime Maps Do: GIS as a Technical Aid to Problem-Oriented Policing

GIS has revolutionized the way in which problem-oriented policing (POP) is conducted. This is largely due to law enforcement's ability to overlay seemingly diverse types of data that all contribute to a true understanding of a particular problem. For example, a series of burglaries taking place between the hours of 1:00 PM and 3:00 PM might be the first thing visually displayed on a crime map. This would correspond with the scanning or problem identification part of the problem-solving model. However, to get at the underlying causes of the burglary problem requires deeper probing and innovative thinking. In this case, the crime analyst might overlay the burglary incident data with available data about land usage in the area. The analyst might then learn that the burglaries are occurring within walking distance of an area high school.

Although this might seem to be an obvious linkage to many, individuals often overlook such connections. By visually displaying overlays of various potential data combinations, GIS can play a critical role in jump-starting the analysis process. With the current example, the police manager might begin to develop a series of hypotheses related to the fact that the burglaries might be caused by troublemaking youths playing hooky from their afternoon classes. In addition to providing a large pool of individuals from which investigators might seek to learn information about the incidents, police planners may also begin to collaborate with the school to develop responses that increase truancy enforcement in area schools.

Types of Data with Mapping Applications

The data that can be used for mapping purposes are many, limited only by the creativity of the planning body. Any data that can be **geocoded**, or for which there is geographic reference information, can be used for GIS analysis (Harries 1999). Although early forms of geocoding only permitted street addresses as the geographic unit upon which to map data, now blocks and

LINKAGES IN LAW ENFORCEMENT
GIS Applications to Sex Offender Management

GIS applications can also help to increase law enforcement's capacity to engage in the collaborative problem solving with other criminal justice and community agencies. The visual representation of information can be a powerful tool in coming to a common understanding of the nature of problems even across planning groups with diverse perspectives.

The authors of this text participated on a citywide task force in New York City composed of representatives from law enforcement, probation and parole, family and criminal courts, mental health, treatment providers, and victim advocates to examine the issue of sex offender management in the community (Grant and Terry 2000). Although New York City had a large registered sex offender population at the time (over 3,000 offenders), there was as yet no comprehensive plan for the management of these offenders in the community involving collaboration between each of the key stakeholders. Building on the recognition across team members of the clear need for such a collaborative approach to sex offender management, as well as a need to better understand the dynamics of the problem through data collection, the New York City Sex Offender Management Team had tremendous momentum from the start, with agencies opening their doors to facilitate the data collection process.

Beginning at the first team meeting, the partners sought to identify a mechanism for gaining a complete understanding of the sex offender population currently residing in the community. Although it was initially suggested that each of the five district attorneys represented conduct searches on sex offenders within their own databases to form an initial population for study, it became immediately apparent that the most efficient access to such data would be to use a database of all registered sex offenders in the city. Based on this initial database, the team sought to get complete information on probation conditions, employment, treatment, living situation, probation officer contacts, mental status, substance abuse history, and so on. In addition, complete criminal histories on the offenders were requested in order to gain a true understanding of the nature of the population being managed so that accurate, comprehensive strategies could be devised. At all points, ethical considerations were paramount in the use of this information, which was always presented in aggregate form and never published beyond the law enforcement planning team purposes.

In a city the size of New York, and with such a large number of offenders, geomapping of offender residences is essential for two reasons. First, depending on the plan developed by the team, it might have been necessary to pilot the demonstration project within one borough, given

Hot spots can be made readily apparent through the use of GIS density-mapping tools. This is an excellent tool in the management of sex offenders in the community. Jeff Greenberg/Alamy Images

the tremendous task and resources required for a citywide approach. Second, geomapping had the tremendous ability to demonstrate to the team the scope of the problem, particularly given the obvious clustering of offenders in several city locations. Mapping enabled researchers to present the planning team with **buffer zones** around each offender, combining offender density in a given area with overlays of key risk factors for reoffending drawn from the relapse–prevention literature and connected to each of the offender residence locations. Examination of these data by schools, day-care locations, and parks, available treatment resources, and so on were all part of the process for meaningful informed problem solving to which GIS proved the essential core tool.

Question

1. How would you go about analyzing a particular problem in your community? Describe the data you would collect to document patterns and arrive at a true understanding of the problem's causes. What role would GIS and hot spot mapping play in this process? How would you use the data to develop a strategic plan? What does the research literature suggest as possible alternatives for dealing with the problem you identified?

census tracts can also be used. Crime incidents are readily applicable for geocoding purposes given that they are almost always available as street addresses or otherwise location based (Harries 1999). Crime-mapping applications of GIS include

- mapping incident types and modus operandi, and
- mapping attributes of victims and suspects (Harries 1999)

Based on an initial pattern analysis, overlays with other forms of data can help to develop a broader understanding of a particular problem. For example, pattern analysis might indicate a problem of disorderly conduct and assaults in an area. An overlay with available liquor stores and bars in the area may present the planner with a series of hypotheses as to what factors might be driving the problem. An additional benefit of GIS analyses is that they are directly compatible with statistical analyses to further refine causal projections. Thus, a city planner might be able to statistically link the rate of disorderly conduct and assaults in city jurisdictions with the overall density of alcohol availability or other possibilities. Although such analyses can only show planners the possible relationship between two variables, or **correlations**, rather than saying conclusively that X causes Y (**causation**), there can be no doubt that such findings greatly enhance the level of informed decision making of law enforcement or other key stakeholders in a city.

Mapping and Accountability: GIS in Action

Crime mapping can increase the accountability of a department by visually demonstrating incident patterns for which departmental administrators can hold commanding officers accountable over time. A proactive police manager should use GIS and other problem-solving tools to create sound strategic and tactical decisions for officer deployment, resource deployment, and partnering with other agencies to facilitate sustained crime reductions. The CompStat model of the New York City Police Department institutionalized the use of GIS for departmental planning purposes with such apparent success that similar versions of CompStat have been implemented in departments across the country.

The NYPD crime control model, or **CompStat**, cannot be oversimplified to refer simply to quality-of-life policing, aggressive policing, or even simply data-driven policing, as is commonly found in the literature about the model. Rather, as police scholar Phyllis McDonald (2002) emphatically states, "this proliferation of singularly focused descriptors does a disservice to the management principles of CompStat and its potential for use in other jurisdictions. CompStat (the abbreviation for "computer-driven crime statistics") is a comprehensive, continuous analysis of results for improvement and achievement of prescribed outcomes" (p. 7). In other words, CompStat involves managing police operations by institutionalizing accountability and analysis processes that are the embodiment of the problem-oriented policing model.

McDonald (2002) offers a concise overview of the key elements of the CompStat model and issues involved in its replication in other departments. To summarize, these elements include the following:

- Specific objectives
- Accurate and timely intelligence
- Effective tactics
- Rapid deployment of personnel and resources
- Relentless follow-up and assessment

Police organizations, like any other form of bureaucracy, are often extremely difficult to change. How then did such a seemingly proactive, forward-looking model become implemented in the country's largest police department? In his prior position as head of the New York City Transit Police in the early 1990s, former police commissioner William Bratton had seen tremendous successes in focusing departmental operations on specific measurable objectives and an ongoing review of outcome achievement. Following a series of complementary strategies in then notoriously dangerous New York City subways, such as increased undercover and uniformed police presence and the removal of graffiti and other signs of disorder, dramatic declines in robberies, fare evasion, and general disorder resulted. New Yorkers once again began to feel safe about riding the subways.

When Bratton came to the helm of the NYPD in 1994, he began a dramatic reengineering effort that included interviews and focus groups involving representatives of every rank and bureau in order to assess the state of command in the department (Silverman 1999). Seven specific objectives were created to guide the future direction of the NYPD (McDonald 2002):

- Get guns off the street.
- Curb youth violence in the schools and on the streets.
- Drive drug dealers out of the city.
- Break the cycle of domestic violence.
- Reclaim the city's public spaces.
- Reduce auto-related crime.
- Root out corruption and build organizational integrity in the NYPD.

To achieve these outcomes, as well as to measure departmental progress toward them, ready access to timely data was essential. However, a significant problem became immediately apparent: The NYPD was not equipped to provide up-to-date crime reports. In fact, there was generally a reporting lag of three to six months for crime statistics, and even then any meaningful analysis on the incident-based level was near impossible (Silverman 1996). Headquarters was not systematically tracking crime activity in the precincts, let alone using such information to evaluate the performance of its commanding officers (Silverman 1999). As a result, precinct commanders did not view crime reduction as a paramount job responsibility. Common to departments across the country, efficiency concerns in responding to crime were seen as being more important. Detective bureaus and other specialized functions thus only rarely collaborated with patrol and often directly clashed over territorial and other concerns.

CompStat was devised as a means of reforming the NYPD by pushing all precincts to generate weekly crime activity reports so that they could be held accountable for the achievement of the seven specific objectives outlined in the reengineering process (McDonald 2002). In the beginning, Patrol Bureau staff computerized the data and compiled it into the "CompStat Book," which featured year-to-date crime complaints and arrests for every major felony category, in addition to gun arrests (Silverman 1999). These data would then be compared on citywide, patrol borough, and precinct levels. In addition, precinct commanders quickly became accountable not only for the crime activity but also for any inaccuracies in the data itself. Over time, data became even more readily available by being downloadable directly from the department's On-Line Booking Service (OLBS). Headquarters eventually came to rank order precincts in terms of overall crime changes within their jurisdiction.

By requiring timely and accurate data, it quickly became clear to precinct commanders that their role had changed; they were now being held accountable for the crime under their charges. As such, they began to realize that they had to stop simply responding to crime and had to begin to proactively think about ways to deal with it from all angles: suppression, intervention, and prevention.

To solidify this message, the department began to hold regularly scheduled CompStat meetings in which precinct commanders and their staff met directly with top departmental brass to discuss crime trends and issues in their precincts. In a very intimidating environment, precinct commanders must stand before a lectern in front of three large video screens that flash GIS-generated maps of recent crime patterns. Commanders are then asked about what **tactics** they have tried to address the patterns, what resources they have tried or needed, and with whom they have collaborated. The session thus becomes a brainstorming problem-solving session about how better to proactively respond to crime. Suggestions for strategy directives are made and are relentlessly followed up upon at subsequent meetings by top brass to further ensure accountability. Having the top brass available as part of this process ensures that departmental resources will be directed to precinct needs, even across precinct and unit lines. Thus, in addition to implementing accountable problem solving, CompStat seeks to reduce the problems of linkage blindness.

In order to be better prepared for the CompStat meetings, each borough implemented **Pattern Identification Modules (PIMs)** composed of housing, transit, patrol, detective, organized crime, and robbery squads to review daily index crime reports and thus identify crime clusters or patterns that need to be addressed. Figure 2 provides a conceptual framework of this planning process.

Over time, the CompStat process has evolved to include other data for analysis, including census data, arrest and summons activity, available resources, average response time, domestic violence incidents, unfounded radio runs, and personnel absences (Silverman 1999). Former Commissioner Howard Safir also added citizen complaints and charges of officer misconduct to the process. Time-of-day photos might also be presented in CompStat meetings to monitor changes in precinct dynamics by shift period.

Many scholars and practitioners have argued that CompStat has played a critical role in the significant crime reductions witnessed by New York City following its implementation (Silverman 1999). Others are more skeptical of these claims, arguing that the crime reduction in

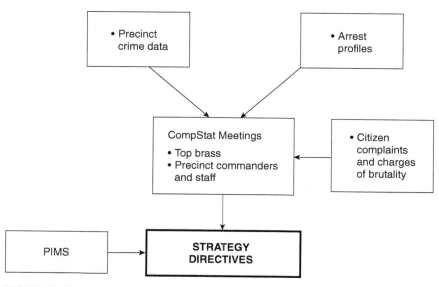

FIGURE 2 Conceptual Framework of the CompStat Planning Process.

New York City can be attributed to larger patterns in society (Karmen 1996). The answer is likely somewhere in the middle; however, the tremendous impact CompStat has had on police management practices internationally cannot be denied. Although some reports have pointed to the demoralizing effects of the process on precinct commanders and officers who feel a pressure to produce numbers, many others cite the significant increases in job satisfaction found by those who feel empowered by the problem-solving aspects brought to the job.

An important concern has been whether the pressure to keep crime statistics low has led to a zero-tolerance policing style that loses sight of community concerns, further inhibiting police–community relations. The answer to this issue is unclear, and it is probably too soon to come to any concrete conclusions. These questions will have to be tracked by practitioners and academicians alike as the model is implemented across diverse contextual conditions within the United States and abroad.

GIS and the Patrol Officer

As GIS crime mapping became recognized as an important tool in both tracking and responding to crime on a neighborhood level, departments across the country sought to expand its use beyond administrative planning to reach the patrol officers and community residents. For example, the Camden New Jersey Police Department began providing officers with access to crime-mapping information on desktop computers and even wireless laptops in patrol cars (*American City and Country* 2002). The department enabled officers to access crime locations, crime types, and times throughout the city in order to focus patrol efforts. The maps also enable officers to pinpoint business contact information when an alarm is sounded, rather than having to call a dispatcher for the information (*American City and Country* 2002).

In 1998, the NIJ awarded the leading GIS software provider, **Environmental Systems Research Institute, Inc. (ESRI)**, a $500,000 grant to work with local law enforcement agencies and universities to effectively utilize GIS as a crime-fighting tool (Carney 1998). Collaborating with several local law enforcement agencies, ESRI developed an accessible GIS interface for large-scale departmental needs.

LINKAGES IN LAW ENFORCEMENT
GIS Applications to Community Policing

Beginning in 1995, the Chicago Police Department (CPD) implemented one of the most easy-to-use and accessible GIS systems in the country as a complement to its department-wide **Chicago Alternative Policing Strategy (CAPS)** community-policing approach. Called **Information Collection for Automated Mapping (ICAM)**, the program enables departmental personnel to generate maps of reported offenses by type, including charts of the ten most frequently reported offenses, through a series of easy mouse clicks (Rich 1996).

CAPS was implemented in 1993 in pilot districts and has since been expanded to all twenty-five of the city's policing districts. CAPS emphasizes officer problem solving by assigning officers to their beats for at least a year, altering dispatch schedules so that the time spent responding to crime outside of their beats is limited, and requiring officer attendance at community meetings (Rich 1996). Early evaluations of CAPS effectiveness showed significant declines in

reported crime, victimization, and fear of crime (Skogan and Hartnett 1996). Based on a thirteen-year study of CAPS, Skogan (2006) concluded that the success of the initiative differed among races. Specifically, Caucasians saw modest improvements, African Americans benefited greatly, and Latinos saw little improvement (Skogan 2006). He comments in his book, "the success of CAPS depended on who you were and where you lived" (Skogan 2006, p. 234).

ICAM is viewed as a complement to CAPS. CAPS enables officers to better understand the problems in their assigned areas and thus be better facilitators of collaborative problem-solving efforts with community residents (Rich 1996). As part of the ICAM development process, focus groups were held with officers and detectives to seek their understanding and cooperation and ensure that the completed program suited their information needs. Once the department got the officers' buy-in, maps were regularly shared at beat meetings. Because of the success of the ICAM, a Citizen ICAM program has been developed. With Citizen ICAM, citizens can generate much of the same information (without specific identifiers) that an officer can, thereby facilitating joint police–community planning efforts. Other departments across the country have produced their own mapping programs, including Web-based citizen crime reports, as will be discussed later.

Questions

1. Does your local police department have a Web site? How does it compare to ICAM?

2. Which GIS elements would you include on a department Web site?

3. What applications of available GIS crime data are there in your community?

Other Applications: Geographic Profiling

Geographic profiling, the combined use of geography, psychology, and mathematics to identify the location of an offender, is most commonly associated with tracking down serial killers, rapists, and arsonists. However, it is actually useful as an investigative tool in any case in which an individual offender has committed criminal activity across a series of locations (including crimes as diverse as robbery, burglary, theft, and fraud). Building from the significant empirical efforts of Brantingham and Brantingham (1981), geographic profiling suggests investigative alternatives based on the "hunting behavior" of the offender. Leading geographic profiler Kim Rossmo argues that criminals are no different in offending as ordinary citizens are in going about their day-to-day activities (Onion 2002).

Following this logic, geographic profiling uses the **nearness principle**, which means that offenders will remain within a limited range that is comfortable to them when committing their offenses (Rossmo 1998), just as animals will tend to forage within a limited range from their base (Onion 2002). Geographic profiling incorporates all possible methods of transportation available to an offender in providing a calculation of the area in which the offender is most likely to reside. Such techniques were utilized to assist in the capture of Derrick Todd Lee, aka the Baton Rouge serial killer, who has been linked to the death of seven women (Weeber 2007).

This research has led to the creation of a computerized geographic-profiling workstation called **Rigel**. Rigel incorporates statistical analyses, GIS, and database management functions to generate investigative suggestions. Crime scenes are broken down into type and then entered by location. Based on the theoretical principles of geographic profiling, addresses of suspects can be evaluated by their probability of being the actual offender (Harries 1999). This can help investigators to sort through their existing databases, such as those of registered sex offenders, and other investigative information. When there is not a specific suspect pool, geographic profiling can help to pinpoint the highest probability areas to focus the search. As with the offender-profiling process, geographic profiling should only be considered an additional tool for investigators; solving the offense will require a sound investigative strategy.

TWENTY-FIRST-CENTURY TECHNOLOGIES IN POLICING

In addition to GIS, over the past decade numerous other technologies have become available to law enforcement, from **record management systems (RMS)** that help departments store and retrieve the immense amount of data they receive on a day-to-day basis all the way to sophisticated weaponry and intelligence technologies that have reached law enforcement by way of the military. Covering all of these advances in significant detail is beyond the scope of this text; however, the remainder of this chapter provides an overview of some significant technological developments that are becoming part of everyday law enforcement activities.

Closed-Circuit Television

The use of **closed-circuit television (CCTV)** and other forms of public surveillance technology in the United States has witnessed significant growth in recent years as not only police departments but also airport security and other public entities have increasingly turned to video surveillance in their efforts to reduce crime and increase public safety. The use of this technology in the United States may not be nearly as prevalent as it is in countries such as England, where there is a camera on nearly every street corner and in every public building; however, it is becoming increasingly popular, particularly following the events of September 11. Law enforcement is now readily turning to surveillance systems such as CCTV as a means of trying to sort through the tremendous traffic at our borders, airports, and dense city streets.

After spending almost two years in CCTV control rooms across England, Goold (2004) concluded that in many cases actual surveillance outcomes have less to do with technological factors than they do with working cultures and the attitudes of individual camera operators. In particular, Goold found that once established, many surveillance systems in public areas quickly become prone to institutional inertia, with both camera operators and scheme managers being either unwilling or unable to update their systems or change their working practices in response to technological advances. Technology does not exist in a vacuum; it is shaped by social factors and by the attitudes and practices of those who use it (Bijkker et al. 1987). In addition, technical workers, such as CCTV operators, often shape the implementation of new technology by fitting it into their existing routines. Technological change may as often be subsumed into existing organizational structures as it effects organizational change (Barley 1986).

Closed-circuit television is becoming an increasingly common form of surveillance in the United States.   istock

No one can erase the images caught on airport CCTV cameras of the September 11 hijackers boarding their plane in Boston. Certainly such retrospective images can be used as evidence of what transpired in a given incident, but law enforcement has become increasingly more interested in finding better ways to harness CCTV technology to identify known offenders passing through a checkpoint, such as a wanted felon or individual on a terrorist watch list. As such, new advances have sought to merge CCTV systems with promising approaches in the field of biometrics, as will be discussed below.

Some agencies have developed innovative ways of overcoming the limitations of private security systems, which in many cases are useful only for recording crimes in progress rather than providing aid to responding units at the scene. For example, the Seal Beach Police Department installed a network that transmits the output of bank security cameras directly to dispatch and to responding units in real time in a high-robbery-incident suburb of Los Angeles (Garcia 2001). The network transmits video over the air through encrypted wireless communication paths in the same manner that images are sent over the Internet.

Global Positioning Systems

Tracking offenders or patrol officer deployments have also been enhanced by the use of Global Positioning Systems. **Global positioning systems (GPS)** use satellite-based technologies for the purpose of tracking the movement of patrol cars or specially equipped stolen vehicles. In some cases, officers can be equipped with GPS-enabled cellular phones, providing an important alternative to conventional address matching for an officer responding to a call. GPS technology has

LINKAGES IN LAW ENFORCEMENT
Surveillance in New York City—The Lower Manhattan Security Initiative

In 2007, the New York Police Department (NYPD) began installing video surveillance cameras, environmental sensors, and license plate readers in lower Manhattan as part of the Lower Manhattan Security Initiative (LMSI). It is a network of 3,000 cameras that will monitor in real time the movement of people and vehicles south of Canal Street, along with license plate readers, and environmental sensors. This information will be sent to a command center staffed by police and private security firms who can then establish moveable roadblocks to investigate suspicious activity. Modeled on London's "Ring of Steel," the LMSI represents the first of its kind in the United States (Josselson 2007). This new counterterrorism strategy aims to deter, monitor, and track terrorist activity. LMSI has received much criticism for intruding on personal privacy, the potential for racial profiling, the cost of the program, and potential for the information to be used unethically for compiling personal information (Josselson 2007). London's camera system was useful in apprehending perpetrators of the 2005 subway bombings and 2007 attempted car bombings (Buckley 2007). However, to date there is no study regarding the effectiveness of surveillance cameras in deterring terrorist activity (Winston 2009b). Some studies on camera surveillance in general have commented that such mechanisms do not reduce crime and may actually displace it (Winston 2009a).

Sources:

Buckley, C. June 9, 2007. "New York Plans Surveillance Veil for Downtown." *The New York Times.* Available at http://www.nytimes.com/2007/07/09/nyregion/09ring.html?ei=5088&en=2644be97bd9577f9&ex=1341633600&partner=rssnyt&emc=rss&page-wanted=print

Josselson, S. September 4, 2007. "New York's 'Ring of Steel.'" *Gotham Magazine.* Available at http://www.gothamgazette.com/print/2278

Winston, A. March 16, 2009a." A Chance for Input on 3,000 New Police Cameras." *City Limits.* Available at http://www.citylimits.org/news/article_print.cfm?article_id=3713

Winston, A. October 9, 2009b. "Is the NYPD 'Ring of Steel' Effective? And is it Work the Cost to Privacy?" *New York Magazine.* Available at http://www.printthis.clickability.com/pt/cpt?action=cpt&expire=&urlID=412346082&fb=Y&url=http%3A%2F%2Fnymag.com%2Fdaily%2Fintel%2F2009%2F10%2Fis_nypd_ring_of_steel_effectiv.html&partnerID=73272

Questions

1. What is surveillance like in your city?
2. Where in your city should surveillance be increased and why?
3. Would there be any detriments to increased surveillance in your city?

also significantly enhanced aerial photography of crime incident locations, allowing for greater visualization of the complete context of a situation (Harries 2001). The State of Iowa has capitalized on the surveillance capacity of GPS to monitor the real-time location of high-risk offenders released from prison. With the use of an offender-monitoring system, law enforcement and correctional agencies can keep offenders away from areas where children are likely to congregate (e.g., schools and day-care centers) (Greene 2003).

The Escambia County Sheriff's Department's SWAT team used a broadband-via-satellite system when responding to an emergency call involving a shooting victim and a barricaded suspect. Through communication with the Mobile Command Center's satellite system, SWAT officers were able to determine that the suspect had fled the scene and that the victim was likely dead (Hughes Network Systems 2002). Pictures of the suspect were immediately obtained via satellite and distributed to patrol, a process that used to take hours or days.

Biometrics

Biometrics involves the automatic, real-time identification of individuals based on their physiology or behavior (Cowper 2003). Biometrics thus encompasses a diversity of technologies, including voice recognition, fingerprint identification, lip movement, retinal scanning, facial recognition software, DNA profiling, thermal imagery, and iris/retinal scanning, to name just a few.

FACIAL RECOGNITION SOFTWARE   The field of biometrics, particularly **facial recognition software**, might overcome the limitations of CCTV systems, both by reducing the need for expensive human operators and by making the suspect identification process faster and more reliable. Currently, fewer than one in ten departments are utilizing such technology, although it is more common in departments with jurisdictions over 1 million or more residents (Hickman and Reaves 2006). Several promising studies support the potential applications of facial recognition software; however, little is known about how such systems will function in real-life situations (Norris and Armstrong 1999).

Like any technology, the potential impact of facial recognition technology—from preventing crime to infringing civil liberties—depends on the quality of the database from which possible "hits" are derived. For example, an under-inclusive database might exclude potential terrorists but "catch" a child support violator; whereas a mistargeted database may send out too large a net that might unnecessarily infringe on people's civil liberties and reduce the effective application of the technology. Cole's (2001) groundbreaking analysis of the history of identification technologies highlights the need for further study of the information elements that comprise biometric databases.

FINGERPRINT IDENTIFICATION SYSTEMS   An advanced system to aid in the processing, storage, and matching of fingerprints has been introduced by the FBI. Called the **Integrated Automated Fingerprint Identification System (IAFIS)**, this enhanced technology offers a two-hour turnaround on electronically submitted criminal print searches from federal, state, and local law enforcement agencies (Smith 1998). IAFIS maintains the largest biometric database in the world with fingerprints and criminal histories of over 55 million people (FBI 2008b). Fingerprints and criminal histories are obtained voluntarily from law enforcement agencies. The cooperation among local, state, and federal agencies has increased interjurisdictional cooperation and crime-fighting efforts.

Interjurisdictional Communication Technologies

At the core of linkage blindness is minimal amount of critical communication that occurs among different law enforcement jurisdictions as well as other sectors of the criminal justice

New technology research seeks to merge facial recognition software with CCTV surveillance cameras, which could help identify known terrorists before they attack.   Corbis/Bettmann

system and community at large. Given the diversity of criminal justice core functions, the gathering and sharing of criminal justice information is particularly complex (Tomek 2001). The need to build information-sharing capacities, both technological and organizational, is evidenced by the NIJ's decision to make information sharing the number one priority for information technology solutions among state and local agencies, as well as internationally (Tomek 2001).

The need for information continuity and access is key for informed decision making by all criminal justice stakeholders. One of the biggest challenges to larger information-sharing collaborations is the large differences across agencies in terms of agency protocols, standards, and even measures for the collection and utilization of data (Tomek 2001). The Department of Homeland Security is working to reduce this difficulty. In law enforcement's effort to prevent terrorism, the DHS has initiated the **Homeland Security Information Network (HSIN)**. HSIN enables state and urban law enforcement agencies to collect and disseminate information among federal, state, and local agencies in order to prevent terrorist activity. This computer-based communications system was developed by state and local authorities in order to connect all fifty states, Washington, D.C., and major metropolitan areas (DHS 2007).

OFFENDER DATABASES   Efforts have been made in recent years to develop sufficient technologies capable of overcoming many of the barriers involved in cross- and interjurisdictional information sharing. The San Diego County **Automated Regional Justice Information System (ARJIS)** warrants further description as to the possibilities in interjurisdictional information sharing. ARJIS combines information from thirty-eight state, local, and federal law enforcement agencies into one Web site that can be accessed by registered police, court, and correctional officials (Walsh 2003). ARJIS includes crime incident databases that are updated every twenty-four hours, most-wanted lists, and interactive maps. Similarly, the Pennsylvania Integrated Justice Network (JNET) connects all of its criminal justice agencies together for the sharing of critical information, including offender photos and images of distinguishing marks. In one case, an offender was apprehended based on the victim being able to describe the perpetrator's tattoo to the police (Walsh 2003).

CROSS-JURISDICTIONAL RADIO COMMUNICATIONS Federal efforts at improving cross-jurisdictional radio communications include the NIJ's **Advanced Generation of Interoperability for Law Enforcement (AGILE)**. AGILE provides direct connections between the radio systems of law enforcement agencies with overlapping or adjacent jurisdictions (Kaluta 2001). The possibilities of such technologies for enhancing national security needs has been demonstrated by early successes of the system as an enhancement to San Diego County's ARJIS (Scanlon 2000). AGILE has also been used to establish an emergency-only radio channel for presidential inaugurations, linking the Secret Service, the FBI, the U.S. Capitol Police, the U.S. Park Police, and the Metropolitan Police Department (Kaluta 2001).

ELECTRONIC WARRANT PROCESSES Some jurisdictions have developed solutions to the numerous problems involved in the arrest warrant process. With the traditional process, courts issue paper warrants that are subsequently used by law enforcement agencies to create a wanted person record in their own systems, which can then be checked by law enforcement officials throughout the country through the use of the FBI's National Crime Information Center. One of the problems with this process is the delay by the court in issuing or canceling a warrant, creating serious officer safety concerns (Perbix 2001). Additional concerns arise from the lack of synchronization across the systems, in which warrants entered into one system are not entered into another (adding to the linkage blindness problem).

Electronic warrant systems, such as the Colorado Integrated Criminal Justice Information System (CICJIS), link the state's main criminal justice systems (including law enforcement, prosecutors, courts, and adult and juvenile corrections) so that data entered by one agency's system are automatically transferred and loaded into another agency's system, thereby reducing linkage blindness and reducing the amount of inconsistent data (Perbix 2001).

INFORMATION SECURITY THROUGH ENCRYPTION Given the confidential information being shared by criminal justice agencies through these enhanced technologies, serious privacy concerns inevitably arise. Secure law enforcement communication over the Internet or intranets can be achieved with **virtual private networking (VPN)**. VPN uses encryption software to scramble the contents of communications so that even if the system becomes available to hackers, they are unable to read the information (Taylor 2000). In addition to an advanced encryption algorithm that is virtually impossible to break, VPNs pass encrypted communications through a "tunnel" between communicating agencies, ensuring that users meet a high level of identification to be able to access the information (Taylor 2000). With the establishment of proper identification and access protocols, VPNs offer law enforcement agencies the ability to exchange and track important information, such as gang memberships, enhancing contact between the communicating agencies.

The World Wide Web and Community Policing

With its focus on collaborative problem solving and communication with the public, community policing is even more information intensive than traditional policing methods (Monahan 1998). New communication technologies such as the Internet have proven instrumental in furthering departmental community policing objectives. Following are the important features that are used by many departmental Web sites in reaching their constituent audiences (Hart 1996):

- Officer photo galleries, including photos and biographical sketches
- Libraries devoted to crime prevention

- Safety tips, including information about known scam cases operating within the jurisdiction
- Virtual tours of the department
- Recruitment tool with links to personnel information about the hiring process
- Citywide and neighborhood crime statistics, including crime-mapping capabilities on more advanced sites, such as the Chicago Police Department's Citizen ICAM
- Departmental wanted lists and upcoming court cases
- Capacity for anonymous and/or confidential reporting of crime information or complaints about officer conduct

Departmental Web sites move beyond the realm of being public relations tools toward true support for community policing activities to the extent that the department shares important details about activities and arrests rather than the filtered information generally provided to citizens by the media (Price 2001). Departmental posting of such information, however, should be balanced against the privacy needs of victims and nonconvicted offenders.

Improving Accountability—Mobile Communications with Patrol

Radio communications with patrol cars revolutionized the ability of departments to monitor the activities of line officers. Although such technology did not take away the high level of discretion available to officers as part of the nature of the job, enhancements to dispatch communications capabilities had a profound effect on the nature of the job. More recently, cellular phone technology has provided an alternate communication forum for some jurisdictions.

MOBILE DIGITAL COMMUNICATIONS **Mobile digital communications (MDC)** offer non-verbal means of communicating information between communication centers and patrol (Thibault et al. 2001). Such communication is achieved through the use of a mobile digital terminal within the patrol car. During 2003, 56 percent of local police departments used mobile computers or terminals (BJS 2006). In some jurisdictions, MDC options allow for electronic submission of reports, thereby reducing the volume of paperwork. More recently, some departments have installed new laptop computers into patrol cars, offering officers instant access to information, such as notes from the communications officer, and even the Internet. Thirty percent of all local departments used vehicle mounted laptops, and 33 percent used portable laptops in the field (BJS 2006). Soon officers will not have to leave their cars to write even more detailed reports (Johnson 2003). The Internet also facilitates interjurisdictional information exchange opportunities immediately available to officers, again providing an important tool in the reduction of linkage blindness.

The Maryland State Police have extended their use of mobile technology to include automation of traffic violations. Prior to stopping a vehicle an officer can enter a motorist license plate number into the computer system to check for outstanding warrants or if the vehicle is stolen. Once stopped, the computer system can scan the license plate again and check federal and state databases for additional information. Currently, thirty-two law enforcement agencies are using this system. This technology has reduced errors due to cross-checking of databases, reduced time spent conducting traffic stops, enhanced officer safety, and improved interagency cooperation (Valcarcel 2009).

AUTOMATIC VEHICLE MONITORING Through the use of **automatic vehicle monitoring (AVM)** technologies, departments are able to know the location and status of patrol vehicles, including whether the door of the vehicle has been left open and so on (Thibault et al. 2001). AVM systems are thus vitally important in aiding officers in high-speed pursuit situations and in determining whether the officer is in need of backup.

Chapter Summary

- Technology has advanced significantly in the past twenty years, and the application of this technology has benefited law enforcement officers in both proactive and reactive methods of policing.
- The most important factors in crime analysis are timeliness, relevancy, and reliability, all of which are necessary to examine data effectively.
- With GIS crime mapping, a map is created that police officers can use to analyze where and when crime occurs. It has many benefits, particularly with regard to proactive policing. It can help the police develop strategies to combat crime, particularly in crime hot spots.
- Advanced technology allows for the collection of more timely and accurate data, helping patrol officers respond more quickly and effectively to crime.

- One of the leading technologies of the twenty-first century is CompStat, which envelopes the problem-oriented policing model and assists in more effective management of areas where crime occurs.
- Surveillance technology such as CCTV is extremely beneficial in tracking all types of criminals, from shoplifters to terrorists. Through the taped monitoring of movements, combined with emerging biometrics of face recognition technology, there are many potential applications of CCTV.
- GPS is important in facilitating law enforcement operation in both investigatory and deployment capacities.
- Interjurisdictional communication technologies useful to law enforcement include offender databases and electronic warrants systems.

LINKING THE DOTS

1. What have been some of the most significant technological advancements in policing since 1980? Explain their significance.
2. What are some of the dangers associated with the advancement in police technology? How are these dangers balanced with the benefits of such technology?
3. Do you think CompStat is partially responsible for the significant drop in crime in New York City over the past decade?
4. How does law enforcement's use of technology benefit the community?
5. How can technology be used to help combat terrorism?

Key Terms

311 system
911 system
Advanced Generation of Interoperability for Law Enforcement (AGILE)
Automated Regional Justice Information System (ARJIS)
Automatic vehicle monitoring (AVM)
Biometrics
Buffer zones
Calls-for-service data
Causation
Chicago Alternative Policing Strategy (CAPS)
Closed-circuit television (CCTV)

CompStat
Correlations
Crime analysis
Crime mapping
Crime trend forecasting
Electronic warrant system
Environmental Systems Research Institute, Inc. (ESRI)
Essential criteria for crime analysis
Facial recognition software
Geocoded
Geographic information systems (GIS)
Geographic profiling
Global positioning systems (GPS)

Homeland Security Information Network (HSIN)
Incident data
Information Collection for Automated Mapping (ICAM)
Integrated Automated Fingerprint Identification System (IAFIS)
Law of accelerating returns
Linkage analysis
Mobile digital communications (MDC)
Nearness principle
Pattern detection
Pattern Identification Modules (PIMs)

Record management systems (RMS)
Relevancy
Reliability
Rigel
Social ecology of crime
Soulliere's stages of technological advancement
Strategic crime analysis
Tactical crime analysis
Tactics
Target profiling
Timeliness
Virtual private network (VPN)

References

Abler, R.F. 1987. "The National Science Foundation National Center for Geographic Information and Analysis." *International Journal of Geographical Information Systems* 1:303–326.

American City and Country. 2002. "Crime Maps Improve Patrols in Camden." *American City and County,* October 1, 2002. Available at www.americancityandcountry.com/ar/government_crime_maps_improve.

Barley, S. 1986. "Technology as an Occasion for Structuring Evidence from Observations of CT Scanners and the Social Order of Radiology Departments." *Administrative Science Quarterly* 31(1):78–108.

Bijkker, M., T. Hughes, and T. Pinch. 1987. *The Social Construction of Technological Systems. New Directions in the Sociology and History of Technology.* Cambridge, MA: MIT Press.

Brantingham, C., and B. Brantingham. 1981. *Environmental Criminology.* Thousand Oaks, CA: Sage Publications.

Canter, P. 2000. "Using a Geographic Information System for Tactical Crime Analysis." In *Analyzing Crime Patterns: Frontiers of Practice,* edited by V. Goldsmith, P. McGuire, J. Mollenkopf, and T. Ross, 3–10. Thousand Oaks, CA: Sage.

Carney, D. 1998. "Arming Beat Cops with GIS Weapons." *Civic.com,* April 13, 1998. Available at www.civic.com.

Clarke, K. C. 1990. *Analytical and Computer Cartography.* Upper Saddle River, NJ: Prentice Hall.

Cole, S. 2001. *Suspect Identities: A History of Fingerprinting and Criminal Identification.* Cambridge, MA: Harvard University Press.

Cowper, T. 2003. "Emerging Technology and the Future of Policing." Paper presented at the International Police Studies Conference, June 12–15, Eastern Kentucky University, Richmond, VA: Kentucky.

DeAngelis, T. February 2000. "GIS: Answering the Why of Where?" *Police Chief* 67(2):12.

Department of Homeland Security (DHS). 2007. "Homeland Security." Available at www.dhs.gov.

Federal Bureau of Investigation (FBI). 2008b. *Integrated Automated Fingerprint Identification System.* Available at http://www.fbi.gov/hq/cjisd/iafis.htm.

Garcia, M., and Zanone, D. 2001. "Force Protection Using Wireless Internet Technology." *Police Chief* 68(12):68.

Goold, B. 2004. *CCTV and Policing: Public Area Surveillance and Police Practices in Britain.* Oxford: Oxford University Press.

Grant, H., and K. Terry. 2000. *The New York City Sex Offender Management Team: Summary Progress Report.* New York: John Jay College of Criminal Justice.

Greene, K. March 30, 2003. "Global Positioning Systems Used for Some Offenders." *Telegraph – Herald.*

Harries, K. 1999. *Mapping Crime: Principle and Practice.* Washington, D.C.: National Institute of Justice.

Harries, K. 2001. *Demonstration of Orthophotographic Representation and Analysis.* Washington, D.C.: National Institute of Justice.

Hart, F. 1996. "How and Why to Implement the Worldwide Web for Community Policing." *Police Chief* 3(1):55.

Hickman, M. J., and Reaves, B. A. 2006a. *Local Police Departments,* Washington, D.C.: Bureau of Justice Statistics, U.S. Department of Justice.

Hughes Network Systems. 2002. *Case Study.* Germantown, MD: Hughes Network Systems.

Johnson, M. 2003. "City Vehicles Receive Laptops." *Daytona Beach News Journal,* April 15, 1.

Kaluta, R. 2001. "New Developments in Interjurisdictional Communication Technology." *Police Chief.* Available at www.iacptechnology.org/library/techtalk/techtalk0401.htm.

Karmen, A. 1996. *New York City Murder Mystery.* New York: NYU Press.

Kelling, G., and M. Moore. 1987. "The Evolving Strategy of Policing." *Perspectives on Policing* 4(1):1–15.

Kurzweil, R. 2001. "The Law of Accelerating Returns." Available at www.kurzweilai.net.

McDonald, P. 2002. *Managing Police Operations: Implementing the New York Crime Control Model: CompStat.* Belmont, CA: Wadsworth.

Monahan, M. September 1998. "Technology Management for Community Policing." *Police Chief* 65(9).

Norris, C., and G. Armstrong. 1999. *The Maximum Surveillance Society: The Rise of CCTV.* New York: NYU Press.

Onion, A. 2002. "Coordinates of a Killer: A Mathematical Method Can Help Investigators Locate Killers." *ABCnews.com,* October 8. Available at www.abcnews.com.

Perbix, M. 2001. "Automating Arrest Warrants Between Courts and Law Enforcement." *Police Chief,* October. Available at www.iacptechnology.org/library/AutomatingArrestWarrantsBTCountsandLE.pdf.

Phillips, P. 1972. "A Prologue to the Geography of Crime." *Proceedings, Association of American Geographers* 4(1):86–91.

President's Commission on Law Enforcement and the Administration of Justice. 1967. *Final Report of the President's Commission on Law Enforcement and the Administration of Justice.* Washington, D.C.: Presidents Commission on Law Enforcement and the Administration of Justice.

Price, C. December 2001. "The Police Web Site as a Community Policing Tool." *Police Chief* 68(12).

Rich, T. 1996. *The Chicago Police Department's Information Collection for Automated Mapping (ICAM) Program.* Washington, D.C.: National Institute of Justice Program Focus.

Rossmo, K. 1998. *Geographic Profiling.* Boca Raton, FL: CRC Press.

Scanlon, P. 2000. "A Successful Partnership: When Police and the Feds Team for Technology." *Police Chief,* October. Available at www.iacptechnology.org/library/techtalk/techtalk/co.

Seaskate, Inc. 1998. *The Evolution and Development of Police Technology.* Washington, D.C.: National Institute of Justice.

Shaw, C., and H. McKay. 1942. *Juvenile Delinquency and Urban Areas.* Chicago, IL: University of Chicago Press.

Silverman, E. 1996. "Mapping Change: How the New York City Police Department Reengineered Itself to Drive Down Crime." *Law Enforcement News,* December 15, 1–6.

Silverman, E. 1999. *NYPD Battles Crime.* Boston, MA: Northeastern University Press.

Skogan, W. 2006. *Police and Community in Chicago.* New York: Oxford University Press.

Skogan, W., and S. Hartnett. 1996. *Community Policing Chicago Style.* New York: Oxford University Press.

Skolnick, J., and D. Bayley. 1986. *The New Blue Line: Police Innovation in Six American Cities.* New York: The Free Press.

Smith, K. 1998. "Integrated Automated Fingerprint Identification System: Twenty-first-century Technology for Law Enforcement." *Police Chief* 62(6):23.

Soulliere, N. 1999. *Police and Technology: Historical Review and Current Status.* Ottawa, ON: Canadian Police College.

Taylor, B. 2000. "Virtual Private Networking: Secure Law Enforcement Communication on the Internet." *Police Chief* 67(1):13.

Terry, K., and J. Furlong. 2004. *Sex Offender Registration and Community Notification: A "Megan's Law" Sourcebook,* 2nd ed. Kingston, NJ: Civic Research Institute.

Thibault, E., L. Lynch, and R. McBride. 2001. *Proactive Police Management,* 5th ed. Upper Saddle River, NJ: Prentice Hall.

Tomek, W. February 2001. "Information Sharing: A Strategic Necessity." *Police Chief* 68(2).

Valcarcel, J. (2009). "Maryland's Pursuit of the Paperless Patrol Car: Using Mobile Technology to Foter Interagency Collaboration and Improve officer Safety." *Police Chief* LXXVI(6). Alexandria, VA: International Association of Chiefs of Police.

Walsh, T. 2003. "Data Sharing Tightens Net for the Law-Agencies Put Criminal Justice Data On-line for Sharing." *Government Computer News,* July 10. Available at www.gcn.com.

Weeber, S. 2007. *In Search of Derrick Todd Lee: The Internet social movement that made a difference.* Lanham, MD: University Press of America.

Crime Mapping and Analysis

From Chapter 13 of *Police Field Operations*, First Edition. Michael Birzer, Cliff Roberson. Copyright © 2009 by Pearson Education, Inc. Published by Pearson Prentice Hall. All rights reserved.

Crime Mapping and Analysis

" Computers have revolutionized the art of crime mapping. Once just an exercise of sticking pins into a map glued to a bulletin board, crime mapping is now built on a foundation of geographic information systems. "

—Diamond, 2004, p. 42

" Geography has become increasingly important in law enforcement and crime prevention. Criminology has long focused on individual propensities toward crime, but it was only during the last few decades that the criminogenic features of *settings* began to take on importance in research and practice. "

—Cohen, 2006, p. 124

CHAPTER OUTLINE

- Introduction
- Crime Analysts
- Crime Mapping
- Should Crime Information Be Made Public?
- Does Crime Mapping Simply Cause Crime to Move Around the Corner?
- Hot Spot Theories on Crime
- Summary

OBJECTIVES

After completion of this chapter, you will be able to do the following:

- Explain the role of crime analysts.
- Briefly discuss the history of crime mapping.
- Explain how computerization changed the concepts involved in crime mapping.
- Illustrate how geographic information systems are currently used in crime mapping.
- Identify the four subparts of a geographic information system.
- Discuss the types of information that crime maps can provide the police.
- Explain what constitutes a hot spot and the issues with hot spots.
- Discuss hot spot theories on crime.
- Discuss the merits of whether crime information should be made public.
- Explain the privacy issues involved in crime mapping.

INTRODUCTION

What locations are hot for auto theft right now? Assume you are a crime analyst employed by a major metropolitan police department. How would you answer that question if it was posed to you by your chief?

This chapter contains an overview of crime mapping. It is not designed to make you proficient in the art. Readers who are interested in further study in crime mapping may refer to three excellent publications that may be obtained without charge from the U.S. Department of Justice: Ronald Clarke and John E. Eck's, "Crime Analysis for Problem Solvers in 60 Small Steps"; Jacqueline Cohen's, "Development of Crime Forecasting and Mapping Systems for Use by Police"; and Keith Harries', "Mapping Crime: Principle and Practice."

CRIME ANALYSTS

Many police agencies do employ one or more crime analysts, but some of the largest and more advanced police organizations do not. When employed, the job of the crime analyst is often narrowly limited to tabulating crimes that occur. In others, it extends to identifying patterns of crimes, with the primary objective of identifying the likely offenders so that they can be apprehended. In its more ambitious form, the crime analyst's job may include identifying factors contributing to a crime pattern, but the job of deciding how to respond to these factors is usually deferred to operational personnel, who then tend to use traditional means for dealing with them.

Meanwhile, the field of crime analysis itself has grown much more sophisticated. A strong literature on its potential is now available. The ability to electronically capture, store, and retrieve massive amounts of data that police routinely collect is infinitely greater than it was just a decade ago. The capacity to map crime geographically is stunning, and is now a major, indispensable tool in crime analysis. Standard approaches have been developed for the collection, analysis, and dissemination of intelligence across jurisdictional lines, but problem analysis is not the exclusive domain of technicians. Everyone in a police agency, from officers on the beat to police executives, and, more broadly, those in both the public and private sector concerned about crime should incorporate the line of thinking set forth here into the perspectives they bring to their work (Clarke & Eck, 2003, v–vi).

CRIME MAPPING

Evidence from clay tablets found in Iraq indicates that crime maps have been around for several thousand years—perhaps tens of millennia (Harries, 1999, p. 4). The French cartographers in the nineteenth century used national maps in attempts to identify crime patterns. European cartographers conducting studies on the social ecology of crime studied the locations of crime in an attempt to provide a number of important insights regarding crime. The studies began with the work of Guerry in France in 1833, Quetelet in Belgium in 1833, and Greg in the Netherlands in 1835. They examined reported incidents of crime and mapped the incidents on topographic maps.

In the 1920s, Parks and Burgess (followed by Shaw and McKay) studied crime rates in Chicago by mapping the reported crimes on a map. They divided the map using concentric zones to support their social disorganization theories of crime causation (Roberson & Wallace, 1998, p. 98).

Shaw and McKay's mapping efforts produced a classic analysis on juvenile delinquency in Chicago. Their work is generally recognized as the landmark piece of research involving crime mapping in the first half of the twentieth century. Shaw and McKay mapped thousands of incidents of juvenile delinquency and analyzed relationships between delinquency and various social conditions (Harries, 1999, p. 6).

Crime mapping has long been an integral part of the process known today as *crime analysis*. The New York City Police Department, for example, has traced the use of maps back to at least 1900 (Vann & Garson, 2003, p. 1). The traditional crime map was a jumbo representation of a jurisdiction with pins stuck in it. The old pin maps were useful for showing where crimes occurred. However, the maps had several serious limitations. When they were updated, the prior crime patterns were lost. While raw data could be archived, maps could not, except perhaps by photographing them. The maps were static; they could not be manipulated or queried. It would have been difficult to track a series of robberies that might overlap the duration (a week or month) of a pin map. Also, pin maps could be quite difficult to read when several types of crime, usually represented by pins of different colors, were mixed together. Pin maps occupied considerable wall space. One researcher noted that to make a single wall map of the 610 square miles of Baltimore County, twelve maps had to be joined, covering 70 square feet. Pin maps had limited value—they could be used effectively, but only for a short time. Pin maps are, however, sometimes used today because their large scales allow patterns to be seen over an entire jurisdiction in detail. The manual approach of pin mapping has generally been replaced by computer mapping (Harries, 1999, p. 3).

Probably the first use of computerized crime mapping in applied crime analysis occurred in the mid-1960s in St. Louis, Missouri, by McEwen and Research Management Associates, Inc. One of the early contributors to computerized crime mapping was Lloyd Haring, who organized a seminar on the geography of crime at Arizona State University around 1970. Early computer mapping efforts used line printers as their display devices, so their resolution was limited to the physical size of the print characters. This precluded the use of computer maps for the representation of point data, at least until plotters that were able to draw finer lines and point symbols came into more general use (Harries, 1999, p. 22). According to Harries (1999, p. 23), even as late as 1980 it was necessary to wait for improvements in desktop computer capacity, printer enhancements, and price reductions before desktop mapping could become an everyday, broadly accepted phenomenon.

Presently, **geographic information systems (GIS)** are used in most major police departments for crime mapping. GIS are computerized systems that consist of a constellation of hardware and software that integrate computer graphics with a relational database for purposes of managing and displaying data about geographic locations. GIS are designed to respond to interactive queries by analyzing and displaying spatial data.

geographic information systems (GIS) / Computerized systems that consist of a constellation of hardware and software that integrate computer graphics with a relational database for purposes of managing and displaying data about geographic locations.

GIS were first developed as tools to manage natural resources and land and to monitor variables about forests, wildlife, and other factors affecting our ecological systems. A Canadian, Roger Tomlinson, is credited with developing the first system in 1963 to help manage Canada's national land inventory (Vann & Garson, 2003, p. 8). By the late 1960s, computer crime mapping began with the use of large mainframe computers and punch cards.

Generally, a GIS has four subsystems: data input, date storage and retrieval, manipulation and analysis, and reporting. The manipulation and analysis subsystem has two aspects: the database management system and the geographic or spatial analysis system.

Using Crime Maps

Constructing a crime map involves taking a set of data and making decisions consistent with the hypothetic–deductive process. Decisions need to be made about the kind of map to be prepared, how symbols or shading will look, how statistical information will be treated, and so forth. These decisions must be based on the objective to be achieved, including consideration of the target audience.

Maps can provide a rich variety of information, including, but not limited to, location, distance, and direction, as well as pattern for maps displaying point or area data. Each type of data means different things to different users.

Location may be the most important of all the types of information to be represented on, or gleaned from, a map from the perspective of a crime analyst. Where things have happened, or may happen in the future, is the most sought after and potentially useful piece of information because it has so many implications for

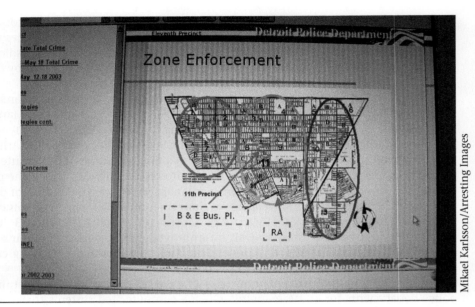

Zone enforcement computer map. Law enforcement often divide a city up into zones depending on crime rates. Different zones will need different approaches to crime prevention and having it divided makes it easier to plan and execute. This is an example of crime mapping.

Mikael Karlsson/Arresting Images

investigators and for the allocation of patrol and community resources, in addition to utility in the realms of planning and politics.

Distance is not much use as an abstract piece of information. It comes to life when translated into some kind of relationship: How far did the victim live from the place where she was robbed? What is the maximum distance police cars can travel within a specific urban environment to provide acceptable response times? How far could a suspect have gone in a particular time period?

Direction is most useful when considered in conjunction with distance, although it is not typically an important piece of map information in crime analysis unless it relates to other relevant processes or conditions. It is generally used in a broadly descriptive context, such as "the hot spot of burglaries is spreading to the west," or "serial robberies are moving southeast," or "the east side is becoming a high-crime area" (Harries, 1999, p. 19).

Pattern is a useful concept in crime analysis, as so much of what crime analysts do involves describing or analyzing the pattern of crime occurrences. Pattern can be a powerful investigative tool because the way points are arranged may tell us something about the process driving that arrangement. Patterns are usually classified as random, uniform, clustered, or dispersed. In a *random arrangement*, points are just as likely to be at any place on the map as at any other. Points are distributed haphazardly around the map. A *uniform pattern* has points that are equally spaced. Alternatively, it can be said that in a uniform distribution the distance between neighboring points is maximized. In a *clustered pattern*, points are clumped together with substantial empty areas. In a dispersed pattern, the points are scattered over the area.

Harries (1999, p. 19) cautions against assuming that the nonrandom distributions (uniform and clustered) automatically mean that some interesting underlying process is at work, providing useful information about crime. This may or may not be true. Harries noted that burglaries may show up in a cluster, suggesting a hot spot, but further investigation shows that the cluster corresponds to a neighborhood with a dense population, so the high frequency is no more than an expression of the geography of risk. The terms describing the types of patterns are subject to some semantic confusion. For example, what does *dispersed* mean? A dispersed pattern could be random or uniform. Is "less dispersed" the same as "clustered"?

Harries (1999, p. 32) notes that maps are often thought of solely as display tools. In fact, maps have a wide-ranging role in the process of research, analysis, and presentation. Mapping is most effective when those broad capabilities are recognized and used to their fullest extent. The map is the end product of a process that starts with the first-responding officer's report that is processed by data entry personnel, entered into a database, and transformed into a symbol on paper. In this narrow interpretation, a map is merely a picture or part of a database.

In visual thinking, the map is used to generate ideas and hypotheses about the problem under investigation. By inspecting a map, we may notice a relationship, or correlation, between environmental factors that otherwise might have gone unnoticed. This correlation may be vertical in the sense that we see connections between different phenomena, such as crimes, land uses, and demographics. Alternatively, we may see a horizontal relationship in which we recognize a common factor across a particular crime type, such as graffiti in similar types of crime locations. Visual thinking is a private activity involving exploration and confirmation.

In the exploratory phase, maps may be crude and are not intended for display or publication. A computer-printed map of burglary patterns for the most recent week might be marked with handwritten information provided by investigators or with other data not in digital form. Information might be transcribed from a mental map to a paper map.

Another possibility, noted by Harries (1999, p. 22), is that the tools of exploratory spatial data analysis (ESDA) are used to find anomalies in data, such as an unexpected cluster of incidents, that could point to unexpected relationships. At this stage, the analyst may generate a formal hypothesis, or educated guess, to explain the process producing the observed crime pattern. Did the observed cluster of burglaries pop up by chance? Is there some recognizable cause? Is a serial burglar operating in the area? Do officers in the field have insight to offer? By developing a hypothesis, the analyst is in the mainstream of scientific research, using a venerable methodology.

Using GIS

There are numerous GIS programs or software that may be used by a crime analyst. The National Institute of Justice has a free program that may be downloaded and used as crime mapping software or as a training aid at www.schoolcopsoftware.com. The program, referred to as the **School COP Program**, does mapping with bitmap images. It contains a setup program that allows you to establish different locations on the image. Incidents (crimes) are geo-coded when you pick the location where they occurred. After the data is entered, you can map all incidents or any subset of incidents.

The Crime Mapping Research Center was established in 1997 by the National Institute of Justice. Its mission is to promote the use of crime mapping in law enforcement. The center was later renamed the National Institute of Justice's

School COP Program / A computer program that does mapping with bitmap images. Incidents (crimes) are geo-coded when you pick the location where they occurred. After the data is entered, you can map all incidents or any subset of incidents.

Mapping and Analysis for Public Safety. Its website may be accessed at www.ojp .usdoj.gov/nij/maps. The website also offers free software, including CrimeStat (spatial statistical tools). It has a Crime Mapping Tutorial, which is a self-paced course that will help you produce crime maps. Many police departments have websites that provide crime pattern and trend data for their jurisdictions. The Oakland, California, Police Department has a **Crimewatch** website that allows individuals to map a selection of various crimes. The crimes may be displayed by police beat, district, or street address. The Oakland website address is www.city .oakcc.com/maproom/crimewatch. The City of Chicago has a similar site at www .cityofchicago.org/CAPS.

Crimewatch / An Oakland, California, Police Department website that allows individuals to map a selection of various crimes. The crimes may be displayed by police beat, district, or street address.

Crime mapping and geographic information systems (GIS) are popular applications within the law enforcement community. In the past decade, law enforcement agencies have shown an increasing interest in a variety of information technologies. Police operations are information driven. Police officers and administrators are more comfortable with technology and its use for analysis and decision making than ever before. Police would like to use technology such as the Internet to reduce requests on staffing, yet still provide services to the community. Expanded functionality in computer-aided dispatch and record management systems, mobile data terminals, the Internet, and GIS have allowed law enforcement to more easily share data and partner with people and organizations in problem solving (Wartell & McEwen, 2001, p. 1).

GIS-based information-sharing systems are increasingly being used by other countries. Crime and Disorder Reduction Partnerships (CDRPs) in England and Wales are used to support their efforts to reduce crime and disorder and improve community safety. At present, there are in excess of twenty major systems distributed at either the regional, county, and/or district level in England and Wales that service CDRPs, with new systems in the planning stages (Chainey, 2006).

Why Map Crime?

As noted by the National Institute of Justice's *Briefing Book on Crime Mapping* (2002), crimes are human phenomena; therefore, their distribution across the landscape is not geographically random. For crimes to occur, offenders and their targets—the victims and/or property—must, for a period of time, exist at the same location. Several factors, from the lure of potential targets to simple geographic convenience for an offender, influence where people choose to break the law. Therefore, an understanding of where and why crimes occur can improve attempts to fight crime. Maps offer crime analysts graphic representations of such crime-related issues.

Mapping crime can help law enforcement protect citizens more effectively in the areas they serve. Simple maps that display the locations where crimes or concentrations of crimes have occurred can be used to help direct patrols to places they are most needed. Policy makers in police departments might use more complex maps to observe trends in criminal activity, and maps may prove invaluable in solving criminal cases. Detectives may use maps to better understand the hunting patterns of serial criminals and to hypothesize where these offenders might live.

Using maps that help people visualize the geographic aspects of crime, however, is not limited to law enforcement. Mapping can provide specific information on crime and criminal behavior to politicians, the press, and the general public.

Police Officer in City of London Traffic Control Room. Similar control rooms are used in all major cities in the United States. The control room is used to allocate police resources.

Hot Spots

Crime is not spread evenly across maps, it clumps in some areas and is absent in others. People use this knowledge in their daily activities. They avoid some places and seek out others. Their choices of neighborhoods, schools, stores, streets, and recreation are governed partially by the understanding that their chances of being a victim are greater in some of these places than in others. In some places people lock their cars and secure belongings, in other places they do not. Along some streets people walk swiftly and view approaching strangers with suspicion. Along other streets they casually stroll, welcome the next interesting person they might meet, and notice others making the same choices in the same areas (Eck et al., 2005).

Areas of concentrated crime are often referred to as **hot spots**. Researchers and police use the term in many different ways. Some refer to hot spot addresses, others refer to hot spot blocks, and others examine clusters of blocks. Like researchers, crime analysts look for concentrations of individual events that might indicate a series of related crimes. They also look at small areas that have a great deal of crime or disorder, even though there may be no common offender. Analysts also observe neighborhoods and neighborhood clusters with high crime and disorder levels and try to link these to underlying social conditions (Eck et al., 2005).

Though no common definition of the term *hot spot* of crime exists, the common understanding is that a hot spot is an area that has a greater than average number of criminal or disorder events, or an area where people have a higher than average risk of victimization. This also suggests the existence of *cool spots*—places or areas with less than the average amount of crime or disorder. It also suggests that some hot spots may be hotter than others; that is, they vary in how far above average they are (Eck et al., 2005, p. 6).

Eck states that if hot spots are merely areas with an above average amount of crime or disorder, why do practitioners and researchers use the term in such a variety of ways? He notes that with recent developments in crime mapping, one can find hot spots of any size—from hot spot places to hot regions. Although all of these

hot spots / Areas of concentrated crime.

perspectives on hot spots have something in common—concentrations of crime or disorder separated by areas with far less crime or disorder—they differ in the area covered by the hot spots. More importantly, according to Eck, the factors that give rise to hot spot places are different from the factors that give rise to hot spot streets, hot spot neighborhoods, or hot spot cities. Further, the actions one takes to deal with a hot spot place will be different from the actions needed to address a hot spot street, hot spot neighborhood, or hot spot city (Eck et al., 2005, p. 11).

Police departments frequently use computer-mapped crime locations to delineate hot spots, or areas with high concentrations of crime. Highlighting such areas helps police direct patrols where they are most needed, thereby optimizing the deterrent effect of police presence. Although concentrations of crime locations may be discernible on a relatively simple point-map of crime locations, multiple crimes occurring at a single address may deceivingly be represented by a single point on such a map. Hot spot analysis is frequently performed using special software, such as the Spatial and Temporal Analysis of Crime (STAC) program developed by the Illinois Criminal Justice Information Authority, which draws ellipses based on the densest concentrations of mapped incidents.

The following map shows locations of residential burglaries and attempted burglaries that occurred over a two-month period in Washington, DC. Using this data, elliptical hot spots were drawn to highlight places of approximately a 1- to 4-block size where concentrations of the crimes occurred. [**Note:** Information and map taken from National Institute of Justice's *Briefing Book on Crime Mapping* (2002).]

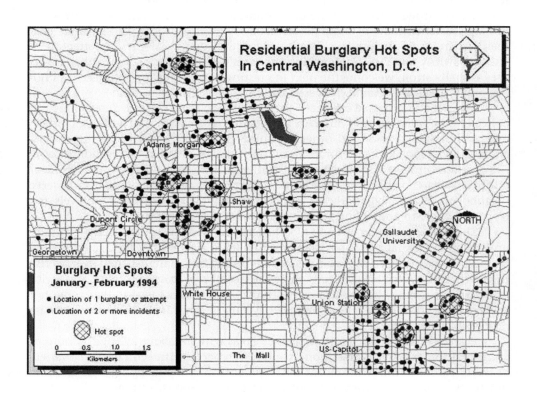

Recovery Locations

Many crime analysts consider the locations where stolen vehicles are recovered to be more relevant in solving crimes than the locations from where they are stolen. Unless a thief has an alternate mode of transportation, a stolen automobile will likely be left close to some desired destination—quite possibly a chop shop, where stolen cars are stripped down for parts. A density map can show the number of automobiles recovered per square mile.

Proximity

The applications of spatial crime analysis extend beyond the production of maps displaying crime locations for police; they provide analytical functions of interest to the general community as well.

The map on the next page of an anonymous small town with a population slightly above 6,500, locates the residences of registered child sex offenders whose addresses have been made public by the local government. These locations were compared with the locations of the town's schools. One-thousand-foot buffers were drawn around the schools to make it easier to observe how close the known offenders live to these potential target areas. Four of the twelve total offender residences fall within the buffered school zones on the map, and several of the others live just outside their perimeters. [**Note:** Information and map taken from National Institute of Justice's *Briefing Book on Crime Mapping* (2002).]

Tracking Serial Offenders

Crime maps can aid in the apprehension of serial criminals. These maps, called **criminal geographic targeting (CGT) models**, help investigators in their attempt to determine where serial criminals most likely reside given the locations of their crimes.

The CGT model adheres to the assumption that a distance relationship exists between the residences of serial offenders and where they choose to commit their crimes. Serial criminals, like everybody else, conduct their routine activities (traveling to and from work, shopping, etc.) within a certain space with which they have become familiar. Within this routine activity space, most people identify with a single anchor point, or place of central importance in their lives, usually the home. The CGT model assumes that serial criminals commit their crimes within their areas of routine activity, but at the same time they are careful not to conduct this activity in the immediate proximity of their residences.

A crime analyst using a CGT model would delineate a hunting area, the region where serial offenders seek out or encounter potential victims. With the aid of special software, each point within this area is assigned a probability of being the residence of the offender. If crime analysts have a significant number of crime locations with which to work, a serial offender's residence can be narrowed down to a small number of probable locations using a CGT model.

Possible residences of serial offenders may be estimated using a three-dimensional map, with the vertical axis representing the probability that each location is the

criminal geographic targeting (CGT) models / Computer-generated models that help investigators determine where serial criminals most likely reside given the locations of their crimes. The CGT model adheres to the assumption that a distance relationship exists between the residences of serial offenders and where they choose to commit their crimes.

Registered Child Sex Offender Representation, "Small" City—March 1997

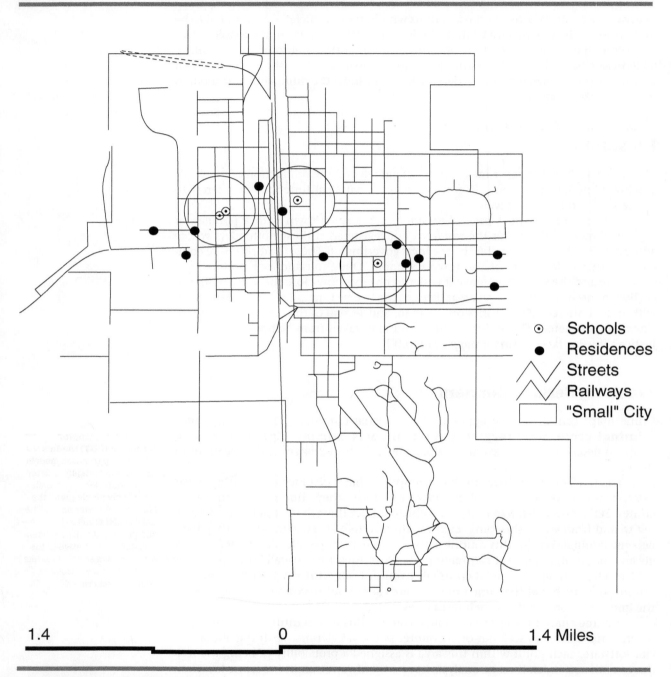

Schools
Residences
Streets
Railways
"Small" City

1.4   0   1.4 Miles

Note: The buffer contains 1,000 ft of the area.
Source: Submitted by Priyamvadha Srinivasan 03/20/97. Fair County Law Enforcement Agencies—March 1997.

residence of the offender. The "peaks" on the map are the most probable locations and correspond with the red and yellow areas on the smaller, two-dimensional inset map in the top right corner. A crime analyst would then overlay this two-dimensional map onto a street map of the area. After comparing the CGT map with other geographic factors, such as land use, police can use the map to concentrate their efforts in certain high-probability areas (Rossmo, 1995).

Mapping Prisoner Reentry

Crime mapping is now being used to address a wide range of criminal justice problems, from allocating police resources to understanding the underlying causes of crime. The mapping of prisoner reentry has been accomplished in only a few cities and only recently. Even fewer cities have attempted to link incarceration and reentry data with other indicators of community well-being. The Urban Institute (UI) in 2002 launched the Reentry Mapping Network (RMN), a partnership of cities engaged in creating community change through the mapping and analysis of reentry and other community indicator data at a highly localized level.

RMN partners use mapping to pinpoint neighborhoods that experience high concentrations of returning prisoners and to examine the extent to which such communities are equipped to address the challenges that prisoner reentry creates. RMN partners use the findings from their mapping and analyses to help mobilize community members and leaders to devise targeted responses to effectively address reentry-related problems. These activities are intended to help corrections officials, community organizations, and service providers develop a better understanding of the dynamics and correlates of prisoner reentry at the local level; engage local

Lester Lefkowitz/PhotoEdit

Emergency service operator. The operator will answer the 911 calls and direct the appropriate police, medical, or fire units to provide assistance.

stakeholders and practitioners in developing strategies to identify opportunities to address reentry-related challenges; facilitate greater coordination and collaboration among state and local agencies and organizations around this work; and expand the knowledge of how to involve communities in using data to identify and address incarceration- and reentry-related challenges.

Mapping can help identify neighborhoods that experience high geographic concentrations of prisoners returning home. Mapping the last known addresses of released inmates (available through the departments of correction in most states) can pinpoint concentrations within cities and neighborhoods, right down to the city block (La Vigne, 2004).

Crime Mapping Software

CrimeStat / A spatial statistics program for the analysis of crime incident locations.

There are many crime mapping software programs available. One of the leading is National Institute of Justice supported software, CrimeStat III. **CrimeStat** is a spatial statistics program for the analysis of crime incident locations, developed by Ned Levine & Associates under a grant from the National Institute of Justice. The program is Windows-based and interfaces with most desktop GIS programs. The program provides supplemental statistical tools to aid law enforcement agencies and criminal justice researchers in their crime mapping efforts. CrimeStat is being used by many police departments around the country, as well as by criminal justice and other researchers. The present version is 3.0 (CrimeStat III) and is available on the Internet for downloading free of charge.

The program inputs incident locations (e.g., robbery locations) in 'dbf', 'shp', ASCII, or ODBC-compliant formats using either spherical or projected coordinates. It calculates various spatial statistics and writes graphical objects to ArcView® MapInfo®, Atlas*GIS™, Surfer® for Windows, and ArcView Spatial Analyst©.

The statistics cover spatial description and distance analysis (for describing the general spatial pattern of crimes), hot spot analysis (for identifying concentrations of crashes), interpolation (for visualizing crime concentrations over a large area), space–time analysis (for understanding temporal and spatial interaction in offender behavior), and journey-to-crime estimation (for estimating the likely residence location of a serial offender). New in version 3.0 is a module for crime travel demand modeling, widely used in transportation planning. It allows a crime analyst to model crime trips over a metropolitan area and to make reasonable guesses at the travel mode and likely routes taken. It can also be used to model possible interventions.

CrimeStat III is accompanied by sample data sets and a manual that gives the background behind the statistics and examples. The software is available for free download, along with full documentation, from NACJD (National Archive of Criminal Justice Data) at ICPSR.

The MAPS program is overseeing the development, by the University of Virginia's (UVA) Systems & Information Engineering Department, of a regional scale spatial data repository for analysis and planning that can support spatial data sharing across agencies and jurisdictions, during critical incident events, as well as in their more routine needs. This repository is called the Geospatial Repository for Analysis & Safety Planning (GRASP) system. GRASP specifically addresses regional issues that relate to standard technologies, shared projections and coordinated systems, seamlessness, multiple data formats, complementary data and types, data sharing policies, and linkages to the larger spatial data infrastructure.

School COP

Developed by Abt Associates, the School Crime Operations Package (School COP) is a software application designed for entering, analyzing, and mapping incidents that occur in and around schools. Target users are persons responsible for enforcing discipline and safety regulations, investigating crime and other incidents, and planning violence prevention initiatives at elementary, middle, and high schools. School COP can be used at a single school or at the school district level. School COP includes a sample database of incidents that illustrate the package's search, reporting, and mapping capabilities. Online help is also available.

School COP runs on Windows 95, 98, NT, 2000, and XP computers and is available for download. The package is free. Abt Associates Inc. developed School COP under a cooperative agreement with the National Institute of Justice (Award No. 1999-LT-VX-K017). More details and software download for School COP are available from Abt Associates Inc.

CASE (Crime Analysis Spatial Extension)

Crime Analysis Spatial Extension (CASE) was developed by NLECTC–Rocky Mountain's Crime Mapping & Analysis Program (CMAP). CMAP, a program of the National Law Enforcement and Corrections Technology Center–Rocky Mountain Region (NLECTC-RM), was released in January 2005, CMAP CASE (Crime Analysis Spatial Extension) for ESRI's ArcGIS 8/9 GIS software.

CMAP CASE contains the spatial functions that many analysts and investigators use to find where offenders live and where they may strike next. CMAP CASE is freely available from their website at www.crimeanalysts.net. It contains a robust help file and supporting documentation explaining how these spatial functions are used to analyze crime. CMAP CASE is made available free to law enforcement agencies.

CompStat

CompStat is a crime-control model and is based on computer-driven statistics. It has been described as "a comprehensive, continuous analysis of results for improvement and achievement of prescribed outcomes" (McDonald, 2002, p. 8). Prior to 1994, the New York Police Department (NYPD), like most major police departments, was organized around avoiding risk and failure. Officers were constrained by regulations and procedures. With the implementation of the CompStat system, the NYPD is now using crime statistics and regular meetings of key enforcement personnel to direct its enforcement efforts. Under the CompStat system, there were major changes in the management style of the NYPD. Precinct commanders were granted more latitude in initiating their own operations and running their precincts. Officers were authorized to assertively enforce quality-of-life laws.

CompStat / A crime-control model based on computer-driven statistics. It has been described as "a comprehensive, continuous analysis of results for improvement and achievement of prescribed outcomes."

NYPD commanders now have daily turn-around on CompStat numbers (crime statistics) and can observe weekly trends in order to take corrective actions. Crime statistics are not the bottom line as to how the police are doing, but they are analyzed on both a precinct-by-precinct and citywide basis. CompStat implementation is based on five basic principles:

1. **Specific objectives:** Examples of crime-specific objectives are decreasing street robberies, drug sales to youths, vandalism, and carjackings.

2. **Timely and accurate intelligence:** If the police are going to respond effectively, officers at all levels must have accurate knowledge of when particular types of crime are occurring, where the crimes are occurring, and how they are being committed.

3. **Effective strategies and tactics:** The tactics must be comprehensive, flexible, and adaptable to the changing crime trends that are identified and monitored.

4. **Rapid deployment of personnel and resources:** Once tactical plans are developed, an array of personnel and other necessary resources should be promptly deployed.

5. **Relentless follow-up and assessment:** An ongoing process of rigorous follow-up and assessment is considered necessary to ensure that the desired results are actually being achieved (McDonald, 2002, p. 8–9).

Despite the national attention that has been paid to the NYPD's CompStat program, there has been little systematic analysis of the programs in policing (Weisburd et al., 2004). Weisburd and others, in a Police Foundation report, noted that only about 33 percent of police departments with more than 100 sworn officers had adopted some form of CompStat and only 11 percent of those departments with less than 100 officers had adopted it. The report concluded that the specific motivations for adopting CompStat varied across police agencies, but most expressed a desire to reduce serious crime and increase management control over field operations. The report noted that larger police agencies were more likely to adopt the NYPD model than the smaller agencies.

Analysis and Planning Level

crime early warning system (CEWS) / A computer program that maps crime forecasts by geographic area to provide a jurisdiction-wide scan for areas perhaps needing changes in tactical deployment of police.

A **crime early warning system (CEWS)** maps crime forecasts by geographic area to provide a jurisdiction-wide scan for areas perhaps needing changes in tactical deployment of police (Cohen, 2006, p. 156).

Time series data, the most frequently used series of measurements, consist of repeated measurements for a fixed observation unit (e.g., census tract, grid cell, car beat, or precinct) and fixed time interval (such as month, quarter, or year), sequenced by time period. Time series methods are the most widely researched and used forecast methods.

At the macro (policy/planning) level, police use crime mapping primarily for the design of precinct and car beat boundaries, in response to changing population and crime patterns (and perhaps budget limitations). The tasks are to design boundaries and staffing levels by precinct and car beat for the purpose of balancing workloads and achieving acceptable response times to calls for service. The corresponding planning horizon is three to five years, requiring long-range forecasts based on demographic trends and forecasts.

The meso-level of decision making corresponds to monthly CompStat meetings for precincts (or similar meetings). While CompStat meetings may be held weekly to accommodate review of a large number of precincts, such as in New York City, each precinct is reviewed only once per month. Hence, the planning horizon is a month and monthly time series data are most relevant.

The purpose of CompStat meetings is manyfold, but two major purposes relative to crime analysis are: (1) to evaluate last month's crime prevention and enforcement performance, and (2) to plan for next month's crime analysis and police activities. Time series forecasting has the potential to play an important role for both of these purposes, providing the basis for evaluation and forecasts of areas with potential crime increases next month. It is here at the meso-level that crime forecasting fits best into crime analysis.

Evaluation of performance within a specific area and month requires making a counterfactual forecast; that is, a forecast of crime level for "business as usual conditions" and no changes in policies or practices from historical conditions. Then if police intervened in special ways for prevention or enforcement during the month for evaluation, or just worked smarter and harder, the difference in the actual crime level from the counterfactual forecast can be attributed to police efforts. Alternatively, changes in the wrong direction might be attributed to changes in criminal activity (e.g., a gang war flare up).

An effective counterfactual forecast is a univariate forecast. Univariate methods capture the existing seasonal and time trend patterns in a time series and then extrapolate or extend them into the future, assuming no pattern changes. For example, the counterfactual forecast for January 2005 would be based on historical data for January 2000 through December 2004, would extend the estimated mean number of crimes for December 2004 by the estimated growth rate (or decline rate) per month to January, and adjust this value for the estimated January seasonal effect. All estimates are based on the historical data.

CompStat does not use univariate forecasts for evaluation, but rather uses the CompStat method. For this method, the counterfactual value for evaluating January 2005 crimes is January 2004 crimes for the same crime type and location. The virtue of this method is that it provides some information on the changes in crime levels over a year's time and at the same seasonal point. Its problems are first that the counterfactual value is a single data point, which is noisy and can yield false information.

The implementation of time series forecasting for use by police takes the form of a crime mapping system called crime early warning system (CEWS). It serves both the meso- and micro-levels of crime analysis.

Micro-level crime analysis includes the familiar day-to-day tasks of crime analysts: reading crime reports, identifying patterns in data, mapping crime points, identifying hot spots, and so on. CEWS includes the point data and records that support these activities (Cohen, 2006).

Crime MAPS allows you to select a jurisdiction (city, unincorporated area in the county, neighborhood, or political district) and a location of interest. The location can be a school, hospital, zip code, tourist attraction, major shopping center, neighborhood, address, or intersection. Except for a zip code or neighborhood, a radius ranging from 500 feet to one mile can be selected to generate an orange shaded area

CASE STUDY: San Diego County, California, Crime Maps

San Diego County, using the Automated Regional Justice Information System (ARJIS), has established a public website at www.mapping.arjis.org/main.aspx. By visiting this site, you can enter a street address, shopping center, or other place and find out what crimes have been reported for that location in recent months.

The law enforcement agencies in San Diego County take reports for all crime cases, arrests, citations, and some traffic collisions within the county. The reports are entered into the ARJIS, which provides the incident data for Crime MAPS. Agencies that provide data to ARJIS include the San Diego County Sheriff, all city police departments in San Diego County, the San Diego Harbor Police, the San Diego Unified School District Police, and the San Diego Community College Police.

Some city police departments and the county sheriff also provide data for some universities and community colleges in their jurisdictions, including: University of San Diego, Point Loma Nazarene, MiraCosta, and Southwestern. Data from UCSD, SDSU, CSU-San Marcos, Cuyamaca, Grossmont, and Palomar are not provided. Also, federal and state law enforcement agencies (military police, FBI, Border Patrol, and CHP) do not provide data to ARJIS.

around the selected location on the resulting map. Incidents will be mapped both inside and outside (twice the radius) this area. Note that neither an entire city nor an unincorporated county can be selected.

Types of Incidents Mapped: Various types of crimes, arrests, citations, and traffic-related incidents are available. Crime types include: aggravated assault, arson, commercial burglary, homicide, malicious mischief/vandalism, rape, residential

Voices of Experience

College Education

Excerpts from an interview between Cliff Roberson and former police officer, John M. Boal. Currently, Professor Boal is a full-time faculty member in the Criminal Justice Program at the University of Akron.

Q: *How important is a college education to a police officer?*

A: I believe education helps you develop your problem-solving abilities. Someone coming out of high school may not have had to face a lot of situations where they were required to use their problem-solving abilities. It

also helps with the ability to engage in critical thinking. This is especially important to a first responder to an emergency situation who needs to make a critical assessment of the situation and determine the resources needed. The officer will need the necessary skills to make a critical assessment. ■

burglary, robbery, sex crimes other than rape, simple assault, theft, vehicle break-in, and vehicle theft. Domestic violence-related assault data are currently not included. Arrest and citation types include: curfew violation, deadly weapon possession, drunk in public, narcotics, prostitution, and truancy. Traffic-related incident types include: DUI, citations, and collisions.

Only incidents with a valid street address or intersection are included. In some cases victims may not know where the crime occurred (e.g., if their pocket was picked somewhere downtown). Such a crime will not have an address and therefore will not be included.

Time Periods of the Incident Data: Crime MAPS is updated with new data every week on Monday. This data includes reports that have been entered in ARJIS up through the previous Saturday. Some law enforcement agencies may be several weeks behind on their data entry, so if you are not getting the expected number of incidents for the most recent week, either search farther back in time or contact your local agency to clarify.

Any time period of ninety-one days or less within the past twelve months can be searched. The period can be defined by start and end dates, times of the day, and days of the week. If you are searching an area with a large number of incidents, you may want to limit your time period to fewer than ninety-one days.

Incident Attributes: The map's *Identify* feature can be used to determine the following attributes or characteristics for each incident or map location at which incidents are mapped: type of incident; hundred-block address or street intersection; and date, day, and time of occurrence. Earliest and latest dates and times are included because some crimes have a range of when they might have occurred. For instance, a car was parked at 10:00 P.M. on the third and discovered missing at 7:00 A.M. on the fourth.

Not all offenses within one report can be queried and mapped. A crime report may contain more than one offense (e.g., a robbery and an assault). Only the primary offense type can be queried and mapped. In this example, the map will show a robbery because it is the more serious offense.

Victim names and exact address data have been removed to protect the privacy of victims. Although the symbols are mapped using the specific address, when the incidents are identified, the addresses only show the hundred-block numbers, not exact addresses.

Incident Locations on the Map: All incidents are mapped at specific street addresses or intersections. The symbols are shown on the streets at those locations. This means that incidents that occur in parks, on school grounds or campuses, at shopping malls, or other such locations are mapped on a street and not at the actual location of the incident in the area. Also, when multiple incidents occur at one address or intersection, the map will show only one symbol. Each symbol can be checked with the map's *Identify* feature to see how many are at the same location.

Comparison with Incident Descriptions in the Media: Some offenses may be shown differently than initially reported in the media. For example, if the victim of a robbery was seriously wounded, the offense may be recorded (and therefore mapped) initially as a robbery, but then changed to a homicide if the victim later dies.

Comparison with Published Law Enforcement Agency Data: There are several reasons why the incident data mapped on this website may not match that published by the various law enforcement agencies. The main one is that not all incidents can be mapped, such as those without a valid street address. For official crime statistics, click on *Crime Statistics* on the ARJIS website (www.arjis.org) or contact your local agency.

Different Results on Different Days: ARJIS is continually receiving police reports for recent as well as older incidents so the incident database is subject to change over time. There can be delays in discovering and reporting crimes (e.g., a home burglary

Learning from Unsuccessful Attempts

The Chula Vista, California, Police Department was aware that the city's building boom could worsen the residential burglary problem. The new houses were intended for affluent couples who would be out during the day when burglaries were most likely to happen. The police, therefore, decided to examine the effectiveness of existing security precautions to see if any of these could be built into new homes or suggested to homeowners. Cathy Burciaga, one of the department's crime analysts, compared completed burglaries with unsuccessful attempts for an eighteen-month sample of 569 homes in the city. This indicated that deadbolts should be installed on both the side and front doors of new houses. Interviews conducted with 250 victims and 50 burglars revealed that not one burglar had tried to enter a house by breaking a double-glazed window. This led to the recommendation that all windows in new housing be double-glazed and meet strict forced-entry standards. The results of Burciaga's study are shown in the following table.

Protective Step	Completed Burglaries	Unsuccessful Attempts	Effective?*
Dusk to dawn light	28%	29%	No
Indoor light on	26%	29%	No
Indoor timer light	9%	11%	No
Deadbolt on front door	28%	25%	No
Deadbolt front and side doors	15%	29%	Yes
Outdoor motion detector	23%	36%	Yes
Radio/TV left on	9%	18%	Yes
Alarm company sign	19%	36%	Yes

* "Yes" means present in a larger percentage of unsuccessful attempts than successful ones.

Source: Research study reported in Clarke & Eck, 2003.

may not be discovered until a person returns from vacation). A robbery may become a homicide if the victim dies later. There can also be delays in entering reports into the ARJIS. In the case of a homicide, it might take several days for the medical examiner to determine that the death was unlawful.

School and Shopping Center Data: The menu of schools includes the public and private school sites in the San Diego Association of Government's (SANDAG) school database: www. sandag.org/resources/maps_and_gis/gis_downloads/downloads/meta-data/schoolsdoc.htm. Not included are colleges, universities, and other institutions of higher education. If a school of interest is not listed, use its street address or the nearest street intersection.

Only major shopping centers are included. These are defined by SANDAG in one of its activity center layers. For the selection criteria, see www.sandag.org/resources/maps_and_gis/gis_downloads/downloads/metadata/majattrsdoc.htm. For smaller shopping centers, use the street address of a specific store or the nearest street intersection.

Help File: A HELP file has been created to guide users through each step of the mapping process. It explains the various options in selecting locations, incidents, and time periods, as well as the use of the various buttons on the map screen. You can see the file by clicking on the HELP button at the top of the Location, Incidents, and Time Period screens, and under Information on the Map screen.

SHOULD CRIME INFORMATION BE MADE PUBLIC?

Note: The following section was taken from *A Guide for Sharing Crime Maps and Spatial Data*, Institute for Law and Justice, NCJ 188739, pp. 4–5. (Citations omitted.)

Why should a law enforcement agency make crime data and crime maps available to researchers, other agencies, and the public?

There are many advantages, including:

1. Providing crime maps through the Internet or another convenient mechanism actually may reduce police workload; that is, fewer calls may be made to the crime analysis section for special requests if the maps are readily available. The Tempe, Arizona, Police Department put a variety of crime maps and information on the Internet to "provide timely information with nearly instantaneous updates and conserve time and resources by reducing mailings and virtually eliminating printing and duplicating costs." In addition, making crime maps and statistics accessible will alleviate common citizen calls such as, "Is this neighborhood safe?" by allowing the agency to refer the citizens to the Internet to make their own judgments.

2. Many police departments have found that the more the community knows about crime and safety issues, the more willing it is to work with the police to solve those problems. In addition, potential victims of a crime pattern may protect themselves better if they are aware of the problem.

3. Maps can assist in community policing and problem solving by showing where problems do and do not exist. While researching gang territories, George Tita, formerly with Carnegie Mellon University, mapped various activity spaces and found that only small portions of a neighborhood were affected. When he shared his maps and results with community developers and gang street workers, their response was that if this information was shared with everyone, people would understand that the whole neighborhood was not gang-infested, and businesses might be more likely to operate and invest in the area.

4. Maps can increase public awareness about neighborhood problems. On one hand, residents of higher crime areas may not want their problems highlighted. On the other hand, some welcome the attention. As an unnamed citizen once stated: "I know that I live in a high-crime area, and [your] publishing the information has only confirmed my opinions. However, it is satisfying that the local council is working in partnership with the police to accurately identify crime hot spots and as a result target crime prevention resources to those areas that most need it, rather than to the middle-class areas where people are more likely to sit on some local committee, shout the loudest, and get funds allocated to an area that in reality is of low priority."

5. Maps facilitate partnerships with researchers and other agencies. If researchers lack accurate, current data they cannot assist departments and the policing field in analyzing and solving crime and disorder problems. Most people recognize the advantage of sharing data among law enforcement agencies and across jurisdictions (because criminals do not usually respect city boundaries). In addition, agencies outside of law enforcement, such as public housing, schools, hospitals, parks and recreation departments, and urban planning divisions can work toward community safety if they are better informed about crime.

6. By providing maps and data, a police department can be sure the data are presented accurately. If the department does not provide maps and data, someone else (such as the media or a neighborhood group) eventually will—then the department risks having its data interpreted and displayed by someone less familiar with them. One nongovernmental website that currently displays crime maps and data is APBnews.com at www.apbnews.com/resource center. Its data contain information and ratings from the CAP Index, a privately developed crime-risk database.

7. Providing maps and data to the public is a means to hold the police department accountable. By making information public, law enforcement agencies are less likely to risk altering the statistics to make themselves look better. In addition, the more the public knows about crime, the more likely it is that someone or some group will ask what the police or, in a true police–community partnership, they can do about it. The concern by officers that the public may have access to up-to-date crime information has led to more internal requests for maps and use of Internet sites by the officers themselves. Officers do not want to be confronted by a community member who is more aware of crime in the neighborhood than they are.

Providing crime maps and data also poses several potential and actual disadvantages, such as:

1. The information might be used for commercial purposes (e.g., alarm companies calling burglary victims), which many citizens may find a violation of privacy or a nuisance. Many departments already release lists of crime incidents to the media, and companies will still not be able to identify specific households from the map, but they could target general areas.

2. Potential offenders may use crime maps to identify areas that have not been targeted and therefore may not be receiving much police attention.

3. Crime maps could conceivably harm a high-crime area by reducing property values or increasing insurance rates. However, no definitive study of the property value concern has been made, and insurance companies (at least in California) have already been using zip code crime information for years to define rates. Taxi drivers, pizza deliverers, and other service people sometimes hesitate to go to high-crime areas, but their reticence is often based more on reputation than on hard data. Crime maps could alleviate concerns.

4. Crime maps are open to misinterpretation by viewers if the maps are too complex or view ers do not understand statistics or crime data. Further, map shading sometimes suggests that an entire area (e.g., beat, neighborhood) has a crime problem, when in fact all the crimes may be concentrated in one or two blocks.

There may also be privacy issues involved in making crime data public, such as:

1. If a map shows the exact location of an offense, such as the victims' residence, or the incident address is released, the victims may be retraumatized by the fear that criminals will see them as an easier target.

2. Victims may decline to assist in investigations and prosecutions if they believe offenders or their associates can find out where they live by looking at crime maps.

3. If persons are victimized again, they may decide not to report the offense because of concerns about publicity through a crime map. An increase in unreported crimes makes it harder for police to respond to public safety concerns.

4. Incident-specific details associated with a map could be misused. If specific addresses are identifiable, all privacy is essentially eliminated.

DOES HOT SPOT PATROLLING SIMPLY CAUSE CRIME TO MOVE AROUND THE CORNER?

Does the concentration of policing resources on hot spots prevent crime? Weisburd and others (2005) studied this question. They concluded that hot spots policing approaches have strong impacts upon crime in targeted sites. They noted that often there is a concern that focusing police resources on hot spots will simply displace the crime to nontargeted areas. According to the researchers, when immediate spatial displacement has been examined, the findings generally support the position that displacement is small and that diffusion of crime control benefits is more likely.

They concluded that there was little evidence of immediate spatial displacement, and strong evidence for diffusion of benefits beyond the targeted areas. This finding, in the context of a controlled study that was designed to directly study displacement and diffusion effects, adds strong support to a policy approach that focuses police resources at crime hot spots. They opined that concentration on hot spots is likely to lead to strong crime prevention benefits not only in targeted sites, but also in areas close to them.

HOT SPOT THEORIES ON CRIME

Note: This discussion on Hot Spot Crime Theories was taken from *Mapping Crime: Understanding Hot Spots* (August 2005), NCJ 209393, by John Eck et al.

Place Theories

place theories / Theories that explain why crime events occur at specific locations.

Place theories explain why crime events occur at specific locations. They deal with crimes that occur at the lowest level of analysis—specific places. They involve looking at specific incidents and asking such questions as, "At what places are burglaries occurring and at what places are they not occurring?" Crime phenomena at this level occur as points, so the appropriate units of analysis are addresses, street corners, and other very small places, which are typically represented on maps as dots. Police action, such as warrants, which specify exact addresses (not blocks or neighborhoods), is very precise at this level.

Street Theories

street theories / Theories that deal with crimes that occur at a slightly higher level than specific places; that is, over small, stretched areas such as streets or blocks.

Street theories deal with crimes that occur at a slightly higher level than specific places; that is, over small, stretched areas such as streets or blocks. A prostitution stroll is an example. At this level of analysis analysts ask such questions as, "On which streets are prostitutes found and on which streets are they not found?" The appropriate units of analysis can be street segments, paths, and sections of highways, which would be represented on maps as straight, bent, or curved lines. Police action is still relatively precise, although not as precise as at the place level. Concentrated patrolling occurs at this level, as well as efforts to change traffic and street patterns.

Neighborhood Theories

Some theories of crime attempt to explain neighborhood differences. At a higher level than place or street, neighborhood theories deal with large areas. Here analysts are interested in such questions as, "What areas are claimed by gangs and what areas are not?" The appropriate units of analysis are quite varied and can include square blocks, communities, and census tracts, to name a few. Two-dimensional shapes such as ellipses, rectangles, and other polygons are used on maps to represent crime phenomena at this level. At this level, police action is far less precise because the areas are typically too large for effective concentrated patrolling. Nevertheless, depending on neighborhood characteristics, relevant action might include efforts to engage residents in collective action against crime and disorder. If offenders are mobile throughout an area, rather than concentrated at a few places, then efforts to deter them should occur at this level.

Other Large Area Theories

Still other theories attempt to explain differences in crime patterns at much higher levels of aggregation. For example, theories of crime differ among cities and regions. On the city level, suggested actions may include citywide changes in economic, transportation, education, welfare, and recreation policies, to name a few. On the multijurisdictional or multistate regional levels, suggested actions against concentrations of crime could include even broader scale policies or social change. Although these are interesting theories, they are far less useful for local police agencies, thus they are not examined here.

Repeat Victimization Theories

Finally, **repeat victimization theories** pertain to questions of why the same victims are targeted repeatedly. They can operate at any of the three levels discussed—points, lines, or polygons—however, not all repeat victimization can be shown on maps.

repeat victimization theories / Theories that pertain to questions of why the same victims are targeted repeatedly.

Types of Hot Spots

The most basic form of a hot spot is a place that has many crimes. A place can be an address, street corner, store, house, or any other small location, most of which can be seen by a person standing at its center. Places typically have a single owner and a specific function—residence, retail sales, recreation, school. Crime often is concentrated at a few places, even in high-crime areas. Although hot spots are often concentrated within areas, they often are separated by other places with few or no crimes.

Routine activity theory helps to explain why crime often is concentrated at specific places. In particular, routine activity points to how behavior is regulated at the location by place managers—owners of places or people acting on an owner's behalf.

SUMMARY

- Most law enforcement agencies have one or more crime analysts, but some of the largest and more advanced police organizations do not. The job of the crime analyst is often narrowly limited to tabulating crimes that occur. In others, it extends to identifying patterns of crimes, with the primary objective of

identifying the likely offenders so that they can be apprehended.

- Crime maps have been around for several thousand years—perhaps tens of millennia. European cartographers studying the social ecology of crime studied the locations of crime in an attempt to provide a number of important insights regarding crime.

- Parks and Burgess, starting in the 1920s, and later, Shaw and McKay, studied crime rates in Chicago by mapping the reported crimes on a map. They divided the map using concentric zones to support their social disorganization theory of crime causation.

- Presently, GIS are used in most major police departments for crime mapping. GIS are computerized geographic information systems that consist of a constellation of hardware and software that integrate computer graphics with a relational database for purposes of managing and displaying data about geographic locations.

- Areas of concentrated crime are often referred to as *hot spots*. Researchers and police use the term in many different ways. Some refer to hot spot addresses, others refer to hot spot blocks, and others examine clusters of blocks.

- CompStat is a crime-control model and is based on computer-driven statistics. It has been described as a comprehensive, continuous analysis of results for improvement and achievement of prescribed outcomes.

- Concentration on hot spots is likely to lead to strong crime prevention benefits not only in targeted sites, but also in areas close to them. Apparently, crime does not move around the corner.

Classroom Discussion Questions and Activities

1. Go to one of the public crime sites and examine the types of crime maps displayed at the site.

2. Plot a crime map involving incidents in your home community.

3. Visit a local law enforcement agency and determine what crime maps the agency keeps and whether some maps are still kept manually.

4. Determine if there are any "auto theft hot spots" near your home.

5. Check and determine how many registered sex offenders live within one mile of your current residence or your school dorm.

References

Block, R., & Block, C. (1995). Space, place and crime: Hot spot areas and hot places of liquor-related crime. In J. E. Eck & D. Weisburd (Eds.), *Crime and place*, Crime Prevention Studies, Vol. 4, pp. 145–184. Monsey, NY: Criminal Justice Press.

Capone, D. L., & Nichols, Jr., W. W. (1975). *Crime and distance: An analysis of offender behavior in space*. Proceedings of the Association of American Geographers, Vol. 7, pp. 45–49.

Chainey, S. (2006). *Review of GIS-based information sharing systems*. London: British Home Office.

Clarke, R. V., & Eck, J. E. (2003). *Crime analysis for problem solvers in 60 small steps*. Washington, DC: U.S. Dept. of Justice, Office of Community Oriented Policing Services.

Cohen, J. (2006 January). *Development of crime forecasting and mapping systems for use by police*. Washington, DC: U.S. Dept of Justice, NCJRS.

Cohen, L., & Felson, M. (1977). Social change and crime rate trends: A routine activities approach. *American Sociological Review*, 44, 588–608.

Diamond, J. (2004, April). Connecting the dots. *Police Magazine*, pp. 42–47.

Eck, J. E., Chainey, S., Cameron, J. G., Leitner, M., & Wilson, R. E. (2005 August). *Mapping crime: Understanding hot spots*. NCJ 209393, Washington, DC: U.S. Department of Justice.

Harries, K. (1999 December). *Mapping crime: Principle and practice*. NCJ 178919, Washington, DC: U.S. Department of Justice.

La Vigne, N. (2004). Why map prisoner reentry? *Crime Mapping News*, 6 (4).

McDonald, P. P. (2002). *Managing police operations: Implementing the New York crime control model–CompStat*. Belmont, CA: Wadsworth.

National Institute of Justice. (2002). *Briefing book on crime mapping*. Washington, DC: U.S. Government Printing Office.

Roberson, C., & Wallace, H. (1998) *Introduction to criminology*. Incline Village, NV: Copperhouse.

Rossmo, D. K. (1995). Place, space, and police investigations: Hunting serial violent criminals. In J. E. Eck & D. Weisburd (Eds.), *Crime and place, crime prevention studies*, Vol. 4. Monsey, NY: Criminal Justice Press.

Vann, I. E., & Garson, G. D. (2003). *Crime mapping: New tools for law enforcement*. New York: Peter Lang.

Wartell, J., & McEwen, J. T. (2001). *A guide for sharing crime maps and spatial data*. Institute for Law and Justice, NCJ 188739.

Weisburd, D., Mastrofski, S. D., Greenspan, R., & White, J. J. (2004, April). *The growth of CompStat in American policing*. Washington, DC: Police Foundation.

Weisburd, D., Wyckoff, L. A., Ready, J., Eck, J. E., Hinkle, J., & Gajewski, F. (2005, October). *Does crime just move around the corner?* Washington, DC: U.S. Dept of Justice, NCJRS.

THE USE OF FORCE

From Chapter 15 of *Policing Today*. Frank Schmalleger, John L. Worrall. Copyright © 2010 by Pearson Education, Inc.
Published by Pearson Prentice Hall. All rights reserved.

THE USE OF FORCE

LEARNING OBJECTIVES

After reading this chapter, students should be able to:

1. Identify the various levels of force, explain how they are controlled by policy, and describe their applications in police work.

2. Describe legal standards associated with the use of deadly force by law enforcement officers, explain the patterns of deadly force, and describe the problem of suicide by cop.

3. Describe legal standards governing nondeadly force, including less-lethal weapons.

4. List three types of excessive force and describe perspectives on the frequency of excessive force.

THINK ABOUT IT

Police brutality cases have been on the rise since the terrorist attacks of September 11, 2001, and federal prosecutors are targeting an increasing number of abusive officers. Brooklyn, New York, tops the list, with 11 criminal prosecutions of police officers during the first 10 months of fiscal year 2007.[1] Several other cities, including Milwaukee; Jackson, Mississippi; New Orleans; Chicago; and Cleveland, have seen a similar upsurge in uncalled for police violence. On the whole, U.S. Justice Department statistics show a 25 percent increase in the incidence of police brutality between 2001 and 2007. The vast majority of police abuse cases are never prosecuted, so the real numbers could be even higher.

One explanation that has been offered for this trend is the growing difficulty that police departments face in finding qualified police officer applicants, partially because of the war in the Middle East. Throughout the country, many agencies have been forced to revise their recruitment policies or lower their standards to fill vacancies. Age, height, and weight requirements have been relaxed; test standards have been revised; hiring bonuses are being offered; and some agencies have become more tolerant of recruits' past drug use.[2] Since many police officers and applicants are steadily being drawn into military service, agencies have had to ramp up their hiring efforts. This raises some interesting questions to keep in mind as you read this chapter:

1. Does a nationwide increase of 25 percent in police brutality cases over a six-year period seem significant?

2. If police brutality has risen substantially since the terrorist attacks of September 11, can those events somehow be blamed?

3. To what extent have relaxed recruitment standards affected police brutality?

4. If it is necessary to relax police hiring standards to meet the realities of police recruiting today, then at what point do we draw the line?

INTRODUCTION

use of force
The use of physical restraint by a police officer when dealing with a member of the public.[i]

Police **use of force** is defined as the use of physical restraint by a police officer when dealing with a member of the public.[3] Law enforcement officers are authorized to use the amount of force that is reasonable and necessary given the circumstances. Most officers are trained in the use of force and typically encounter numerous situations during their careers when the use of force is appropriate—for example, when making some arrests, restraining unruly combatants, or controlling a disruptive demonstration. Force may involve hitting; holding or restraining; pushing; choking; threatening with or using a baton, a flashlight, or chemical or pepper spray; restraining with a police dog; using a Taser or a similar energy weapon; or threatening with or using a gun.

WEB PATROL 1

Analysis of Police Use-of-Force Data
http://www.justicestudies.com/pubs/analysis.pdf

excessive force
"The application of an amount and/or frequency of force greater than that required to compel compliance from a willing or unwilling subject."[ii]

A more complex issue is the use of *excessive* force. The International Association of Chiefs of Police defines **excessive force** as "the application of an amount and/or frequency of force greater than that required to compel compliance from a willing or unwilling subject."[4] When excessive force is employed, the activities of the police often come under public scrutiny and receive attention from the media and legislators. A police officer's use of excessive force can also result in lawsuits by members of the public who feel that they have been treated unfairly. Whether the use of excessive force is aberrant behavior on the part of an individual officer or is the practice of an entire law enforcement agency, both the law and public opinion generally condemn it.

Kenneth Adams, an expert in the use of force by police, notes that there is an important difference between the terms *use of excessive force*, such as shoving or pushing when simply grabbing a suspect would be adequate, and the *excessive use of force*, which refers to the phenomenon of force being used unacceptably, often on a department-wide basis. The distinction "deals with relative comparisons among police agencies, and there are no established criteria for judgment."[5] The *use of excessive force* and the *excessive use of force* may also be distinguished from the *illegal use of force*, which refers to situations in which the use of force by police violates a law or statute.[6]

Excessive force can be symptomatic of **problem police officers**. Problem officers are those who exhibit problem behavior, as indicated by a large number of citizen complaints, frequent involvement in use-of-force incidents, and other evidence.[7] The **Christopher Commission**, which studied the structure and operation of the Los Angeles Police Department (LAPD) in the wake of the **Rodney King** beating, found a number of "repeat offenders" on the force.[8] According to the commission, approximately 1,800 LAPD officers were alleged to have used excessive force or improper tactics between 1986 and 1990. Of these officers, more than 1,400 had only one or two allegations against them. Another 183 officers had four or more allegations, 44 had six or more, 16 had eight or more, and one had 16 such allegations. The commission also found that, generally speaking, the 44 officers with six complaints or more had received positive performance evaluations that failed to record "sustained" complaints or to discuss their significance.

THE USE OF FORCE

Recall that *use of force* and *use of excessive force* are not one and the same. Most of this chapter is concerned with the legitimate use of force. We save the discussion of improper force for the end of the chapter. What, then, are the types of force? When can force be used? How often do officers use force? What distinguishes deadly force from nondeadly force? What are the rules governing an officer's use of force? We answer these and related questions in the next few sections.

Levels of Force

Whether police officers use force properly or improperly, seven levels of force have been identified:

1. *Mere presence.* It is believed that the simple presence of an officer, the embodiment of the authority of the state, will deter dangerous and criminal behavior.

2. *Verbalization.* When officers speak, they are taught to do so persuasively. If verbalization doesn't work, officers move on to more forcible options.

problem police officer

An officer who exhibits problem behavior, as indicated by a large number of citizen complaints, frequent involvement in use-of-force incidents, and other evidence.[iii]

Christopher Commission

The commission that studied the structure and operation of the Los Angeles Police Department in the wake of the Rodney King beating incident.

Rodney King

A suspect whose videotaped beating by members of the Los Angeles Police Department led to civil unrest across the nation.

WEB PATROL 2

Early Detection of the Problem Officer
http://www.justicestudies.com/pubs/problemofficers.pdf

A protestor is arrested in New York City during the 2004 Republican National Convention. When is police use of force legitimate?

© Robert Galbraith/Reuters/CORBIS/All Rights Reserved

3. *Command voice.* An officer's command voice is more vibrant than his or her speaking voice, and the officer's request takes the form of an order: "Sir, I asked you for your vehicle papers once. Now I'm *telling* you to give them to me *now*."

4. *Firm grips.* These are physical grips on the body directing a suspect when and where to move. They are not intended to cause pain.

5. *Pain compliance.* These tactics seek the suspect's compliance by causing pain. They should not cause lasting physical injury.

6. *Impact techniques.* Impact techniques may involve physical contact or the use of chemical spray or stunning weapons.

7. *Deadly force.* This is force that is capable of killing the suspect. Examples include the "sleeper hold" (a choke-hold which can interfere with a person's breathing), the "bar arm control hold" (in which the forearm is squeezed against the neck to cut off the flow of air), and the use of guns.[9]

Our concern in this chapter is primarily with the last two types of force. These are the most likely to result in the injury or death of a suspect. Moreover, of all of the levels of force, they attract the most attention. All too often, it seems, bystanders record what they perceive to be police brutality. Sometimes such recordings *do* reveal brutality. Other times, though, untrained bystanders may fail to understand that what an officer did to apprehend a resistant suspect followed the police agency's policy to the letter.

WEB PATROL 3

Citizen Complaints about Police Use of Force
http://www.justicestudies.com/pubs/citizencomplaints.pdf

Use-of-Force Policy

force continuum

The spectrum of force available to a police officer, from the absence of physical force to the use of a deadly weapon.

Justifiable force is not applied arbitrarily. Police officers are trained to use only the necessary level of force to gain control over a situation or to subdue an unruly suspect. Sometimes they are taught a **force continuum,** or use-of-force continuum. Other times their policy manuals contain elaborate descriptions of proper and improper force. Some agencies combine both approaches. Figure 1 contains some force-related terminology that will help you work through this section.

Figure 1 • Force-Related Terminology

Suspect resistance

No resistance. Suspect was cooperative and followed all verbal instructions given by the officer.

Slight resistance. Suspect resisted the officer's actions, and the officer had to use strong directive language or minimal force (skills) to encourage suspect to cooperate and follow directions.

Moderate or high resistance. Suspect impeded officer's movement or resisted cuffing or placement in a car This level of resistance required the officer to use arm/wrist locks or distraction techniques or fighting skills to gain compliance and control.

Violent or explosive resistance. In this, the most extreme, level of resistance, the suspect struggled or fought violently and required the officer to (1) use fighting skills to disengage, (2) use a chemical agent, baton, or firearm, or (3) continue

fighting to gain control. In some cases in this resistance category, the officer decided that he or she needed to use weapons or other special tactics to gain control instead of engaging the suspect directly.

Officer force

No force. Officer used typical verbal commands.

Slight force. Officer had to use strong directive language or minimal physical force to encourage the suspect to cooperate and follow directions.

Forcibly subdued suspect with hands. Officer used an arm/wrist lock, takedown, block, punch, or kick, or struck or wrestled the suspect.

Forcibly subdued suspect using methods other than hands. Officer used chemical agent, baton, gun, or other special tactics or weapons.

Source: G. P. Alpert and R. G. Dunham, "The force factor: Measuring police use of force relative to suspect resistance," in *Use of force by police: Overview of national and local data* (Washington, DC: Bureau of Justice Statistics, 1999), p. 55. Full report available at http://www.ojp.usdoj.gov/bjs/abstract/ufbponld.htm (accessed July 21, 2008).

Figure 2 • Use-of-Force Continuum

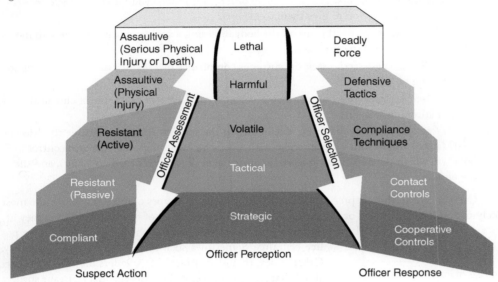

Source: Federal Law Enforcement Training Center, Department of Homeland Security.

An example of a use-of-force continuum, this one from the Federal Law Enforcement Training Center (FLETC), appears in Figure 2. The left side looks at the suspect's action. The right side looks at the appropriate response the officer should use. So, for example, if the suspect is compliant, an officer should only use "cooperative controls." These include verbal commands. At the other end of the continuum, if the officer perceives that the suspect is assaultive and likely to inflict serious injury or death, deadly force is justified.

Another force continuum appears in Table 1. This one is from the Phoenix (Arizona) Police Department. Seven categories of suspect behavior are listed alongside seven categories of police response. No resistance should equate with no force. Passive resistance, such as laying down and obstructing a road or entrance to a facility, should be met with control and restraint, sometimes coupled with arrest and use of handcuffs. Finally, a suspect who wields a firearm could very likely be shot—and justifiably so.

More often than not, law enforcement agencies adopt use-of-force policies that are far more detailed and restrictive than the force continuums just presented. The Allegan County (Michigan) Sheriff's Office, for example, limits use of force as follows:

> It is the policy of the Sheriff's Office to employ in all situations only those levels of force that are reasonable and necessary to control behavior of the offender. Reasonable and necessary levels of force are those levels that permit the officer to restrain or control the offender while maintaining

Table 1 • Phoenix Police Department Force Continuum

Police	Suspects
0. No force	0. No resistance
1. Police presence	1. Psychological intimidation
2. Verbal commands	2. Verbal noncompliance
3. Control and restraint (handcuffs)	3. Passive resistance
4. Chemical agents	4. Defensive resistance
5. Tactics and weapons[a]	5. Active aggression
6. Firearms/deadly force	6. Firearms/deadly force

[a]Includes all physical tactics and weapons except chemical agents and firearms.

Source: J. Garner and others, *Understanding the use of force by and against the police* (Washington, DC: National Institute of Justice, 1996), p. 5.

a high level of safety for themselves, their fellow officers, and the public. Reasonable physical force may be used in the following situations:

1. Self-defense.
2. To protect, defend or aid fellow officers.
3. To protect, defend or aid civilians or prisoners.
4. To prevent a person from harming themselves whether intentionally, recklessly or accidentally.
5. To prevent a crime or escape.
6. To effect an arrest.
7. To maintain public order or stop a disturbance.
8. To protect or preserve evidence or a crime scene.[10]

Additionally, the agency's policy manual explains in detail what type of force can be used and when. A list of suspect actions is provided, along with proper responses deputies can use. This portion of the Allegan County (Michigan) Sheriff's Office policy manual appears in Figure 3.

In a study reported in 2001, police experts Geoffrey Alpert and Roger Dunham found that the **force factor**—the level of force used by the police relative to the suspect's level of resistance—is a key element to consider in attempting to reduce injuries to both the police and suspects.[11] The force factor is calculated by measuring both the suspect's level of resistance and the officer's level of force on an equivalent scale and by then subtracting the level of resistance from the level of police force used. Results from the study indicate that, on average, the level of force that officers use is closely related to the type of training that their departments emphasize.

> **force factor**
> The level of force used by a police officer relative to the suspect's level of resistance.

Applications of Force

The National Institute of Justice estimates that nearly 45 million people nationwide have face-to-face contact with the police over a typical 12-month period and that approximately 700,000 of them are subjected to the use of force or the threat of force.[12] When handcuffing is included in the definition of force, the number of people subjected to force increases to 1.2 million, or slightly more than 2.5 percent of those having contact with the police. Other studies show that police use weaponless tactics in approximately 80 percent of use-of-force incidents and that half of all use-of-force incidents involve merely grabbing or holding the suspect.[13]

Studies show that police use force in fewer than 20 percent of adult custodial arrests. Even in instances where force is used, the police primarily use weaponless tactics. For example, a study of more than 7,000 police arrests in Phoenix revealed that no weapon was displayed, much less used, in about 95 percent of the arrests (see Table 2).[14] In addition, female officers are less likely to use physical force and firearms and are more likely to use chemical weapons (mostly pepper spray) than are their male counterparts. The use of weapons by suspects, a decidedly different issue, is detailed in Table 3.

Who is most likely to experience police force? Perhaps not surprisingly, males, African Americans, and younger people are most likely to experience force:

> Blacks (4.4%) and Hispanics (2.3%) were more likely than whites (1.2%) to experience use of force during contact with police in 2005. Blacks accounted for 1 out of 10 contacts with police but 1 out of 4 contacts where force was used. Persons age 16 to 29 (2.8%) who had contact with police were more likely than those over age 29 (1.0%) to have had force used against them. Persons age 16 to 29 made up a smaller percentage of persons who had a police contact (34.5%) compared to the percentage of persons experiencing force during a contact (60.3%). The median age of those experiencing force was 26.[15]

The nature of the contact is also associated with whether force is used. People whose contact was initiated by the police were much more likely to see force used. Indeed, about 80 percent of the contacts involving use of force were initiated by the police. This, too, is not surprising because police-initiated contacts are those where officers generally witness a criminal act or a person they suspect of having committed a crime. Sometimes these suspects flee, and force is required to stop them.

Figure 3 • Sample Use-of-Force Policy

INACTIVE RESISTANCE

Subject Action: Inactive Resistance

Resistance may include psychological intimidation or verbal resistance (blank stares, clenching of fists, verbal disagreement, for example). The subject complies, however, with verbal attempts to control.

Officer Response: Presence or Verbal Direction

The presence of a uniformed officer or verbal direction alone may control the incident.

PASSIVE RESISTANCE

Subject Action: Passive Resistance

The subject does not attempt to defeat the officer's attempts to touch or control but will not voluntarily comply with verbal or physical attempts to control (dead weight, does not listen to verbal commands).

Officer Response: Compliance Controls

The officer responds with soft empty-handed techniques. They may inflict pain and are used to gain control (joint locks, pressure points). They are used when verbal orders have not been effective and the subject does not comply with lawful orders. Selection of a reasonable control method is critical in this situation.

ACTIVE RESISTANCE

Subject Action: Active Resistance

The subject attempts to prevent an officer from gaining control (pulling or pushing away, blocking). This is not an attack against the officer, but an overt attempt to keep the officer from gaining control.

Officer Response: Physical Controls

The officer responds with hard empty-handed techniques, chemical agents, or electromuscular disruption (strikes, takedowns, chemical agents, Advanced Taser). Based on the totality of circumstances, controls available, and officer's ability, the control response may vary.

ACTIVE AGGRESSION

Subject Action: Active Aggression

The subject initiates physical actions or assaults against an officer or another person with less than deadly force (challenging, punching, kicking). The resistance is aimed specifically against another person or the officer.

Officer Response: Intermediate Controls

The officer responds with an intermediate weapon like an impact weapon or less-than-lethal munitions (baton, 12-gauge less-than-lethal munitions).

DEADLY FORCE ASSAULT

Subject Action: Deadly Force Assault

The subject uses deadly force against an officer or another person, which may result in great bodily harm or the loss of human life.

Officer Response: Deadly Force

The officer responds with deadly force, which may result in great bodily harm or the loss of life. A deadly force assault leaves little room for officer response options; he or she must act immediately to stop the assault and to neutralize the threat.

Source: Allegan County (Michigan) Sheriff's Office, "Use of force," February 11, 2004, http://www.less-lethal.org/docs/30/Policy (accessed July 21, 2008).

Table 2 • Weapons Threatened, Displayed, or Used by Police in 7,512 Arrests

	Used		Displayed or Used		Threatened, Displayed, or Used	
	Arrests	Percentage of Arrests	Arrests	Percentage of Arrests	Arrests	Percentage of Arrests
No weapon involved	7,354	97.9	7,151	95.2	7,130	94.9
Weapon involved	158	2.1	361	4.8	382	5.1
All arrests	7,512	100.0	7,512	100.0	7,512	100.0
Type of weapon[a]						
None	7,354	97.9	7,151	95.2	7,130	94.9
Baton	15	0.2	39	0.5	43	0.6
Flashlight	41	0.5	72	1.0	73	1.0
Handgun	11	0.1	202	2.7	204	2.7
Chemical agent	88	1.2	118	1.6	130	1.7
Rifle/shotgun	7	0.1	31	0.4	32	0.4
Motor vehicle	15	0.2	21	0.3	21	0.3
Canine	20	0.3	31	0.4	37	0.5
Other	19	0.3	19	0.3	19	0.3

[a]Because some arrests involved the use, display, or threatened use of more than one weapon, the percentages under Type of weapon do not add up to 100 percent.

Source: J. H. Garner and C. D. Maxwell, "Measuring the amount of force used by and against the police in six jurisdictions," *Use of force by police: Overview of national and local data* (Washington, DC: Bureau of Justice Statistics, 1999), p. 31, http://www.ncjrs.gov/pdffiles1/nij/176330-2.pdf (accessed July 21, 2008).

Table 3 • Weapons Threatened, Displayed, or Used by Suspects in 7,512 Arrests

	Used		Displayed or Used		Threatened, Displayed, or Used	
	Arrests	Percentage of Arrests	Arrests	Percentage of Arrests	Arrests	Percentage of Arrests
No weapon involved	7,460	99.3	7,411	98.7	7,367	98.1
Weapon involved	52	0.7	101	1.3	145	1.9
All arrests	7,512	100.0	7,512	100.0	7,512	100.0
Type of weapon[a]						
None	7,460	99.3	7,411	98.7	7,367	98.1
Stick	17	0.2	31	0.4	56	0.7
Knife	18	0.2	34	0.5	42	0.6
Handgun	12	0.2	29	0.4	47	0.6
Chemical agent	5	0.1	5	0.1	7	0.1
Rifle/shotgun	5	0.1	14	0.2	16	0.2
Motor vehicle	14	0.2	14	0.2	15	0.2
Canine	4	0.1	4	0.1	6	0.1
Other	9	0.1	14	0.2	17	0.2

[a]Because some arrests involved the use, display, or threatened use of more than one weapon, the percentages under Type of weapon do not add to 100 percent.

Source: J. H. Garner and C. D. Maxwell, "Measuring the amount of force used by and against the police in six jurisdictions," in *Use of force by police: Overview of national and local data* (Washington, DC: Bureau of Justice Statistics, 1999), p. 32, http://www.ncjrs.gov/pdffiles1/nij/176330-2.pdf (accessed July 21, 2008).

DEADLY FORCE

Generally speaking, **deadly force** is force that is likely to cause death or significant bodily harm. *Black's Law Dictionary* adopts a more general definition, namely "force that may result in the death of the person against whom the force is applied."[16] According to a report released by the Bureau of Justice Statistics in 2001, the number of justifiable homicides by police averages nearly 400 per year.[17]

deadly force
Force that is likely to cause death or significant bodily harm.

The use of deadly force by law enforcement officers, especially when it is *not* considered justifiable, is one area of potential civil liability that has received considerable attention in recent years. Historically, the "fleeing-felon rule" applied to most U.S. jurisdictions. It held that officers could use deadly force to prevent the escape of a suspected felon, even when that person represented no immediate threat to the officer or to the public. This, as we will see, has changed.

WEB PATROL 4

Excessive Force 101
http://www.justicestudies.com/pubs/excessiveforce.pdf

Legal Standards

The 1985 U.S. Supreme Court case of ***Tennessee v. Garner***[18] specified the conditions under which deadly force can be used to apprehend a suspected felon. Edward Garner, a 15-year-old suspected burglar, was shot to death by Memphis police after he refused their order to halt and attempted to climb over a chain-link fence. In an action initiated by Garner's father, who claimed that his son's constitutional rights had been violated, the Court held that the use of deadly force by the police to prevent the escape of a fleeing felon could be justified only where the suspect could reasonably be thought to represent a significant threat of serious injury or death to the public or to the officer and where deadly force is necessary to effect the arrest. In reaching its decision, the Court declared that "[t]he use of deadly force to prevent the escape of *all* felony suspects, whatever the circumstances, is constitutionally unreasonable."

Tennessee v. Garner
The 1985 U.S. Supreme Court case that specified the conditions under which deadly force could be used to apprehend suspected felons.

More specifically, the Court ruled that deadly force may be used when two criteria are present: (1) It is necessary to prevent the suspect's escape, and (2) the officer has probable cause to believe that the suspect poses a serious threat of death or serious physical injury to others. Given the nature of the *Garner* case, one would think the Court would have handed down a unanimous decision, but three justices dissented, noting that the statute struck down by the majority "assist[s] the police in apprehending suspected perpetrators of serious crimes and provide[s] notice that a lawful police order to stop and submit to arrest may not be ignored with impunity."[19] In any case, to further grasp the reach of *Garner*, it is important to consider the notion of what kind of offender poses a "serious threat." Courts will generally consider present and/or past dangerousness.

Present Dangerousness. According to Victor Kappeler of Eastern Kentucky University, "[A] dangerous suspect is, generally, an armed suspect who can inflict serious physical harm."[20] As such, suspects who are armed with a deadly weapon, be it a gun, knife, or other object, can safely be considered dangerous. Moreover, the weapon must be capable of inflicting death or serious bodily harm. Fingernail clippers, for example, cannot be considered a deadly weapon.

It is not enough that the suspect be merely armed for deadly force to be justifiably used. In addition, the danger posed by the suspect must be *immediate*. If, for example, the suspect is armed with a gun, the gun must be pointed at a police officer or some other individual. Deadly force may not be considered justified if the suspect's hand is not raised (or being raised) into the shooting position. In one illustrative case, one of the federal district courts concluded that the police used deadly force inappropriately in killing a woman (Hegarty) when

> Hegarty repeatedly asked the officers to leave, but she neither threatened them nor did she fire any shots while the officers were present. In fact, the officers decided to enter Hegarty's home forcibly only after it appeared that she had put down her rifle. Hegarty did not threaten injury to herself at any time, nor were there other individuals in danger.[21]

WEB PATROL 5

Curbing Police Brutality: What Works?
http://www.justicestudies.com/pubs/curbing.pdf

Past Dangerousness. A suspect can also pose a serious threat based on his or her past conduct or based on the nature of the crime in question. It is easier to defend deadly force against suspects who have committed murder, armed robbery, and similar offenses, in contrast to less serious offenses like burglary or motor vehicle theft. These less serious offenses, in general, do not enhance the police authority to use deadly force.

It should be emphasized that only a handful of courts have permitted deadly force based solely on past dangerousness, and the U.S. Supreme Court has never sanctioned such action. In fact, a federal circuit court of appeals has held that the use of deadly force to apprehend a suspect charged with a serious crime is unconstitutional.[22] For example, if a suspect committed robbery but was then confronted by the police and, following their orders, raised his hands, he could not then be shot.

Finally, if police are going to defend deadly force based on past dangerousness, then the serious offense that the suspect is alleged to have committed must have been committed in the recent past. In other words, officers should avoid deadly force if too much time has elapsed between the crime and the use of deadly force. For example, if a police officer used deadly force based solely on the fact that a suspect committed homicide several months ago, the officer's actions would probably be considered unconstitutional. This is especially true if the officer could have used other methods besides the use of deadly force to apprehend the suspect.

Federal Policy. In 1995, following investigations into the actions of federal agents at the deadly siege of the Branch Davidian compound at Waco, Texas, and the tragic deaths associated with a 1992 FBI assault on antigovernment separatists in Ruby Ridge, Idaho, the federal government announced that it was adopting an "imminent danger" standard for the use of deadly force by federal agents. The imminent danger standard restricts the use of deadly force to situations in which the lives of agents or others are in danger. When the new standard was announced, federal agencies were criticized for not adopting it sooner. The federal deadly force policy, as adopted by the FBI, contains the following elements[23]:

Defense of life. Agents may use deadly force only when necessary—that is, only when they have probable cause to believe that the subject poses an imminent danger of death or serious physical injury to the agent or to others.

Fleeing subject. Deadly force may be used to prevent the escape of a fleeing subject if there is probable cause to believe that the subject has committed a felony involving the infliction or threatened infliction of serious physical injury or death and that the subject's escape would pose an imminent danger of death or serious physical injury to the agents or to others.

Verbal warnings. If feasible, and if doing so would not increase the danger to the agent or to others, a verbal warning to submit to the authority of the agent should be given prior to the use of deadly force.

Warning shots. Agents may not fire warning shots.

Vehicles. Agents may not fire weapons solely to disable moving vehicles. Weapons may be fired at the driver or other occupant of a moving motor vehicle only when the agent has probable cause to believe that the subject poses an imminent danger of death or serious physical injury to the agent or to others and when the use of deadly force does not create a danger to the public that outweighs the likely benefits of its use.

Patterns of Deadly Force

Studies of killings by the police have often focused on claims of discrimination—that is, that African American and minority suspects are more likely to be shot than whites. But research has not provided solid support for such claims. While individuals shot by police are more likely to be minorities, an early study by criminologist James Fyfe found that police officers will generally respond with deadly force when mortally threatened and that minorities are considerably more likely to use weapons in assaults on officers than are whites.[24] Complicating the picture further, Fyfe's study showed that minority officers are involved in the shootings of suspects more often than other officers, a finding that may be due to the assignment of minority officers to poor inner-city areas. However, a later study by Fyfe, which analyzed police shootings in Memphis, Tennessee, found that African American property offenders were twice as likely as whites to be shot by police.[25]

Although relatively few police officers ever fire their weapons at suspects during the course of their careers, those who do may become embroiled in social, legal, and personal complications. It is estimated that in an average year, 600 suspects are killed by police officers in America, while another 1,200 are shot and wounded, and 1,800 are shot at and missed.[26] The personal side of police shootings is well summarized in the title of an article that appeared in *Police Magazine*. The article, "I've Killed That Man Ten Thousand Times," demonstrates how police officers who have to use their weapons may be haunted by years of depression and despair.[27] According to author Anne Cohen, all departments did to help officers who had shot someone was to "give him enough bullets to reload his gun." The stress and trauma that police officers suffer from having shot someone are now being realized, and many departments have developed mechanisms for dealing with them.[28]

Suicide by Cop

Police officers have particular difficulty dealing with instances of **suicide by cop**, in which individuals who are determined to die engage in behavior that causes responding officers to resort to deadly force. On March 10, 2005, for example, John T. Garczynski, Jr., a father of two preteen boys, died in a hail of 26 police bullets fired by officers who had surrounded his vehicle in a Boca Raton, Florida, condominium parking lot.[29] Garczynski, a Florida Power and Light Company employee, appeared to have been despondent over financial problems and the breakup of his marriage. The night before his death, Garczynski met his wife at a bowling alley and handed her a packet containing a suicide note, a typed obituary, and a eulogy to be read at his funeral. After he left, Garczynski's wife called police, and officers used the help of a cell phone company to locate Garczynski. As deputies surrounded Garczynski's 2003 Ford Explorer, he attempted to start the vehicle. One of the officers yelled "Freeze," and then "Let me see your hands." It was at that point, deputies said, that Garczynski pointed a gun at them and they fired.

Rebecca Stincelli, author of the book *Suicide by Cop: Victims from Both Sides of the Badge*,[30] says that an incident like the one involving Garczynski can be devastating for police officers. "In the past, people have used rope, a gun, gas, jumped off a building. A police officer is just another method," says Stincelli. "They say it's nothing personal. [But] they are wrong. It's very personal" for the officers involved.[31] The FBI notes that "suicide-by-cop incidents are painful and damaging experiences for the surviving families, the communities, and all law enforcement professionals."[32]

A study of fatal shootings by Los Angeles police officers found that an astonishingly large number—more than 10 percent—could be classified as suicide by cop.[33] Recently, researchers have identified three main categories of suicide by cop: direct confrontations, in which suicidal subjects instigate attacks on police officers for the purpose of dying; disturbed interventions, in which potentially suicidal subjects take advantage of police intervention in their suicide attempt in order to die; and criminal interventions, in which criminal suspects prefer death to capture and arrest.[34]

Several steps for managing suicide-by-cop scenarios have been suggested:

- Contain the area, while remaining aware that too close a containment may allow the precipitator [the suicidal person] to provoke a deadly confrontation.
- If time and circumstances allow, make a clear demand for compliance—a demand that will usually be ignored.
- Ask the person what he or she wants (specifically, ask if they are trying to die).
- If family, friends, or acquaintances of the subject are present, ask if they are aware of the subject's mental health history, chemical dependency or any criminal record.
- Remain a good listener, while avoiding making promises or committing to anything.
- Use a less-than-lethal weapon only as a diversionary tactic before making a planned attempt to apprehend but never as a stand-alone tactic, as the use of such devices without an immediate attempt to apprehend may in fact escalate the situation.[35]

suicide by cop
An incident in which an individual who is determined to die engages in behavior meant to provoke responding officers to resort to deadly force.

It may seem silly to ask the apparently suicidal individual about his or her intentions, but failure to do so can result in needless death:

> While the individual shot by police may have committed a suicidal act, he may not have been suicidal. In fact, the offender's physical survival probably did not enter his thought processes at the moment he made his fateful decision. Instead, this person was momentarily indifferent to the consequences of his threatening behavior. Rather than suicide by cop, he committed "death by indifference."[36]

WEB PATROL 6

Understanding the Prevalence and Severity of Force Used by and against the Police

http://www.justicestudies.com/pubs/understandingforce.pdf

NONDEADLY FORCE

nondeadly force
Force that is unlikely to cause death or significant bodily harm.

We defined *deadly force* as force that is likely to cause death or significant bodily harm. **Nondeadly force** is basically the opposite: force that is *unlikely* to cause death or significant bodily harm. We cannot safely say that nondeadly force will always prevent injury or preserve loss of life because sometimes—rarely—people die as a result of injuries suffered from nondeadly force. This is more true of so-called less-lethal weapons, which we will introduce shortly, than physical force, although people sometimes die or suffer long-term injury from physical force, too.

Legal Standards

Graham v. Connor
The 1989 U.S. Supreme Court case in which the Court declared that claims of excessive nondeadly force must be judged under the Fourth Amendment's reasonableness clause.

In the 1989 case of **Graham v. Connor**,[37] the U.S. Supreme Court declared that claims of excessive nondeadly force must be judged under the Fourth Amendment's reasonableness clause:

> [A]ll claims that law enforcement officers have used excessive force—deadly or not—in the course of an arrest, investigatory stop, or other "seizure" of a free citizen should be analyzed under the Fourth Amendment and its "reasonableness" standard.[38]

The Court also said that whether deadly force has been used appropriately should be judged from the perspective of a reasonable officer on the scene and not with the benefit of 20/20 hindsight. The justices wrote, "The calculus of reasonableness must embody allowance for the fact that police officers are often forced to make split-second judgments—in circumstances that are tense, uncertain, and rapidly evolving—about the amount of force that is necessary in a particular situation."[39]

In helping to decide what a reasonable police officer would do, courts need to consider three factors: the severity of the crime, whether the suspect poses a threat, and whether the suspect is resisting or attempting to flee the scene. Generally, if the crime in question is a serious one and the suspect is dangerous or resists arrest, the suspect will have difficulty prevailing with a claim of excessive force.

WEB PATROL 7

Understanding the Use of Force by and against the Police in Six Jurisdictions

http://www.justicestudies.com/pubs/understandingforcereport.pdf

WEB PATROL 8

Early Warning Systems: Responding to the Problem Police Officer

http://www.justicestudies.com/pubs/warning.pdf

YOU DECIDE
Back Me Up

You and your partner are on patrol when a car roars through a red light at a high speed. You give chase. The driver does not pull over right away, yet he does not appear to be evading you. He is just continuing to drive, as if looking for a place to stop. Your partner is getting increasingly agitated and mutters that when he gets his hands on the driver, "He's going to get what he deserves." You know your partner is on edge anyway, as he just went through a nasty divorce and has been having problems at work. As the vehicle finally pulls over, your partner jumps out and says, "Back me up!" He then draws his gun and shouts to the driver, "Get out of the car with your hands up!" The driver, a juvenile, gets out of the vehicle and appears visibly scared. Your partner then yells, "Get on the ground, facedown!" The driver appears confused and does not immediately respond. Your partner takes out his nightstick and, with one hit to the legs, brings the driver to the ground. The driver never fights back or resists, but your partner looks as though he is about to strike another blow. What should you do?

Less-Lethal Weapons

Less-lethal weapons offer what may be a problem-specific solution to potential incidents of suicide by cop, as well as a generic solution to at least some charges of use of excessive force. Less-lethal weapons are designed to disable, capture, or immobilize, rather than kill.

Efforts to provide law enforcement officers with less-lethal weapons like stun guns, Tasers, rubber bullets, beanbag projectiles, and pepper spray began in 1987.[40] More exotic types of less-lethal weapons are available today. They include snare nets fired from shotguns, disabling sticky foam that can be sprayed from a distance, microwave beams that heat the tissue of people exposed to them until they desist or lose consciousness, and high-tech guns that fire bolts of electromagnetic energy at a target, causing painful sensory overload and violent muscle spasms. The National Institute of Justice says, "The goal is to give line officers effective and safe alternatives to lethal force."[41]

As their name implies, however, less-lethal weapons are not always safe. On October 21, 2004, for example, 21-year-old Emerson College student Victoria Snelgrove died hours after being hit in the eye with a plastic pepper-spray-filled projectile. Police officers had fired the projectile at a rowdy crowd celebrating after the Red Sox won the American League championship. Witnesses said that officers fired into the crowd after a reveler near Fenway Park threw a bottle at a mounted Boston police officer.[42] The following sections look at three families of less-lethal weapons. There are others besides those we discuss here, but these are some of the most widely used.

less-lethal weapon
A weapon that is designed to disable, capture, or immobilize, rather than kill.

WEB PATROL 9

Less-Lethal Weaponry Case Study (Long Beach, California)
http://tinyurl.com/2ltc3o

Conducted Energy Devices. The most popular **conducted energy device (CED)** is the familiar Taser. The most common Taser models are the X26 and M26. The Taser International website explains how the X26 works (the M26 performs similarly):

> The Taser X26 uses a replaceable cartridge containing compressed nitrogen to deploy two small probes that are attached to the Taser X26 by insulated conductive wires with a maximum length of 35 feet (10.6 meters). The Taser X26 transmits electrical pulses along the wires and into the body affecting the sensory and motor functions of the peripheral nervous system. The energy can penetrate up to two cumulative inches of clothing, or one inch per probe.[43]

Some Tasers have two modes: "probe" and "touch stun." In the "probe" mode, a cartridge projects and attaches to a suspect's clothing or penetrates the skin with barbs. Between the barbs and the pistol-like Taser unit are two small wires. An electrical charge is then sent down the wires, disabling the suspect. The "touch stun" mode requires the officer to touch the suspect with the unit (similar to a stun gun); wires are not used. For obvious reasons, the "probe" mode is safer for the officer.

Another recently developed conducted energy device is the so-called Sticky Shocker. Developed by Titan, the device is intended to fill the gap between a Taser or pepper spray and impact munitions. (We will discuss pepper spray and impact munitions shortly.) According to its developer,

conducted energy device (CED)
A device that uses electrical shock to incapacitate a suspect. Examples are the Taser and the Sticky Shocker. Also called *electromuscular disruption technology*.

> The Sticky Shocker idea evolved in response to the need for a nonlethal weapon bridging the gap between kinetic rounds (e.g., rubber bullets, beanbags, wooden batons) and devices designed for use at close-in range, such as electric stun devices with darts and pepper spray (effective only within 5 m) or stun guns (arms-length range). The Sticky Shocker concept puts stun gun technology on a wireless self-contained projectile, allowing temporary incapacitation of a human target at safe, stand-off distance, using a widely accepted 40 mm or 37 mm projectile configuration and conventional launchers. The Sticky Shocker can extend the range of electrical stun technology out to 10 m and potentially further. The projectile contains a battery pack and associated electronics that will impart a short burst of high-voltage pulses. Pulse amplitudes are near 50 kV with pulse widths of a few microseconds and repetition rate between 10 to 15 pulses per second. The pulse characteristics are similar to those of commercial stun guns. The pulses are not lethal but will disable a human target temporarily, with full recovery from impact within a few minutes.[44]

There are some concerns over the use and safety of conducted energy devices. Researchers, too, have fixed their sights on CEDs. A recent Police Executive Research Forum study called attention to the need for national guidelines governing their use, particularly the use of Tasers, and the organization offered more than 50 recommendations for proper and safe operation of the devices.[45] Their recommendations included the following:

1. CEDs should only be used against suspects who are actively resisting or exhibiting active aggression or to prevent individuals from harming themselves or others. CEDs should not be used against passive suspects.

2. No more than one officer at a time should activate a CED against a person.

3. When activating a CED, law enforcement officers should use it for one standard cycle (five seconds) and stop to evaluate the situation. If subsequent cycles are necessary, agency policy should restrict the number and duration of those cycles to the minimum activations necessary to place the subject in custody.

4. Training protocols should emphasize that multiple activations and continuous cycling of a CED appear to increase the risk of death or serious injury and should be avoided where practical.

5. Officers should be trained to recognize the limitations of CED activation and should be prepared to transition to other force options as needed.[46]

The need for such guidelines is critical because despite their supposedly nonlethal nature, conducted energy devices *have* been implicated in some deaths. In fact, Amnesty International, the well-known human rights group, has called for a moratorium on Taser use until its risks can be properly assessed. According to the Amnesty International report, which was published in 2006, the number of Taser-related deaths has passed 150.[47] Here is a story of one Taser death from the Amnesty International report:

> Russell Walker, aged 47, died after being tasered by Las Vegas police officers on 7 June 2005. Officers were called to a hotel at 8 p.m. when Walker was reported as creating a disturbance. Officers tasered him when he began to struggle with them, and they then placed him in handcuffs. Once handcuffed, Russell Walker again began struggling and the taser was used again. The taser was used a third and final time when Walker had been placed on a gurney, and he then stopped breathing. He was pronounced dead at hospital at 9 p.m. Although the Las Vegas policy on tasers stipulates that they may not be used on handcuffed suspects, and may not be used multiple times, a grand jury inquest into the death of Russell Walker found that the actions of the officers were justified. The coroner in the case ruled that Russell Walker died of "heart arrhythmia during restraint procedures" and commented that the struggle with officers together with the amount of cocaine Walker had ingested was a "recipe for disaster."[48]

Amnesty International attributes deaths like that described here primarily to the use of Tasers. In the vast majority of cases, however, it appears that the suspects were under the influence of illicit drugs or had heart conditions, and the Taser apparently exacerbated an existing condition. Medical examiners have also attributed some Taser-related deaths (and other deaths in police custody) to a condition known as **excited delirium**, an overdose of adrenaline that can occur in heated confrontations with the police.

Impact Munitions. Earlier in this chapter, we mentioned a force continuum. There is also a **weapons continuum**. Traditional less-lethal technologies require that officers be in close proximity to suspects. Whether employing a baton, a can of pepper spray, or a Taser in "touch stun" mode to get the job done, an officer has to be a few feet from the suspect. Lethal weapons, especially guns, by contrast, do not require close proximity. These devices can be put on a continuum that moves the threat of injury to the officer from low to high. Guns generally present a low risk to officers, whereas batons present a fairly high risk. In response to this problem, less-lethal technologies have been developed that can be used from a distance. Such devices are most commonly called **impact munitions**. According to the National Institute of Justice,

excited delirium
A condition in which a suspect experiences an overdose of adrenaline during a heated confrontation with the police.

weapons continuum
The array of nonlethal and lethal weaponry available to police officers, the selection of which depends on the situation.

impact munitions
Munitions designed to stun or otherwise temporarily incapacitate a suspect or a dangerous individual so that law enforcement officers can subdue and arrest that person with less risk of injury or death to themselves and to others.[iv]

A Taser demonstration gone awry. A Dane County (Wisconsin) sheriff's department sergeant rushes to catch deputy Krist Boldt after Boldt was stunned by an M26 Taser during a demonstration. Boldt, who was expected to fall forward, fell backward instead, injuring his head. When might the use of conducted energy devices like the Taser be appropriate?

Wisconsin State Journal/Craig Schreiner/AP Wide World Photos

These devices can be fired at a greater distance from the target, thus reducing the risk to officers and the likelihood they will resort to lethal force. . . . Impact munitions are designed to stun or otherwise temporarily incapacitate a suspect or dangerous individual so that law enforcement officers can subdue and arrest that person with less danger of injury or death for themselves and others.[49]

Impact munitions include foam rubber bullets, wooden dowels, beanbags, and other projectiles that are usually fired from 12-gauge shotguns or 37/40-millimeter gas grenade launchers. For example, the 12-gauge launching cap produced

WEB PATROL 10

Use of Force, Civil Litigation, and the Taser
http://www.justiceprograms.com/pubs/taserissues.pdf

by Combined Tactical Systems (CTS) can fire a large rubber projectile from a distance of 75 to 100 meters. Beanbags can also be fired from these types of devices.

The company's 12-gauge point round is another example of a less-lethal technology. According to CTS, "The point target cartridge round delivers a strong blow to the body with the capability to stun individuals without penetrating the body. The round is designed to be fired at the center mass of an adult subject at distances between 10 and 20 meters."[50]

So-called area rounds are 12-gauge shotgun shells full of rubber pellets that deliver strong blows to people without penetrating the body (although they can break the skin). Sponge point grenades and similar projectiles, fired from grenade launchers, also function to subdue unruly individuals. Even rubber pellet–filled hand grenades have been developed. Finally, flash grenades or flash-bang stun hand grenades are available in the law enforcement arsenal. All of these devices pose minimal risk of death, though they can certainly cause injury.

Law enforcement officers need to be careful to use impact munitions from proper distances. When employed from too great a distance, less-lethal weapons can be ineffective. On the other hand, when fired from less than 30 or so feet, these devices can cause serious injury, including broken bones. Death can even occur if the devices are not used as intended. A National Institute of Justice study of 373 incidents involving impact munitions found that eight individuals died as a result of injuries sustained from the weapons.[51] Most of the deaths were caused by broken ribs that pierced the heart or lungs. At least one suspect died as a result of being hit in the neck with a beanbag round. Additional findings from this study appear in Figure 4.

Figure 4 • Findings from a Study of 373 Incidents Involving Impact Munitions

The Targets

The study found that 181, or nearly half, of the reported 373 incidents involved emotionally disturbed individuals who were armed and showed signs of suicidal intent. The reported incidents also included

- Nonsuicidal but armed individuals in open areas who had refused police orders to drop their weapons (70 incidents)
- Individuals barricaded inside buildings or vehicles (48 incidents)
- Hostage takers (nine incidents)

The data showed the characteristics of those who were shot by law enforcement officers firing impact munitions:

- Most individuals were in their 30s, though ages ranged from 14 to 83.
- Nearly all were men (291 of 315 cases in which gender was recorded).
- Nearly two-thirds were white (200 out of 301 where information on race or ethnic group was included), followed by Hispanics (49) and African Americans (40).

Armed and Dangerous

Subjects were armed in almost 90 percent of the 306 cases for which weapons data were available. (In the few instances where suspects possessed multiple weapons, the researchers counted only the most dangerous one.)

- Cutting instruments (knives, swords, axes, machetes)—50 percent of the 306 cases
- Firearms (handguns, shotguns, rifles)—29 percent
- Blunt instruments (bats, clubs, sticks)—6 percent
- Other objects (rocks, bottles, Molotov cocktails)—4 percent
- No weapon—11 percent

Number of Shots Fired

Law enforcement officers fired one to 141 shots at individual targets. Often, multiple shots were needed to subdue an individual because a single hit by an impact munition was not always immediately effective. In the overwhelming number of cases, however, the number of shots fired was few.

Ten or fewer rounds were fired in 98 percent of the 316 cases for which information was available, five or fewer in 93 percent, and one shot in 38 percent of the cases.

Respondents in 313 of the cases reported on the number of shots that struck their intended target, with the number of hits ranging from one to 13. In one case, the individual being fired at surrendered after the shots missed. Others surrendered when follow-up shots missed but the initial shots hit their target.

Type of Munition Used

The type of impact munition used was identified in 962 of the 969 reported discharges of devices. Of the 21 different types of munitions used, beanbags shot from 12-gauge shotguns were the most common, accounting for 65 percent of all the projectiles fired. Plastic baton rounds were the second most common, used in 28 percent of the cases.

Where Struck

Most often, targets were struck in the abdomen (34 percent) or the chest (19 percent), followed by the legs (15 percent), arms (14 percent), and back (11 percent). Only 2 percent of the impacts were on the head, and only 1 percent each in the groin and neck, the more vulnerable parts of a person's body. Of the 969 reported discharges of impact munitions, 782 resulted in injuries. Of those, more than 80 percent were bruises and abrasions, both relatively minor injuries that may not require medical treatment. Bruises accounted for 51 percent of the injuries, and abrasions added another 31 percent. More serious lacerations accounted for 5.5 percent of the injuries; broken bones accounted for 3.5 percent. Of the 782 injuries, there were 14 instances (1.8 percent) in which the impact munition penetrated the target's skin and caused a more serious injury.

Impacts to the head produced a greater proportion of nonfatal serious injuries than other areas struck. Of the 19 head impacts reported, 14 resulted in a laceration, bone fracture, or penetration wound.

Source: National Institute of Justice, *Impact munitions use: Types, targets, effects* (Washington, DC: National Institute of Justice, 2004), pp. 4–5, http://www.ncjrs.gov/pdffiles1/nij/206089.pdf (accessed July 21, 2008).

Pepper Spray (Oleoresin Capsicum).

Pepper spray, or oleoresin capsicum (OC), is a so-called lachrymatory (inflammatory) agent that causes irritation to the eyes and skin. Pepper spray, like tear gas, causes the eyes to close tightly and tear up, and it may even cause temporary blindness. It also causes the mucous membranes of the nose, throat, and sinuses to burn and swell, making breathing difficult. OC spray is very effective when used to subdue a resistant suspect. Note that pepper spray is not the same as tear gas. There are two forms of tear gas: chlorobenzylidenemalononitrile (CS) gas and chloroacetophenone (CN) gas. These gases are irritants and are used more often than pepper spray to control unruly crowds, rather than to gain compliance from an individual.

The active ingredient in pepper spray is capsaicin, a derivative of the fruit from plants in the *Capsicum* genus, which includes certain peppers, notably the cayenne pepper—hence the term *pepper spray*. The spray is usually packaged in small pressurized canisters that are carried on the person and can be dispensed quickly to subdue a suspect or for self-defense. The spray is most effective when sprayed in the eyes. Pepper spray, unlike some of the other less-lethal technologies, can be acquired legally by non–law enforcement personnel, but not in all states. Most states that permit its sale have laws that penalize improper use of the spray.

Pepper spray is aptly called a less-lethal weapon because some people *have* died as a result of its use.[52] A study of pepper spray's effectiveness was conducted by researchers at the University of North Carolina.[53] They examined injuries to officers and suspects and complaints of excessive force before and after police departments adopted the use of pepper spray. The researchers found an overall decline in officer injuries, but the decline apparently preceded the introduction of pepper spray, and the effect varied across police departments. The researchers found fewer suspect injuries due to the introduction of pepper spray. Finally, complaints of excessive force declined markedly after pepper spray came into use.

Another study looked at in-custody deaths following the use of pepper spray. Researchers at the University of Texas Southwestern Medical Center identified 63 such cases and concluded, for the most part, that pepper spray was not the culprit. According to one summary of this research,

> For pepper spray to cause death, it would have to make breathing difficult by closing or narrowing the bronchial tubes. The subject would have to struggle to both inhale and exhale. These effects would be noticeable shortly after the application of pepper spray. Yet, except for the two cases in which the subjects were classified as asthmatics, comments regarding breathing (other than "ceased breathing") were found in only five case reports, none of which referred to a struggle to breathe. In none of these cases did death immediately follow pepper spray application.[54]

The researchers went on to conclude that pepper spray did not cause *or* contribute to death in 61 of the 63 identified cases. The two remaining deaths were of asthmatics whose conditions were exacerbated by pepper spray. Table 4 contains a summary of the causes of death in these 63 cases. Po-

pepper spray
A so-called lachrymatory (inflammatory) agent that causes irritation to the eyes and skin. Also called *oleoresin capsicum (OC)*.

Table 4 • Causes of Death in 63 Cases Where Pepper Spray Was Used

Category	Number of Cases
Category I: clear cut	23
IA: Drugs alone	12
IB: Drugs and disease	4
IC: Positional asphyxia	7
Category II: combined effects	32
IIA: Confrontational situation + drugs	23
IIB: Confrontational situation + disease	5
IIC: Confrontational situation + drugs and disease	4
Category III: outliers (uncategorizable)	6
Category IV: asthma	2
Total cases examined in study	**63**

Source: National Institute of Justice, *The effectiveness and safety of pepper spray* (Washington, DC: National Institute of Justice, 2003), p. 9.

sitional asphyxia, which is mentioned in the table, sometimes occurs when suspects are placed, usually with handcuffs behind their backs, in a prone position. The position sometimes makes breathing more difficult.

On the subject of positional asphyxia, researchers at the University of California, San Diego, measured the effects of both pepper spray and a placebo spray on police recruits who were then placed in either a sitting position or in the "hogtie" (feet and hands bound behind the back) position.[55] The study found that pepper spray alone does not cause respiratory problems in either position. It should be noted, however, that the study participants were healthy police recruits and that they were allowed to wear goggles to minimize the harmful effects of the pepper spray. Even so, it is safe to say that pepper spray is likely the safest less-lethal weapon, especially when compared to some of the other weapons we have discussed in this chapter.

Indirect Force

Questions sometimes arise about whether officers go too far in their efforts to apprehend a suspect. Injury could occur to the suspect, but also to innocent bystanders. Either way, one could allege that an officer's decision to pursue effectively amounted to excessive force. This is best understood as **indirect force**, however. It is indirect in the sense that if injury or death occurs, it is not directly at the hands of a police officer, as it would be in the case of a shooting.

indirect force
Actions by an officer that indirectly expose a suspect or an innocent bystander to potential injury but that do not involve the intentional application of direct physical force. A high-speed automobile pursuit is an example.

Some U.S. Supreme Court cases are illustrative. In *Brower v. County of Inyo* (1989),[56] for example, Brower stole a vehicle and led the police on a high-speed chase over a 20-mile stretch of highway. Officers used an 18-wheeler to block both lanes of the highway on which Brower was driving. They also pointed the headlights of their police cars in Brower's direction, hoping to blind him. Brower crashed into the roadblock and was killed, and the police were subsequently sued by Brower's family members, who alleged that the roadblock violated Brower's Fourth Amendment rights. The U.S. Supreme Court ruled that "Brower's independent decision to continue the chase can no more eliminate [the officers'] responsibility for the termination of his movement effected by the roadblock than Garner's independent decision to flee eliminated the Memphis police officer's responsibility for the termination of his movement effected by the bullet."

In other words, the Court found that the law enforcement officers involved in setting up the roadblock had seized Brower within the meaning of the Fourth Amendment.

WEB PATROL 11
Police Attitudes toward Abuse of Authority
http://www.justicestudies.com/pubs/policeattitudes.pdf

In *County of Sacramento v. Lewis* (1998),[57] a patrol officer witnessed a motorcycle approaching at breakneck speed. A sheriff's deputy gave chase. During the pursuit, the motorcyclist lost control and tipped over. The pursuing deputy was unable to bring his cruiser to a halt before running into the crashed motorcycle and killing its operator. Representatives of the motorcyclist's estate brought a lawsuit against the police, but the U.S. Supreme Court did not see the indirect force applied in this case as excessive:

> Respondents' allegations are insufficient to state a substantive due process violation. Protection against governmental arbitrariness is the core of due process . . . , including substantive due process . . . , but only the most egregious executive action can be said to be "arbitrary" in the constitutional sense . . . ; the cognizable level of executive abuse of power is that which shocks the conscience. . . . In the circumstances of a high-speed chase aimed at apprehending a suspected offender, where unforeseen circumstances demand an instant judgment on the part of an officer who feels the pulls of competing obligations, only a purpose to cause harm unrelated to the legitimate object of arrest will satisfy the shocks-the-conscience test. Such chases with no intent to harm suspects physically or to worsen their legal plight do not give rise to substantive due process liability.

In other words, the pursuing officer could not be held responsible for the motorcyclist's death because the officer did not intend for the man to die, nor could he have reasonably foreseen the outcome of the pursuit.

In a decision welcomed by police officers everywhere, the U.S. Supreme Court recently held, in the case of *Scott v. Harris* (2007),[58] that police officers cannot be sued for their decision to chase fleeing motorists, even if such a chase results in serious injury to the suspect. As the Court put it,

"[A] police officer's attempt to terminate a dangerous high-speed car chase that threatens the lives of innocent bystanders does not violate the Fourth Amendment, even when it places the fleeing motorist at risk of serious injury or death."

EXCESSIVE FORCE AND ABUSE OF AUTHORITY

Recall that excessive force is not the same as use of force. Excessive force is *inappropriate* force. To clarify even further, consider the distinction between ends and means. In our democratic system of government, we are very concerned with process. Applied to policing, *process* refers to the means or procedures police use to perform their jobs. We are nervous about the prospect of giving police unlimited authority. On the other hand, we don't like to ignore the ends either—in other words, crime control. We want police to control crime *and* preserve our liberty. But when the ends become more of a concern than the means, inappropriate or excessive force is a likely result.

Excessive force is not the only form of inappropriate police conduct. It is also possible to abuse one's authority. Abuse of authority can be thought of as something of an umbrella under which excessive force falls. An officer can abuse his or her authority without resorting to physical force. In either case, the end result is a person who is improperly and unjustly made to suffer in one way or another.

Types of Excessive Force

Excessive force and abuse of authority take at least three distinct forms. Neither is quite the same as, say, accepting a gratuity or receiving a kickback. Each leads to a measure of discomfort, if not pain or even death, on the part of a criminal suspect—or even an innocent person. Physical brutality, verbal and psychological abuse, and other so-called rights violations are discussed in this section. Think of these as appearing on a continuum that moves from most to least serious.

Physical Brutality.
Perhaps the most notorious example of police brutality in recent years is the infamous 1991 Rodney King incident, which was mentioned at the beginning of this chapter. King was stopped for speeding and for fleeing from police. He did not cooperate once he was stopped, and officers applied force to subdue him, but a bystander's video recording of the incident revealed something else. King was hit and kicked more than 50 times, as 27 officers from various agencies stood by. What's more, the beating continued even after King appeared to be under control. King received 11 fractures to his skull, a broken ankle, and several other serious injuries. So serious was the incident that an independent commission, the Christopher Commission (named for Warren Christopher, former deputy attorney general and deputy secretary of state for the United States), was appointed to investigate it—along with other alleged problems in the Los Angeles Police Department. Three officers who were criminally charged in the incident were acquitted in 1992, inciting one of the largest riots in Los Angeles history.

In 2008, LAPD officers were once again criticized by the press for their handling of another incident, an immigration rally. Two officers were reassigned after the incident, but this has not stopped people from trying to connect the dots—from Rodney King to the Rampart Division scandal, to the crackdown at the 2000 Democratic National Convention which took place at Los Angeles' Staples Center. Critics argue that the LAPD is plagued by a warrior culture that, like an ocean liner, is difficult to turn around.[59]

According to Michigan State University criminologist David Carter, physical brutality and excessive force go hand in hand:

> Operationally, this classification [excessive force] includes (1) any officer behavior involving the use of more force than is necessary to effect an arrest or search, and/or (2) the wanton use of any

degree of physical force against another by a police officer under the color of the officer's office. The key test is whether there was any physical force directly used against an individual with no distinction between injurious and noninjurious incidents with the proposition that the causal variables are the same.[60]

In other words, physical brutality is concerned with the force used, *not* with the end result. This makes sense because some people are more resistant to injury than others, so it would be unfair to ignore applications of excessive force simply because they do not result in injury to the suspect.

Verbal and Psychological Abuse.

The old idiom "Sticks and stones may break my bones, but words will never hurt me" couldn't be further from the truth. We know from some high-profile school shootings that words definitely hurt. Any child of a dysfunctional family, even one where physical abuse was never a problem, knows that communication problems and insults can take their toll. There is no reason why police officers should be excused when they engage in verbal abuse. When the things they say and do exclusive of the application of physical force go beyond standards of acceptability, they can be considered abusive. Such actions include everything from insulting suspects to denying them basic necessities during the course of an aggressive interrogation. As Carter observed,

> These are incidents where police officers verbally assail, ridicule, or harass individuals and/or place persons who are under the actual or constructive dominion of an officer in a situation where the individual's esteem and/or self-image [is] threatened or diminished. Also included in this category [verbal and psychological abuse] is the threat of physical harm under the supposition that a threat is psychologically coercive and instills fear in the average person.[61]

There is a fine line between psychological pressure and abuse. Consider police interrogation. Assume that a detective lies to a suspect by saying that an accomplice has implicated him. Is this abuse or just good detective work? On the one hand, it is not a verbal assault, ridicule, harassment, or even a threat of harm. It is, however, something that could instill fear. What if, to take it one step further, the detective *indirectly* threatened the suspect, perhaps by claiming that a jury would surely find him guilty? This type of deception is increasingly common, especially in the wake of the U.S. Supreme Court's famous *Miranda* decision. *Miranda* has, for better or for worse, made it more difficult for police to secure confessions. As such, they have had to resort to creative means of doing so, including deception.

Richard Leo, a researcher who has documented this trend, summarized one exchange between a detective and a suspect that illustrates the point:

> Detective: If you take this to a jury trial, they're going to hit you hard. They're going to slam you real hard. He's trying to lie to us, he must think we're stupid. Ladies and gentlemen of the jury, we have the evidence that shows he broke the window. He says "no, I didn't do it." Now do you want to be lenient with this guy?
>
> The suspect interjects: No, I'm not going to go for this one.
>
> Detective: Fine, we'll take it to a jury trial, but they're going to say he's guilty, he's guilty. You had a chance to tell the truth. They'll say: he had a chance. The sergeants talked to him and gave him an opportunity to explain how it happened, to give his side of the story, and what did he do? He lied. That's what he's going to say. He's going to say you lied. You had a chance to tell the truth but you lied. That's exactly what he's going to say.[62]

We are not suggesting that this exchange amounts to abuse, but at what point does deception go too far? This is not an easy question to answer. Gone are the days where psychological pressures were combined with physical force in a mix commonly called the **third degree**, but words alone can go pretty far toward directly harming an individual.

Other Rights Violations.

If an officer physically and unnecessarily abuses a suspect during an arrest, there is a clear rights violation that might enable the suspect to claim a violation of the Fourth Amendment right to be free from unreasonable seizures. Likewise, a detective who coerces a suspect into confessing or who violates the suspect's *Miranda* rights also commits a rights violation. Specifically, the detective violates the suspect's Fifth Amendment right to be free from compelled self-incrimination. There are other rights, however, that can also be violated

third degree
A formerly common coercive interrogation technique that combined psychological pressures with physical force.

without physical abuse and in the absence of verbal or psychological abuse. David Carter calls this **legal abuse**:

> This form of abuse occurs with greater frequency than the other categories. Legal abuse is defined as any violation of a person's constitutional, federally or state-protected rights. Although the individual may not suffer any apparent psychological damage in the strictest sense, an abuse of authority has nonetheless occurred. In all cases of physical abuse and in many cases of verbal abuse, there will also be a legal question. However, legal abuse can—and does—occur frequently without the other forms.[63]

What if, for example, a police officer pushes a suspect up against a brick wall before conducting a pat-down search, and the suspect bumps his head, causing it to bleed? The injury is by no means serious, and we would probably be remiss to call it brutality. A bystander may not even take notice. But what if the force is unnecessary? If it is not abuse and it is not psychological pressure, what can the suspect do? If the seizure in this case is not justified, what remedies are available? There are not too many, but this doesn't make the incident any more acceptable than a full-on physical assault.

Perspectives on the Frequency of Excessive Force

Excessive force and abuse of authority are the exception, not the norm, in police work. This may not have rung true before the civil rights era, when abuses were serious and commonplace, but much has happened since then. The courts have handed down important decisions clarifying constitutional protections. Police departments have changed their policies and training procedures in response to these court rulings and to the rising tide of litigation. The police professionalism movement has also served to rein in misbehavior and to screen out the unfit. There are, of course, exceptions, and just as we have seen police abuses in the past, we will see them again in the future. This raises an important question: Is there cause for concern? We will wrap this chapter up with some yes and no answers to this question.

Perspective 1: Brutality Is Still a Problem.
Human Rights Watch asserts that police corruption and brutality are anything but behind us. The organization's report, *Shielded from Justice: Police Brutality and Accountability in the United States*, although published nearly a decade ago, is still available on the organization's website.[64] The report discusses 14 large American cities and presents several noteworthy examples of police officers run amok. Its authors were very critical of big-city policing:

> Police officers engage in unjustified shootings, severe beatings, fatal chokings, and unnecessarily rough physical treatment in cities throughout the United States, while their police superiors, city officials, and the Justice Department fail to act decisively to restrain or penalize such acts or even to record the full magnitude of the problem. Habitually brutal officers—usually a small percentage of officers on a force—may be the subject of repeated complaints but are usually protected by their fellow officers and by the shoddiness of internal police investigations. A victim seeking redress faces obstacles at every point in the process, ranging from overt intimidation to the reluctance of local and federal prosecutors to take on brutality cases. Severe abuses persist because overwhelming barriers to accountability make it all too likely that officers who commit human rights violations escape due punishment to continue their abusive conduct.[65]

Human Rights Watch also criticized the lack of effective accountability mechanisms. While there may seem to be several methods of ensuring police accountability, most apply only in limited circumstances and are reserved for the most egregious of civil rights violations. According to *Shielded from Justice*,

> Victims of police brutality have many options for reporting abusive treatment by officers but little chance of seeing those officers punished or prosecuted. Citizen review agencies are often overwhelmed and understaffed; reporting an abuse to such an agency may, eventually, lead to an investigation, but it is unlikely to result in the offending officer's being appropriately punished. Filing an abuse complaint with a police department's internal affairs unit can be

legal abuse
Any violation of a person's constitutionally, federally, or state-protected rights.[v]

intimidating, and police departments' excessive secrecy usually means that the complainant learns nothing about any disciplinary action that may have been taken against the accused officer. Filing a civil lawsuit is an option for some victims, but success rates vary widely from city to city, and typically it is the municipality rather than the officer that is held financially responsible. Also, most victims of abuse correctly perceive that criminal prosecution, either locally or federally, is rarely an option—except in highly publicized cases. As a result, resentment and frustration often exacerbate the original abusive treatment. Because it is an open secret that oversight procedures for police abuse do not function effectively, many abuse victims do not even bother to pursue a complaint at all. This series of factors results in violent officers remaining on the job.

Perspective 2: Brutality Is the Exception. Human Rights Watch, like Amnesty International, has traditionally adopted a liberal political orientation. Since the vast majority of law enforcement officials tend to adopt a more conservative stance, it is no surprise that many disagree with the *Shielded from Justice* report. Although the incidents described in the report did happen, critics feel that Human Rights Watch may have exaggerated the extent of police brutality in the United States, giving the misleading impression that it is somehow rampant. One researcher has argued that it is impossible to put police brutality into context without some attention to how often officers are assaulted or killed. In other words, violent physical altercations between police and citizens are often a two-way street; officers will respond with force if they are attacked. While the following observation was made more than 10 years ago, its message still rings true today:

> While the FBI's civil rights division reports 2,450 complaints involving law enforcement officers in 1989, during the same period, 62,712 law enforcement officers were the victims of assaults. In 1990, there were more than 71,794 assaults against law enforcement officers nationwide, according to the Uniform Crime Reports. Sixty-five officers were killed.[66]

What, then, explains perceptions that police brutality is rampant? These are a few of the possible explanations:

1. The media are responsible. Media accounts of police violence unduly emphasize the exceptional and fail to report on the vast majority of police-citizen encounters where there is no physical altercation. In addition, some media have a liberal bias and seem intent on casting the police in an unfavorable light.

2. Reports of police brutality tell only part of the story. A person who files a complaint of excessive force, for instance, may be airing a contrived complaint against the police. For this reason, many reports of police brutality are found to be unsubstantiated.

3. Citizens and the media are not trained in the use of force and thus cannot discern what is and is not excessive. It may seem abusive to an observer to see a police officer hit a suspect with a nightstick, but the officer may have been trained to do just that under the circumstances.

Some critics have alleged that the media take isolated incidents and spin them into something much bigger. Consider one author's account of the Rodney King incident in Los Angeles:

> When a videotape of LAPD officers raining blows on King filled television screens across the country in March 1991, the news pages began to fill with claims that police brutality had long been rampant in Los Angeles. But police misconduct had not been an important issue for the city's premier news organization, the *Los Angeles Times*. In fact, the *Times* had marginalized the issue for years. Yet when the King video was released to a local television news station, the *Times* helped build the story into a serious crisis for LAPD chief Daryl Gates and played a major role in constructing the brutality problem that would drive Gates from office.[67]

In other words, the *Los Angeles Times* took what was arguably a shameful display of police brutality and made an agenda out of it. It used the incident to move brutality to center stage. In doing so, it gave the impression that the problem pervaded the LAPD when, in fact, the incident was quite isolated given the size of the department, which today employs nearly 10,000 sworn officers. Morale suffered for the whole organization following the Rodney King incident.

SUMMARY

- Use of force and excessive force are not the same thing. Police officers are authorized to use force when necessary, but excessive force is *unnecessary* force. Levels of force range from an officer's mere presence all the way up to deadly force. Use-of-force policies usually refer to a force continuum that describes the appropriate levels of force to use in response to the level of resistance or force used by the suspect. Force is applied infrequently. For example, force is used in less than 20 percent of custodial arrests, to say nothing of encounters that do not result in arrest. The use of excessive force may be symptomatic of problem police officers.

- Deadly force is force that is likely to cause death or significant bodily harm. Strict legal standards govern the use of deadly force. In general, it is unconstitutional for an officer to shoot an unarmed fleeing felon. Such shootings are permissible, however, if the officer has probable cause to believe that the suspect poses a serious risk of danger to others. Roughly 3,600 suspects are shot at by police officers each year. Of these, about 600 die from injuries they receive. Suicide by cop refers to situations in which individuals who are determined to end their lives engage in behavior that causes responding officers to resort to deadly force.

- Nondeadly force is the opposite of deadly force; it is force that is unlikely to cause death or significant bodily harm. Claims of excessive force are judged under the Fourth Amendment's reasonableness clause. Nondeadly force would be excessive if a "reasonable person" would feel it was unreasonable to employ such force in a given situation. Less-lethal weapons, including conducted energy devices, impact munitions, and pepper spray, have been developed as alternatives to (but not replacements for) deadly force. Indirect force, or actions by an officer that indirectly expose a suspect or an innocent bystander to potential injury but that do not involve the intentional application of direct physical force—as in the case of a high-speed automobile pursuit—was also discussed in this chapter.

- Excessive force falls into three general categories: (1) physical abuse, (2) verbal and psychological abuse, and (3) other rights violations. The latter includes constitutional rights violations that result from police actions besides abuse. An example would be a push. There are differing views on whether excessive force is still a problem today. Human Rights Watch and other liberal-minded groups feel that it is. Law enforcement groups and conservative thinkers feel that it is not.

COMING FULL CIRCLE

For Discussion

Return to the questions posed at the start of this chapter. Have any of your answers changed since you read the chapter? What portions of this chapter helped you answer these questions?

Writing Assignment

Using material from this chapter and additional resources, write a 500-word essay in response to one of the questions presented at the beginning of the chapter. Submit your essay to your instructor if asked to do so.

KEY TERMS AND NAMES

Christopher Commission
conducted energy device (CED)
deadly force
excessive force
excited delirium
force continuum
force factor

Graham v. Connor
impact munitions
indirect force
legal abuse
less-lethal weapon
nondeadly force
pepper spray

problem police officer
Rodney King
suicide by cop
Tennessee v. Garner
third degree
use of force
weapons continuum

WEB INTERACTIVITY

Visit the Bureau of Justice Statistics on the Web, and view the page "Use of Force by Police: Overview of National and Local Data," which can be found at http://www.ojp.gov/bjs/abstract/ufbponld.htm. The findings available through that page constitute a joint report by the National Institute of Justice and the Bureau of Justice Statistics. Read through the findings and summarize what they reveal about the extent and nature of police use of force and the circumstances under which force is applied. Submit your summary to your instructor if asked to do so.

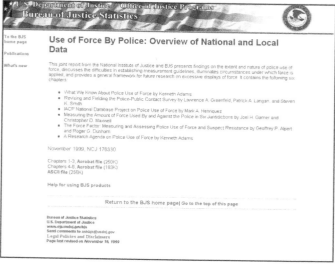

U.S. Department of Justice, Bureau of Justice Statistics

REVIEW QUESTIONS

1. What are the levels of police use of force that this chapter discusses? Which level is most commonly used by police officers?

2. What legal standards govern the use of deadly force by police officers?

3. What legal standards govern the use of nondeadly force by police officers? How might today's less-lethal weapons be effectively employed in place of deadly force?

4. Identify three types of excessive force, and provide examples of each. Do you believe that excessive force is a serious problem in policing today? Explain.

NOTES

i. Adapted from National Institute of Justice, *Use of force by police: Overview of national and local data* (Washington, DC: National Institute of Justice, 1999).

ii. International Association of Chiefs of Police, *Police use of force in America, 2001* (Alexandria, VA: International Association of Chiefs of Police, 2001), p. 1.

iii. S. Walker, G. P. Alpert, and D. J. Kenney, *Responding to the problem police officer: A national study of early warning systems* (Washington, DC: National Institute of Justice, 2000).

iv. National Institute of Justice, *Impact munitions use: Types, targets, effects* (Washington, DC: National Institute of Justice, 2004).

v. D. L. Carter, "Theoretical dimensions in the abuse of authority by police officers," in *Police deviance*, 3rd ed., ed. T. Barker and D. Carter (Cincinnati: Anderson, 1994), pp. 269–290.

1. K. Johnson, "Police brutality cases on rise since 9/11," *USA Today*, January 18, 2007, http://www.usatoday.com/news/nation/2007-12-17-Copmisconduct_N.htm (accessed August 16, 2008).

2. See, e.g., B. Taylor and others, *Cop crunch: Identifying strategies for dealing with the recruiting and hiring crisis in law enforcement* (Washington, DC: Police Executive Research Forum, 2006); A. Sharp, "Departmental divergences on marijuana use and new recruits," *Law and Order* 51 (2003): 80–84; S. F. Domash, "Who wants this job?" *Police* 26 (2002): 34–39; L. K. Decker and R. G. Huckabee, "Raising the age and education requirements for police officers: Will too many women and minority candidates be excluded?" *Policing: An International Journal of Police Strategies and Management* 25 (2002): 789–802; and T. Anderson and J. Kandel, "Wanted: Cop recruits," *Los Angeles Daily News*, http://www.lapd.com/article.aspx?&a=2737 (accessed January 16, 2008).

3. Some of the material in this section is adapted or derived from National Institute of Justice, *Use of force by police: Overview of national and local data* (Washington, DC: National Institute of Justice, 1999).

4. International Association of Chiefs of Police, *Police use of force in America, 2001* (Alexandria, VA: International Association of Chiefs of Police, 2001), p. 1.

5. K. Adams, "Measuring the prevalence of police use of force," in William A. Geller and Hans Toch eds., *Police violence: Understanding and controlling police abuse of force* (New Hartford: Yale University Press, 2005), pp. 52–93.

6. *Police use of force in America, 2001*, op. cit.

7. S. Walker, G. P. Alpert, and D. J. Kenney, *Responding to the problem police officer: A national study of early warning systems* (Washington, DC: National Institute of Justice, 2000).

8. Some of the wording in this paragraph is adapted from Human Rights Watch, "The Christopher Commission report," http://www.hrw.org/reports98/police/uspo73.htm (accessed March 30, 2002).

9. J. P. Crank, *Understanding police culture* (Cincinnati: Anderson, 1998), p. 78. See also J. H. Skolnick and J. J. Fyfe, *Above the law: Police and the excessive use of force* (New York: Free Press, 1993).

10. Allegan County (Michigan) Sheriff's Office, "Use of force," February 11, 2004, www.less-lethal.org/docs/30/Policy (accessed May 18, 2007).

11. G. P. Alpert and R. G. Dunham, *The force factor: Measuring police use of force relative to suspect resistance—A final report* (Washington, DC: National Institute of Justice, 2001).

12. M. R. Durose, E. L. Smith, and P. A. Langan, *Contacts between police and the public* (Washington, DC: Bureau of Justice Statistics, 2007).

13. J. H. Garner and C. D. Maxwell, "Measuring the amount of force used by and against the police in six jurisdictions," in *Use of force by police: Overview of national and local data* (Washington, DC: Bureau of Justice Statistics, 1999), p. 41. Full report available at http://www.ncjrs.gov/pdffiles1/nij/176330-2.pdf (accessed July 21, 2008).

14. Ibid., p. 30.

15. Durose, Smith, and Langan, *Contacts between police and the public*, p. 8.

16. S. W. Lathrop, "Reviewing use of force: A systematic approach," *FBI Law Enforcement Bulletin* (October 2000): 18.

17. *Black's law dictionary*, 6th ed. (St. Paul, MN: West Publishing Co., 1990), p. 398.

18. *Tennessee v. Garner*, 471 U.S. 1 (1985).

19. Ibid., p. 28.

20. V. E. Kappeler, *Critical issues in police civil liability*, 3rd ed. (Prospect Heights, IL: Waveland, 2001), p. 72.

21. *Hegarty v. Somerset County*, 848 F.Supp. 257 (1994), p. 257.

22. *Hemphill v. Schott*, 141 F.3d 412 (1998).

23. J. C. Hall, "FBI training on the new federal deadly force policy," *FBI Law Enforcement Bulletin* (April 1996): 25–32.

24. J. Fyfe, *Shots fired: An examination of New York City Police firearms discharges* (Ann Arbor, MI: University Microfilms, 1978).

25. J. Fyfe, "Blind justice? Police shootings in Memphis," paper presented at the annual meeting of the Academy of Criminal Justice Sciences, Philadelphia, March 1981.

26. See W. Geller, *Deadly force study guide*, Crime File Series (Washington, DC: National Institute of Justice, no date).

27. A. Cohen, "I've killed that man ten thousand times," *Police Magazine* (July 1980).

28. For more information, see Joe Auten, "When police shoot," *North Carolina Criminal Justice Today*, 4:4 (Summer 1986): 9–14.

29. Details for this story come from S. Slater, "Suicidal man killed by police fusillade," *Palm Beach Post*, March 11, 2005, p. 1A.

30. R. Stincelli, *Suicide by cop: Victims from both sides of the badge* (Folsom, CA: Interviews and Interrogations Institute, 2004).

31. Slater, "Suicidal man killed by police fusillade."

32. A. J. Pinizzotto, E. F. Davis, and C. E. Miller III, "Suicide by cop: Defining a devastating dilemma," *FBI Law Enforcement Bulletin* 74:2 (February 2005): 15.

33. "Ten percent of police shootings found to be 'suicide by cop,'" *Criminal Justice Newsletter*, September 1, 1998, pp. 1–2.

34. R. J. Homant and D. B. Kennedy, "Suicide by police: A proposed typology of law enforcement officer–assisted suicide," *Policing: An International Journal of Police Strategies and Management*, 23:3 (2000): 339–55.

35. A. L. Honig, "Police-assisted suicide: Identification, intervention, and investigation," *Police Chief*, October (2001): 89–93, quote on p. 93.

36. G. T. Williams, "Death by indifference," *Law and Order* (December 2003): 66–69, quote on p. 67.

37. *Graham v. Connor*, 490 U.S. 386, 396–397 (1989).

38. Ibid, p. 490.

39. Ibid.

40. D. W. Hayeslip and A. Preszler, *NIJ initiative on less-than-lethal weapons,* NIJ Research in Brief (Washington, DC: National Institute of Justice, 1993).

41. Ibid.

42. T. Farragher and D. Abel, "Postgame police projectile kills an Emerson student," *Boston Globe*, October 22, 2004, http://www.boston.com/sports/baseball/redsox/articles/2004/10/22/postgame_police_projectile_kills_an_emerson_student (accessed July 25, 2007).

43. Taser International, "Taser X26," http://www2.taser .com/products/law/Pages/TASERX26.aspx (accessed May 18, 2007).

44. Titan, "Sticky Shocker," http://www.jaycor.com/ web-content/eme_ltl_sticky.html (accessed May 18, 2007).

45. J. M. Cronin and J. A. Ederheimer, *Conducted energy devices: Development of standards for consistency and guidance* (Washington, DC: Police Executive Research Forum, 2006), http://www.policeforum.org/upload/ CED-Guidelines_414547688_2152007092436.pdf (accessed July 21, 2008).

46. Ibid., p. 23.

47. Amnesty International, *Amnesty International's continued concerns about Taser use* (New York: Amnesty International, 2006), http://web.amnesty.org/library/index/ engamr510302006 (accessed July 21, 2008).

48. Ibid.

49. National Institute of Justice, *Impact munitions use: Types, targets, effects* (Washington, DC: National Institute of Justice, 2004).

50. National Institute of Justice, *Department of defense nonlethal weapons and equipment review: A research guide for civil law enforcement and corrections* (Washington, DC: National Institute of Justice, 2004), http://www .ncjrs.gov/pdffiles1/nij/205293.pdf (accessed July 21, 2008).

51. National Institute of Justice, *Impact munitions use,* p. 3.

52. For some research in this area, see R. J. Kaminski, S. M. Edwards, and J. W. Johnson, "Assessing the incapacitative effects of pepper spray during resistive encounters with police," *Policing: An International Journal of Police Strategies and Management* 22 (1999): 7–29; and R. J. Kaminski, S. M. Edwards, and J. W. Johnson, "The deterrent effects of oleoresin capsicum on assaults against police: Testing the velcro-effect hypothesis," *Police Quarterly* 1 (1998): 1–20.

53. National Institute of Justice, *The effectiveness and safety of pepper spray: Research for practice* (Washington, DC: National Institute of Justice, 2003), http://www.ncjrs.gov/ pdffiles1/nij/195739.pdf (accessed July 21, 2008).

54. Ibid., p. 10.

55. Ibid., p. 11.

56. *Brower v. Inyo County,* 489 U.S. 593 (1989).

57. *County of Sacramento v. Lewis,* 523 U.S. 833 (1998).

58. *Scott v. Harris,* No. 05-1631 (2007).

59. See, e.g., http://www.cnn.com/2007/US/05/12/la.cops .ap/ index.html?eref=rss_us.

60. Cited in R. Roberg, K. Novak, and G. Cordner, *Police and society,* 3rd ed. (Los Angeles: Roxbury, 2005), p. 333. See also D. L. Carter, "Theoretical dimensions in the abuse of authority by police officers," in *Police deviance,* 3rd ed., ed. T. Barker and D. Carter, pp. 269–90 (Cincinnati: Anderson, 1994), p. 273.

61. Ibid.

62. R. A. Leo, "*Miranda's* revenge: Police interrogation as a confidence game," *Law and Society Review* 30 (1996): 259–88, quote on p. 278.

63. Cited in R. Roberg, K. Novak, and G. Cordner, *Police and society,* 3rd ed. (Los Angeles: Roxbury, 2005), p. 333. See also Carter, "Theoretical dimensions in the abuse of authority by police officers," p. 273.

64. See Human Rights Watch, *Shielded from justice: Police brutality and accountability in the United States,* http://www.hrw.org/reports98/police (accessed July 21, 2008).

65. Human Rights Watch, "Summary and Recommendations," *Shielded from justice: Police brutality and accountability in the United States, Summary and recommendations,* http:// www.hrw.org/reports98/police/uspo06.htm (accessed July 21, 2008).

66. L. B. Sulc, "Police brutality is not a widespread problem," in *Policing the police,* ed. P. Winters, pp. 79–85 (San Diego: Greenhaven, 1995), p. 80.

67. R. G. Lawrence, *The politics of force: Media and the construction of police brutality* (Berkeley: University of California Press, 2000), p. 62.

Technoprison

Technology and Prisons

Janice Joseph

INTRODUCTION

The great technological advances in the last 25 years are having an impact on prisons. Combined with the ever-present need to reduce prison cost and increase security, the use of technology is becoming prevalent in the penal system. Less than 15 years ago, there were perhaps very few computers, technology review committees, or technology products of any kind in prisons. However today, technology has emerged as a critical issue in prisons and is used in many aspects of prison life. Technological innovations have occurred in internal security with the use of advanced X-ray devices, closed-circuit monitoring, magnetic "friskers," and officer tracking/alerting systems. Drug and alcohol abuse testing packages, telemedicine, and videoconferencing all are products of advances in technology used in prison. This chapter examines several types of technological devices used in prisons and the issues surrounding their use. The chapter focuses primarily on biometrics, technology to detect illegal activities in prison, smart cards, electroshock devices, monitoring and surveillance technology, and teleconferencing technology.

BIOMETRIC SCANNING

Biometrics, which means "life measurement," is based on the principle that everyone has unique physical attributes that a computer can be programmed to recognize. It is a science of using a particular biological aspect of the human body (National Law

Enforcement and Corrections Technology Center 2000) and uses mathematical representations of those unique physical characteristics to identify an individual (Desmarais 2000; Wood 2001). Biometric technologies automate the process of identifying people based on their unique physical or behavioral characteristics such as the finger, hand, eye, face, and voice.

Biometric scanning is used for identification and verification of individuals. *Identification* is defined as the ability to recognize a person from among all those enrolled (all those whose biometric measurements have been collected in the database) and seeks to answer the question: Do I know who you are? It involves a one-compared-to-many match (or what is referred to as a "cold search"). Biometrics is also used for *verification,* which involves the authentication of a person's claimed identity from his previously enrolled pattern. Verification seeks to answer the question: Are you who you claim to be? and involves a one-to-one match (see Campbell, Alyea, and Dunn 1996; Miller 1996). In order to accomplish this, the system has to (1) receive biometric samples from a candidate/user; (2) extract biometric features from the sample; (3) compare the sample from the candidate with stored template(s) from known individual(s); and (4) indicate identification or verification results (Idex 2000).

There are two phases in the system; one is the enrollment phase, and the other is the verification phase. During the enrollment phase, individuals submit a "live sample" of their biometric information (e.g., the eyes, face, or fingerprints), which is scanned and stored in a database along with the subject's name and any other identification information. During the verification phase, individuals present their biometric information, and the recognition system compares the current scan with the sample stored in the database. While biometric technologies come in many forms, the procedure for storing and retrieving biometric information is uniform (Isaacs 2002a). Biometric scanning involves the scanning of the fingers, eye, hand, and face.

Finger Scanning

Finger-scan technology is the oldest and most prominent biometric authentication technology used by millions of people worldwide. It measures the unique, complex swirls on a person's fingertip. The swirls are characterized and produced as a template requiring from 250 to 1,000 bytes. What is stored is not a full fingerprint but a small amount of data derived from the fingerprint's unique patterns (Chandrasekaran 1997). Finger-scanning extracts certain characteristics of the image into templates known as "minutiae" that are unique to each finger. Optical, silicon, and ultrasound are mechanisms that are currently used to capture the fingerprint image with sufficient detail and resolution (Finger-Scan.com 1999). After the fingerprints are scanned by the reader, templates are recorded and compared with the templates that are stored on the databases (ZDNet 1999). The County of Los Angeles and Middlesex County in Massachusetts use finger scanning (Esser 2000). The Pierce County Sheriff's Department uses finger-scanning identification systems made by Tacoma, Washington-based Sagem Morpho to verify inmates upon release (Issac 2002b). Overall, the biometric industry made $196 million in 2000, with finger imaging being the most popular tool (Pries 2001).

Eye Scanning

Eye scanning is probably the fastest growing area of biometric research because of its promise for high scan accuracy. There are two types of eye scanning: retinal scanning and iris scanning.

Retinal scans examine the blood vessel patterns of the retina, the nerve tissue lining the inside of the eye that is sensitive to light. An infrared light source is used to illuminate the retina of the eye. The image of the enhanced blood vessel pattern of the retina is analyzed for characteristic points. A retinal scan can produce almost the same volume of data as a fingerprint image analysis. By emitting a beam of incandescent light that bounces off the person's retina and returns to the scanner, a retinal scanning system quickly maps the eye's blood vessel pattern and records it into an easily retrievable digitized database (Ritter 1999; Tierney 1995).

While retinal scanning uses lasers that focus on the back of the eye, iris scanning zooms in on the front. Iris scans digitally process, record, and compare the light and dark patterns in the iris's flecks and rings, something akin to a human bar code. Iris scanning works by capturing the image of a person's iris; using a video conferencing camera; and establishing a 512-byte code of the image's unique characteristics (McManus 1996). Iris recognition stands out as perhaps the most "hygienic" of the biometric technologies in that no part of the user's body has to touch anything to operate the system. A retinal scan can produce almost the same volume of data as a fingerprint image analysis. Along with iris recognition technology, iris scan is perhaps the most accurate and reliable biometric technology (Woodward 1997).

Iris recognition gives prison officials absolute assurance that the right inmate is being released and eliminates the risk of human error in matching a face with photograph identification. In addition, the iris recognition system lets the prison administration determine if a new inmate was previously incarcerated there under a different name. The Sarasota County Detention Center in Florida uses iris scanning to prevent former prisoners from visiting former inmate friends (National Law Enforcement and Corrections Technology Center 2000). The Lancaster County Prison and the York County Prison in Pennsylvania also use iris scanning to verify prisoners before they are released from prison for routine events such as court appearances and medical visits. There are currently 30 county prisons and 10 state prisons using iris scanning. Inmates are verified by iris recognition before they are released from prison at the end of their sentences and for routine events such as court appearances and medical visits (Center for Criminal Justice Technology Newsletter 2001; Pries 2001).

Hand Scanning/Hand Geometry

With hand geometry, the biometric hand unit employs a miniaturized camera to capture a digital template of the back of the individual's hand. These photographs analyze the size, shape, width, thickness, and surface of the hand. In effect, a digital map of the outline of a person's hand is created. The biometric hand readers simultaneously analyze over 31,000 points and instantaneously record over 90 separate measurements of an individual's hand. The results are converted into a less than 10-byte code and are stored in the system's memory for future comparisons (Chandrasekaran 1997; Zunkel 1998).

Hand scanning/geometry has been used to identify inmates, employees, and visitors to correctional facilities. The Federal Bureau of Prisons, for example, uses hand geometry to verify the identity of visitors and staff members in order to avoid mistaken identifications. Inmates use it for access to the cafeteria, recreation, lounge, and hospital. In San Antonio, Texas, hand geometry helps to prevent escape attempts. The Florida Department of Corrections currently also utilizes hand scanning in 19 of its facilities (The Corrections Connection 2001).

Facial Recognition

The facial recognition technique is one of the fastest growing areas. It measures the peaks and valleys of the face, such as the tip of the nose and the depth of the eye sockets, which are known as nodal points—the human face has 80 nodal points, only 14–22 are needed for recognition—concentrating on the inner region, which runs from temple to temple and just over the lip. The scan also reads the heat pattern around the eyes and cheeks; and the ability to scan the dimensions of an individual's head. It then comes up with a face print (National Law Enforcement and Corrections Technology Center 2000). It also measures such characteristics as the distance between facial features (from pupil to pupil, for instance) or the dimensions of the features themselves (such as the width of the mouth). Facial recognition software uses a camera attached to personal computer to capture and map key identifying features (ZDNet 1999). In addition to photographs, the system records other identifying attributes such as scars, tattoos, and gang insignia. Identification cards are produced for department employees, inmates, and offenders, and face-recognition technology is utilized for positive identification. The advantage of the facial recognition system is that it can work with people still at a distance. As one approaches, the system could recognize the face and activate the system, such as turning on a computer or unlocking a door stages (Desmarais 2000).

The Facial Recognition Vendor 2000 (FRVT 2000) was tested at a correctional facility in Prince George's County, Maryland, to assist correctional officers in their decision to unlock an electronically controlled door providing access to the facility (Bone and Crumbacker 2001). In 1998, the Wisconsin department of corrections awarded Viisage Technology, Incorporated, a $1.4 million contract to develop a biometric facial identification system for the State's prison system. The facial recognition system is used in more than 44 locations throughout the State (Colatosti 1998). The Ohio Department of Rehabilitation and Corrections also uses facial recognition to identify inmates (Prison Talk Online, 2004).

ILLEGAL ACTIVITIES DETECTION TECHNOLOGY

To prevent illegal activities in prisons, manufacturers have developed new detection technologies. These include technologies to detect illegal drugs, concealed weapons, pulse radar, and the number of heartbeats in vehicles.

Illegal Drugs

Attempts to control the influx of drugs entering prison facilities have ranged from closed-circuit television in visiting areas to an increased use of drug dogs and pat- or rub-down searches of visitors. Unfortunately, a large amount of controlled substances continue to penetrate many prisons. So today, scanners such as Ion Track Instruments' ITEMISER and VaporTracer are used to detect traces of microscopic particles associated with 40 different types of drugs. Generally, drug detection systems are categorized as trace detectors or bulk detectors. Bulk detectors are typically much larger, less mobile, and less sensitive than trace detectors. Most trace detection systems in use today are based on ion mobility spectrometry (IMS), which is a highly portable equipment and with capabilities that, until recently, were confined to the laboratory. Originally developed for medical imaging and diagnosis, trace detectors can determine if items have been in the presence of drugs or touched by people who have been using, handling, or hiding drugs. Another use for trace detection is in the nonintrusive inspection of cargo and containers. Drug residue on the exterior or vapors seeping from the interior can be detected to signal inspectors that an enclosure needs further scrutiny. Trace detectors operate in two basic modes: vapor detection and particle detection and can use a "wipe and spray" method to detect drug residue (Wright and Butler 2001).

Drug detection systems are used on both prisoners and visitors. In most situations, the scanner is positioned at the security checkpoint where the visitors' access into the prison is located. Before entry into visiting rooms is permitted, visitors can be screened for controlled substances. Typically, if traces of drugs are found on the visitor, either entry is refused into the visiting area or the visitor is subjected to further search procedures before being permitted entry (Ion Track 2002). Some prisons have chosen to use trace detection technology for searching inmates' cells for drugs. Individual cells can be checked and analyzed on location with the portable, battery-operated VaporTracer or by running the ITEMISER from a portable power supply, and personal items, such as furniture and virtually any surface, can be checked for drugs. Because some drugs can easily be hidden in or on a letter or envelope, contraband screening of all incoming mail is essential. The prisons also scan multiple letters and parcels for drugs in just seconds. If a detection is made, the letter or parcel is opened and searched according to that prison's standard procedures. The machine can also search for particles that are gathered on paper used to wipe hands or clothing or through a special vacuum (Bucsko 2001).

The Department of Corrections in Pennsylvania purchased 3 ion scanners and 15 ITEMISERS for the prisons. In 1998, 22,074 visitors were scanned, and 734 were found to be carrying drugs (Caramanis 1999). The Federal Bureau of Prison uses the explosive/drug detectors, from IonTrack Instruments, which can change from detecting narcotics to explosives in 10 seconds (Gaseau 1999). California, a leader in particle-sniffing technologies, has a system that requires inmates and visitors to wipe their hands on a tissue, which is then inserted into an analyzer sensitive to trace amounts of narcotics in parts per trillion. The machine can not only indicate what narcotic the inmate has but also the quantity of that narcotic. California has also been using the Rapidscan 500 in its prisons to detect contraband in packages. It breaks down the molecular structure of what is inside a package and when it finds the drug, it circles it on the monitor and tells the operator it has found the preprogrammed substance (Wired News 1997).

Concealed Weapons

Inmates can easily hide metallic objects such as tweezers, lighters, safety pins, needles, and other items in orifices on their bodies, but the "Big BOSS" (Body Orifice Scanning System), which is a chair that scans and detects metallic objects hidden on or in the body, has been improving security in Arizona's prisons. The chair, which costs $6,500, scans an inmate's head, lower digestive tract, groin, rectum area, and feet, and sounds an alarm if any foreign objects are detected. Arizona purchased five 5 of these chairs and with this system Arizona caught 17 inmates hiding weapons on their bodies. The problem is that the machine cannot be used for extended periods of time so it has to be shut down and be allowed to cool off before resuming operation. Physical contact, however, is still required to find nonmetallic foreign objects that inmates hide from officers (*Directions* 2001; Lau 2001).

Heartbeat Detectors

Perhaps one of the weakest security links in any prison has always been the sally port where trucks unload their supplies and where trash and laundry are taken out of the facility. Over the years inmates have hidden in loads of trash, old produce, laundry—any possible container that might be exiting the facility. Oak Ridge National Laboratory has produced sound detectors or seismometers that count the number of heartbeats in service vehicles as they leave the prison, reducing the need for routine searches. Likewise the Springfield, Virginia Ensco Incorporation and Houston's Geo Vox Security have also developed sensors that can detect the heartbeats of those hiding inside cars or trucks at prisons and which use magnets and tiny weights to sense minute vibrations. The Advanced Vehicle Interrogation and Notification System (AVIAN)—being marketed by Geo Vox Security—also works by identifying the shock wave generated by the beating heart, which couples to any surface the body touches. A potential escapee can be identified in less than 2 minutes after two specialized AVIAN sensors are placed on the vehicle. Prisons can buy the system for $50,000 or lease it for $1,000 per month. The average cost of locating and capturing an escaped inmate is estimated at $750,000 (deGroot 1997). About 6 of the 25 state prisons in Pennsylvania use the Geovox system to detect escapees before vehicles leave the prison, and one state prison in New Jersey has installed the system developed by Ensco. These devices are also now in use at other facilities, most notably at Riverbend Maximum Security Institution in Nashville, Tennessee, where four inmates escaped in a hidden compartment in a flatbed truck several years ago (Weed 2001).

Pulsed Radar

Special Technologies Laboratories has created a new technological device, GPR-X—with GPR standing for ground penetrating radar, and X indicating the new generation of technology that GPR represents. The device transmits energy into the ground, and by measuring the time it takes for that energy to be reflected, it can detect changes in ground material. GPR can, therefore, detect contraband buried in the recreation yard, for instance, or a tunnel being built under the prison (deGroot 1997).

Contraband Cellular Phones

Cellular phones have become the latest epidemic in prison contraband, posing a danger that extends beyond prison walls. Cellular phones have become more valuable in prison than drugs or other contraband. They have become the new prison cash because the inmates can sell minutes or cellular phone use to other inmates. As cellular phones become smaller, it has become very easy to smuggle them inside correctional facilities and easier for inmates to continue their criminal activities, harass victims, or transmit photographs of information. Prisoners are willing to pay between $350 and $600 to have a phone smuggled into prison. The cellular phones are smuggled into the prison inside mayonnaise jars, hidden in compost piles, shoved into the soles of shoes, and slipped inside hollowed-out blocks of cheese. More importantly, corrupt correctional officers sometimes smuggle cellular phones into the prison for the inmates. In Texas, for example, a correctional officer was charged with trying to smuggle a cell phone and drugs into a prison. In Philadelphia, a sweep of three city jails in 2002 netted more than 60 phones. New Jersey, Maryland, and Tennessee are having similar problems with cellular phones in prison. At least three states—Texas, Pennsylvania, and Iowa—have made it a crime for inmates to possess cell phones (Cellular-news 2006; Demsky 2005; Sullivan 2006).

Equipment that would jam or intercept cell phones also would interfere with the signals needed by prison personnel, so prison officials are using a technological device that can pinpoint cell phone activity within a small area, like a single pod inside a prison. The GEO Group Inc., the second largest private prison management company in the United States has created a high-tech equipment for detecting and locating hidden contraband cellular phones (even if the phone is not transmitting or even turned off). The equipment, the ORION Non-Linear Junction Detector (NLJD) can respond to electronic components, allowing the user to detect and locate electronic items (such as hidden cellular phones). Previously correction institutions were limited to physical searches and this technology makes detection of contraband easy. Florida and Pennsylvania have been using this system (Cellular-news 2006).

Smart Card

A smart card is a standard-sized plastic card with an embedded computer microchip containing a central processing unit (CPU) and up to 8K bytes of electronic, updatable memory. It is a photo identification card containing embedded computer chips that electronically store inmates' personal identification and medical information. Smart card technology has been emerging over the past two decades and there are now millions in circulation. The card stores all types of information about an inmate, including his or her movement, medical care, commissary purchases, treatment needs and meals eaten. They can also provide access to restricted areas and some are service-related, like telephone calling cards or those that deduct purchases from a holder's account. Some can be used for identification purposes only, while others enable remote payment, money access, and information exchange via computer, telephone, or television "set-top boxes" (Jackson 1998a).

Australia is believed to be the first country in the world to use smart card technology as an integral part of the operation of a prison—providing greater security, efficiency and flexibility. Fujitsu Australia's SmartCity smart card system has been incorporated throughout Western Australia's new Acacia Prison, the most advanced medium security prison in the world. The smart cards allow prison officers to monitor the movements of individual prisoners within the jail and also replace cash inside the institution. The cards are used to keep two prisoners from having any contact by restricting them from moving into the same area of the prison at the same time. Smart card also increases security considerably during prisoner transfers. Money that prisoners earn by working is credited to their smart card, and they use the card to purchase snacks, cigarettes, toiletries, magazines, or pay for telephone calls, and so forth (Fujitsu Australia Limited 2001).

Smart-card technology is still in its infancy and they are used in prison primarily to dispense medication in United States. When an inmate's smart card is inserted into a reader, that inmate's medication history is displayed on a computer screen. Any administration of medicine is entered into the record electronically, including the date and time of the dispensation—information that can be retrieved at any time by the institution's medical staff (Gaseau 1999).

The Ohio Department of Rehabilitation and Correction (ODRC) has conducted a project which was funded by the National Institute of Justice to manage inmate information with a "smart card." Initially, the cards were used to track the medication activity of 2,300 inmates in a medium-security men's facility. In this system, the inmate's photo is electronically stored, indicating who the inmate is and what his inmate number is. When an inmate needs service, such as the library, he/she puts the card into a reader that scans the information on the microchip contained in the card. These smart cards will be integrated with the ODRC's electronic photo-imaging system, so that when the card is used, it will automatically bring up a picture of the inmate on a computer screen. In the future, the smart card will be a multiuse card that will be used in prison to control many aspects of prison life. Inmate classification, medical and mental health information, education status and parole information will be stored on the microchip (Justice Technology Information Network 1998).

ELECTRO-SHOCK DEVICES

Stun Belt

The stun belt is an electronic shocking device secured to a person's waist and is available in two styles: a one-size-fits-all minimal-security belt (a slim version designed for low visibility in courts) and the high-security transport belt, complete with wrist restraints. Both come attached to a 9-volt battery. When activated, the stun belt shocks its wearer for 8 seconds, with 3–4 milliamps and 50,000 volts of stun power. Guards like it because they do not have to get near prisoners who wear the belt. They can set off the 8-second, 50,000-volt stun from as far away as 300 feet. It shocks the left kidney, blood channels, and nerve pathways.

Stun Tech, manufacturer of the stun belt, recommends the belt as a psychological tool, an effective deterrent for potentially unruly inmates, and a humane alternative to guns or nightsticks. More than 100 county agencies have employed the belt for prisoner transport, courtroom appearances, and medical appointments (Schulz 1999; Yeoman 2000).

In 1995, the use of stun belts was reported to be illegal in Illinois, Hawaii, New Jersey, New York, Michigan, Massachusetts, and Rhode Island and some municipalities. However, these shock devices have been adopted by at least 19 state prison systems including Oklahoma, Arizona, Florida, Wisconsin, and Iowa, as well as by the federal government. They are currently used in both medium- and high-security prisons; on chain gangs, during prisoner transport including transport to and from medical facilities; and on prisoners deemed a "security risk" during court appearances. At Red Onion State Prison in Virginia, 10 inmates were required to wear the belts while meeting with an attorney investigating charges of human rights violations; one prisoner who refused to wear the device was barred from speaking to the lawyer. There have been few tests run to determine the safety of stun belts; and these tests that have been conducted have led to highly suspect and vague results (Schulz 1999; Yeoman 2000).

Electric-Stun/Lethal Fences

Perhaps the largest contributor to keeping inmates locked up has been the introduction of electric fences, also known as *lethal fences*. These fences are erected around the perimeter of the facility and often carry about 10,000 volts of electricity, more than enough to take a human life. They are usually positioned between double perimeter fences and the electrified fence serves as an unmanned lethal barriers or deterrents. The fences usually consist of galvanized posts spaced approximately 30 feet apart supporting wires powered with high voltage and are located approximately 10 feet from the outer perimeter fence and approximately 15 feet from the inner perimeter field. Any movement of the wire or variation in the current will trigger an alarm and a lethal jolt. These fences would shock would-be escapees with a lethal dose of 5,000 volts, or more than double the jolt of an electric chair. Guards in the command center can watch a graphic representation of the fenced perimeter that instantly pinpoints any change in current; the same system also sends a message to the watch commander's beeper in the event of an incident (Jackson 1998a).

In 1992, California began installing the first electric fences around its prisons. At the time, skeptical industry observers said the system would never work and would never be widely accepted in the field. Today, all of California's 33 prisons are surrounded by electric fencing, and several other states have installed them as well (deGroot 1997). Nevada, Colorado, Missouri, Wisconsin, Arkansas, Alabama, Arizona, Pennsylvania, Illinois, and the federal government use this type of fencing (Brustad 2001; Scolforo 2005).

Verichip

A company in Florida called Applied Digital Systems has marketed the "Verichip," which is the size of a grain of rice and can be embedded beneath a person's skin. The information on this chip could include a person's medical records, banking records, how much the person owes on his or her mortgage, credit cards, and other personal loans. It could also be used to track your activities anywhere in the world. It would replace all of a person's present forms of identification such as passport, driver's license, social security, and credit/debit cards. The chip would also include data on your family history, address, occupation, criminal record, income tax information, and so forth. The chip is powered electromagnetically through muscle movement or can be activated by an outside monitoring facility. One will not be able to withdraw money from the bank without it, receive benefits from the government without it, buy or sell anything without it. This is one of the dangers of the chip; once a person has it, the person can be controlled by someone else. The technology is used in some U.S. prisons where prisoners have a chip implanted in their bodies; when they become violent, the guard simply pushes a button on a remote control and paralyses the prisoner (The Ultimate Scam 2002).

MONITORING AND SURVEILLANCE TECHNOLOGY

Perimeter Security Control Devices

A prison is only as secure as its perimeter. The basic role of a perimeter security system is fourfold: deter, detect, document, and deny/delay any intrusion of the protected area or facility. Six factors affect the probability of detection of most surveillance sensors, although to varying degrees. These are (1) the amount and pattern of emitted energy, (2) the size of the object, (3) distance to the object, (4) speed of the object, (5) direction of movement, and (6) reflection and absorption characteristics of the energy waves by the intruder and the environment (e.g., open or wooded area, or shrubbery) (Jackson 1998b). Electronic sensors monitor the tension in barbed-wire barricades, seismometers detect any suspicious shaking of chain-link fences, and microwave beams pick up motion in the deserted areas between fences. A positive signal from any of the systems sounds an alarm, swings surveillance cameras to the appropriate spot, and sets off warnings in a guard booth and the perimeter patrol car. A few of the newest prisons, including the Toledo Correctional Institution in Ohio, use "smart" perimeters that can eliminate the need for staffed watchtowers (Weed 2001).

Control of Inmate Movement Inside Prison

The number of inmates in the United States has doubled over the past decade to nearly 2 million, so it has become difficult to monitor prisoners. Prisoners can be fitted with tamper-proof transmitter wristbands that broadcast a unique serial number via radio frequency every 2 seconds. Antennas throughout the prison pick up the signals and pass the data via a local area network to a computer. This system can alert a monitor when a prisoner gets dangerously close to the perimeter fence or when an inmate does not return from a furlough on time; it can even tag gang members and notify guards when rival gang members get too close to each other (prison employees also carry transmitters with panic buttons) (Roberti 2002). Prisons in Arizona and Texas have tested a similar system developed by Motorola in which prisoners and officers wear bracelets that transmit personal radio IDs (PRI). Correctional facilities in California, Michigan, Illinois, and Ohio have implemented the Alanco's TSI PRISM(TM) RFID officer safety and inmate management system. Under this system, every inmate is issued a bracelet when he or she is processed. The bracelet, which is approximately the size of a divers' watch, includes an active RFID tag as well as a bar code if the correctional system.

With RFID tags worn by inmates and RFID readers deployed throughout the prison. This allows correctional officers to continuously monitor and track the location and movement of approximately inmates. Receivers pick up the signals and relay them to a computer that displays everyone's exact location in the prison. The TSI's wristbands for inmates transmit signals every two seconds to a battery of antennas mounted in the prison facility. With this PRI, each prisoner can be seen on a map of the prison as a red dot, and each officer as a blue dot. A single officer monitoring the display can keep track of thousands of prisoners. The computer can alert a guard if a dangerous prisoner comes into his area, or raise an alarm if someone is out of place. It can also track two prisoners who hate each other and selectively block access through certain checkpoints to make sure they never come in contact. The computer can also keep a log of everyone's movements, aiding investigations of assaults or other crimes. The device also has a sensor that is designed to set off an alarm in 15 seconds if it loses contact to skin (Swedberg 2005).

VIDEO TELECONFERENCING

The uses of teleconferencing and videoconferencing have become common in prison. The individuals can see and talk to one another from any place around the world with picture and audio as clear as if we were having a face-to-face conversation. This tool is now readily available to all criminal justice agencies. Teleconferencing allows prisoners more virtual contact with the outside world and can be used in court hearings, prison visits, and telemedicine.

Video Court Appearances/Video Arraignment

Videoconferencing is used in prisons for routine court hearings, thus reducing the number of inmates transferred out for their hearing. This basically enables prisoners to be arraigned without physically being present in a courtroom or allows witnesses from across the country to testify electronically, thus completing cases faster. Also, with the video technology, an inmate with an open warrant from a surrounding community is placed on the videoconferencing list. The judge can recall or resolve the warrant, appoint counsel, schedule a trial date, or resolve the case all in one day. States like Montana and Wisconsin have recently begun videoconferencing initial court appearances for inmates (The Associated Press State & Local Wire 2002; Miller 2002). The use of videoconferencing in prisoner civil rights proceedings was authorized by Congress in the Prison Litigation Reform Act. The Judicial Conference also has encouraged courts to use videoconferencing in certain proceedings, and currently 100 federal court sites make use of the technology (The Third Branch 2001).

The cost for commercial packages for video teleconferencing can run as high as $90,000 (Gaseau 1999). However, the Hampden County, Massachusetts, Correctional Center bought its own equipment and used existing fiber optics to run the technology at a cost between $7,000 and $10,000 per site. The Eastern District of Texas and the Central District of Illinois were among the first courts to receive funding for videoconferencing for court hearings for prisoners (The Third Branch 2001).

The Conference Court Administration and Case Management Committee reviewed the merits of using videoconferencing in court proceedings and found that a potential for savings in personnel time and travel costs existed and this can outweigh the cost of purchase and operation of videoconferencing systems when used in prisoner civil rights proceedings. In support of this observation, the Committee, in collaboration with the Conference Automation and Technology Committee, established the Prisoner Civil Rights Videoconferencing Project, which analyzed courts' use of videoconferencing technology for prisoner proceedings. Between 1996 and 2001, approximately 58 videoconferencing sites within the district courts were funded under this project (The Third Branch 2001).

Prison Visits/Video Visiting

Inmate visitation is required in all correctional agencies but it can be difficult to manage. One facility in Colorado, however, is working on a way to automate and simplify the process. The automated visitation system, created by the Arapahoe County, Colorado, Detention Facility and AMA Technologies, allows visitors to call and schedule dates and times for visits, using an identification (ID) number (the last four digits of the photo ID that will be presented upon arrival). This system is integrated with a television system at the facility. When the visitor arrives at the facility at the scheduled time, he or she enters by a separate entrance into a visitor reception center and sits at a 27-inch interactive screen to visit with the inmate, who will sit at one of 80 video stations throughout the facility. Inmates in the infirmary who once had to be transported to booking for a visitation can sit in their beds and have visitation directly from the infirmary (Gaseau 1999). A similar situation exists in Arizona, where inmates can remain in their housing units and visit their relatives and friends who are located in the visiting room (Villa 2005). Friends and family can avoid standing in line by scheduling videoconferences with inmates. Because inmates remain in their housing units, this form of video visitation cuts down on movement in the prison, thereby reducing the number of assaults and eliminating the opportunities for contraband to be smuggled into prison.

Telemedicine

 Telemedicine is one of the newest and most exciting advances in medicine. The process allows a doctor in the prison to examine the patient with a stethoscope or performs an electrocardiogram, and the results are then relayed over the Internet to a remote medical specialist who sends back a diagnosis. It could provide prisoners with adequate, cost-effective health care in the future. Taking a prisoner to a specialist outside the prison can pose a danger to the correctional officers and the community by giving the prisoner an opportunity to escape. Telemedicine allows physicians to consult with on-site medical personnel through videoconferencing and compatible medical devices such as medical microcameras. Telemedicine also helps prisons comply with a court order mandating standardized and uniform health care for inmates. Georgia, Michigan, Ohio, Arizona, and Texas are the major states that are providing telemedicine in the field of corrections (The Third Branch 2001).

According to a report prepared by Abt Associates (1999) and funded by the National Institute of Justice (NIJ), prisons that use telemedicine systems instead of conventional care could save approximately $102 per specialist encounter. In addition, telemedicine can improve the quality of care available to prisoners by reducing the waiting time between referral and consultation with specialists and by increasing access to distant physicians who specialize in prison health care (Weed 2001).

ISSUES REGARDING THE USE OF TECHNOLOGY

Usefulness

Many of these technological devices are very useful to the operation of the prison system. They save time and money. The smart card system, for example, can be used to manage to process inmate data at a fast rate to dispense medication. While it could take one minute per patient to dispense medication to patients, the smart card can reduce the time for this process to a few seconds. Electric perimeter fences in California eliminated the need for 24-hour watchtower surveillance, thus saving about $32 million per year, about $1 million per prison. Heartbeat sensors used to detect inmates can be cost effective and can identify an escapee in less than two minutes after two specialized AVIAN sensors are placed on the vehicle. Prisons can buy the system for $50,000 or lease it for $1,000 per month. This may seem high, but the average cost of locating and capturing an escaped inmate is estimated at $750,000 (deGroot 1997). Pennsylvania's Luzerne County has saved $120,000 in six months on court transportation, manpower, and cost on local correctional facility because of their innovative use of teleconferencing (Weiss 2003). The benefits of telemedicine are obvious: (1) travel costs are reduced dramatically because the number of vans needed to transport inmates is substantially reduced and (2) through telemedicine, dozens of medical specialists serve several inmates right into a prison (Weed 2001).

Many of these technological devices used in prison can enhance the effectiveness and efficiency of institutional security. Explosive/drug detectors from Ion Track Instruments can reduce contraband, and field-monitoring devices can prevent inmates from entering restricted areas in the prison. According to Stewart (2000) "we are beginning to see the application of technology widely influencing virtually every aspect of institutional security. In some respects, this influence can be described as a revolution in security innovation" (p. 8). Telemedicine's most valuable asset may be its ability to minimize security risks associated with taking inmates outside of a corrections facility for health care (Weed 2001).

Technoprison

Despite the usefulness of technological devices in prisons, there are some serious problems with their use. These include constitutional issues, reliability, cost, and the inhumane nature of these devices.

CONSTITUTIONAL ISSUES

One of the most controversial legal issues regarding technology and prisons is the right to privacy. Some of these technological devices, for example, retina and iris and hand geometry biometrics can be invasive and may capture information about a person's health and medical history. Recent scientific research suggests that finger imaging might also disclose sensitive medical information about a person. There is a relationship between an uncommon fingerprint pattern, known as a digital arch, and a medical disorder called chronic, intestinal pseudo-obstruction (CIP) that affects 50,000 people nationwide. In addition, Turner syndrome, Klinefelter syndrome, and certain nonchromosomal disorders, such as leukemia, breast cancer, and Rubella syndrome, may cause certain unusual fingerprint patterns (see Chen 1988).

The availability of medical and other types of personal information on individuals whether they are inmates, employees, or visitors who are subjected to biometrics raises concern about the right to privacy. It is quite possible that personal information on individuals stored in correctional databases for the purposes of identification and verification could be disseminated to other sources, since a biometric system in one correctional facility may be connected with other databases in the correctional system. Once in use, therefore, a biometric system in a prison may not be confined to its original purpose. The more people have access to a database, the less likely that this information will remain private.

The right to privacy becomes a bigger issue when biometrics is used in conjunction with smart cards. Smart cards, which may contain data, such as medical, financial, health history, and criminal record, can be stolen or lost. Unauthorized individuals who possess lost or stolen smart cards and have means to decrypt the biometric data could discover information that are very personal to the card owners (Esser 2000).

Another constitutional issue relates to the Eighth Amendment, concerning cruel and unusual punishment. There is a great deal of criticism of the use of electroshock devices in prisons as their use in prison is viewed as a violation of the Eighth Amendment. Stun belts, which have two metal prongs positioned just above the left kidney, leave welts that can take up to six months to heal, and the belt could cause fatalities. Like the stun belt, the taser, and the stun gun, the shield is an electronic shocking device. Guards frequently use the shield when removing prisoners from their cells, but the death of a Texas corrections officer who suffered a heart attack shortly after receiving a shock from an electric shield similar in design to the stun belt raises serious questions about the belt's safety. As part of the training, Officer Landis was required to endure two 45,000-volt shocks, but on December 1, 1995, something went terribly wrong. Shortly after the second shock, Landis collapsed and died. Although the maker of the shield denied that it had killed

Landis, the Coryell County justice of the peace who conducted an inquiry into Landis's death reported that Landis's autopsy showed that he died as a result of cardiac dirhythmia due to coronary blockage following electric shock by an electronic stun shield. The electric shock threw his heart into a different rhythmic beat, causing him to die. The Texas Department of Criminal Justice, which had used the shields to subdue prisoners since September 1995 immediately suspended their use (Cusac 1996; Roberti 2002). In another incident in Virginia, the state used a stun gun repeatedly to shock a 50-year-old prisoner, Lawrence James Frazier, who was already in the infirmary because of his diabetes. Frazier lapsed into a coma and died five days later. Although the Virginia Department of Corrections later claimed that a "medical study" proved that the use of the stun gun did not cause Frazier's death, the study was actually only a review of policies and procedures and did not include an examination of the body or forensic reports (Amnesty International 2000).

The electric/lethal fence has been criticized for its cruelty. At Calipatria prison (California), the electric fence has caused the deaths of wild and endangered birds that came in contact with the fence. This outraged bird lovers and after the "death fence" (as it became known as) had become an international environmental scandal, the state was forced to create a birdproof fence (the only one in the world) by using vertical mesh netting that envelops both sides of the electrified fence, thus making it an ecologically sensitive death fence. It also now consists of a warning wire for curious rodents, antiperching deflectors for wildfowl, and tiny passageways for burrowing owls. It has also built an attractive pond for visiting geese and ducks (Davis 1995).

One of the greatest concerns over the user of electroshock devices is their abuse by the officers and the institution. In a prison, operators of these devices could use them (and the threats of their use) for simply sadistic purposes or to coerce prisoners to do whatever the operator wants. This would allow these guards to take retribution on the prison population. Amnesty International has criticized the use of high-tech weapons in prisons as torture, especially the stun belt. It has argued that there is something frightening about them. Since there is no independent medical testing, Amnesty International found it outrageous that prison officials use the stun belt on inmates with HIV/AIDS in Old Parish Prison in New Orleans. At Parish Prison, inmates must sign a release form granting prison officials authorization to fit them with the belt for transportation to health facilities for life-saving medical treatment. What was especially disturbing to Amnesty International was that if an HIV-positive inmate refuses to sign the release, he or she would be denied transportation and thus denied urgent medical care (Schulz 1999). Amnesty International has recommended that federal, state, and local authorities (1) ban the use of remote control electroshock stun belts by law enforcement and correctional agencies and (2) prohibit the manufacture, promotion, distribution, and transfer (both within and from the United States) of stun belts and all other electroshock weapons, such as stun guns, stun shields, and tasers pending the outcome of a rigorous, independent, and impartial inquiry into the use and effects of the equipment. The organization also suggested that American companies should cease production of the remote control stun belt and suspend all manufacture, promotion, and transfers of all other stun weapons, pending the aforementioned inquiry (Schulz 1999).

Reliability and Accuracy

One of the major issues regarding technological devices is their reliability and accuracy. Automated biometric systems, for example, are not 100 percent foolproof. Although fingerprints, the face, and the voice, for example, remain constant from day to day, small fluctuations, such as cold or moist hands, different degree of lighting for face recognition, and background noise for voice authentication can confuse the devices. Setting the sensitivity too low increases the odds of an imposter's logon being accepted (false positive). High-sensitivity setting means greater security, but it also means that an authorized user may be erroneously rejected (false negative) (Gunnerson 1999).

Recently, a scanner that registers traces of microscopic particles associated with 40 different types of drugs at the State Correctional Institution in Woods Run, Pittsburgh, Pennsylvania, gave several false positive results, including one for a prison guard's shift commander (Bucsko 2001). Also on January 20, 2001, six inmates escaped by circumventing a 5,000-volt malfunctioning electric fence in Alabama by using a broomstick to pry up the electric fence and slide under it. The alarms of the electric fence did not go off (*News Tribune Online Edition* 2001).

The geophone-based detector for detecting heartbeats of inmates trying to escape in a vehicle is not without shortcomings as well. The main problem is that it can be used only on a vehicle that is cushioned from the ground—for instance, by shock absorbers, springs, and rubber tires. If the vehicle is not cushioned from the ground, the earth itself serves as a kind of vibrational damper. That is, the vehicle and the earth virtually become one solid body. Vibrations from heartbeats are strong enough to move a truck but not strong enough to move the earth. This means that ships, which are essentially one with the water they rest in, and railroad cars, whose rigid steel wheels ride on steel tracks, will not vibrate strongly enough for heartbeats to be detected by the geophones (Strauss 1997).

High Cost

Although technology has reduced prison cost in many instances, start-up cost can be high. The cost for technological devices in prison is too high for some states. Although high-tech solutions may ultimately reduce staffing demands, they require funds for construction, installation, and training (Weed 2001). The price tag attached to implementing telemedicine can be high. In Ohio, for example, the largest investment in its telemedicine program was the video hardware, which includes video codecs (coder/decoder), cameras, and monitors. The initial cost of hardware per site was approximately $87,000 and there is the possibility the equipment will not be usable beyond five years (NASCIO 2001). Likewise, in Texas, telemedicine units alone cost $50,000. The total package, including the unit, communications system, equipment on the receiving end, and software, adds up to a cost per facility of $100,000–$300,000 (Proctor 2000). Smart cards could be expensive; each card can cost $8.88; readers, $59; and handheld readers, $8,000. Hardware and software can cost $125,000; systems engineering, $175,000; conversion, $50,000; and support, another $50,000 (Guseau 1999). The installation of

Arizona's lethal fence will cost $1.2 million (Tugan 2000) and the chair in Arizona's prison that scans inmates for weapons costs $6,500 (Lau 2001).

Apart from the specific problems discussed above, there are still some general issues and questions regarding the use of technology. One is the effect that technology will have on the relationship between inmates and correctional officers. One wonders whether the increased isolation (because of technology) between inmates and officers will increase the hostilities of the inmates for officers. After years of being this coercive environment of technological devices, how would the inmates adapt to society on the outside once they are released? What are the physical and psychological effects of years of exposure to technological devices on inmates? What are the goals of all this technological gadgetry and are these goals being achieved? Finally what types of prisoners are being created with this extensive use of technology; will inmates be turned into robots? These are some of the unanswered questions that have not been addressed as society continues to create prisons with the prison system using the "Big Brother is Watching You" strategy.

RECOMMENDATIONS

Although technological devices are beginning to revolutionalize the prison system, they are subjected to manipulation. More needs to be done to prevent abuses. The following are some recommendations designed to improve the use of technological devices:

1. To curtail the unauthorized use of technology by prison personnel, Congress should pass legislation regulating the use of the technology. The legislation should clearly stipulate that the use of technological devices should be limited to its original purpose. Violation of the legislation should result in criminal sanctions.

2. State and federal governments should ensure that technological databases in prison are physically secured. Any physical documents pertaining to the database should be kept in a secured area, which could be protected by security personnel, alarm systems, video surveillance, and other related security devices to prevent unauthorized access to the information (see Woodward 1997).

3. To prevent constitution challenges to the use of technology in prisons, manufacturers should work closely with legal scholars to ensure that their systems are secure and free from constitutional challenges.

4. To maximize the use of technology, all states should establish technology review committees in prison to evaluate various technologies before purchased or used. The benefit of such committees is that the prison agency becomes more knowledgeable about technological needs and requirements.

5. State and federal governments should force manufacturers of these devices conduct comprehensive tests to determine their reliability, accuracy, and safety of these technological devices.

SUMMARY

Over the last decade, technological innovation has spurred the development of new devices to improve supervision in prisons. Technological advances have occurred in virtually every aspect of prison life and have led to changing roles for prison officials. Management information systems and smart cards have been introduced as a more affordable and comprehensive means of tracking inmate activities. Perimeter detectors, biometrics, and electroshock devices can prevent prison escapes. Drug and alcohol abuse testing packages, telemedicine, and videoconferencing all are products of advances in technology in prisons.

The extensive use of technology in prison has created images of an Orwellian nightmare "Big Brother" society since these technological devices are being used to watch, detect, secure, and contain inmates all across the United States. It is expected that technology will increase its appeal to prison administrators and politicians because of its versatility. Consequently, future prisons will become more and more technologically sophisticated.

It is undeniably true that through the use of these technological gadgetry, a large number of inmates can be supervised. However, as the prisons continue to be an integral part of the technological revolution, there are challenges ahead. Administrators should be cautious not to rely on technology to the point where safety is compromised. It is also important for prison officials to remember that technologies are devices that require well-trained staff to operate them. It is also perhaps too early to evaluate whether high-tech supervision will, in the long run, be the cost-effective, cost-efficient, and safer way to operate prisons. All new technology has it pitfalls and problems, and only time will tell how effective they really are. What is quite clear is that prisons have become part of the technological landscape and technology will continue to affect the way prisons are operated in the United States.

REFERENCES

ABT ASSOCIATES (1999, July 9). Abt Associates Finds Use of Telemedicine Can Reduce Health Care Costs in Prisons. [Retrieved February 15, 2003, from http://www.abtassoc.com/html/newsroom/press-releases/pr-telemedicine.html]

AMNESTY INTERNATIONAL (2000, July 11). After Prison Stun Gun Death, Virginia Refuses Amnesty International Visit: Amnesty International demands VA Suspend Electro-Shock Stun Gun Use. Washington, DC: Amnesty International (Author). [Retrieved February 14, 2003, from http://www.amnestyusa.org/news/2000/usa07112000.html]

BUCSKO, M. (2001). Scanning of prison visitors under fire: Inaccurate drug detector prompts unfair penalties. *Pittsburgh Post-Gazette:* B5

BONE, J. M. and C. L. CRUMBACKER. (2001, July). Facial Recognition—Assessing its Viability in the Corrections Environment. *Corrections Today*, 62–64.

CAMPBELL, J. P., L. A. ALYEA, and J. DUNN. (1996). *Biometric Security: Government Applications and Operations.* At 1 in CardTech/SecurTech (CTST). Government Conference Proceedings. [Retrieved March 15, 2003, from http://www.biometrics.org/REPORTS/CTSTG961]

CARAMANIS, C. B. (1999). Detection and monitoring technologies help DOC become virtually drug-free. *The Corrections Connection.* (February). [Retrieved February 15, 2003, from http://www.corrections.com/news/technology/detection.html Post (March 30): H1.

CELLULAR-NEWS. (2006). Locating Cell Phones Inside Prisons. [Retrieved April 13, 2007 from http://www.cellular-news.com/story/18558.php]

CENTER FOR CRIMINAL JUSTICE TECHNOLOGY NEWSLETTER. (2001, June 18). Biometrics at York County (Pa) prison. [Retrieved February 11, 2003, from http://www.mitretek.org/business_areas/justice/cjiti/ccjtnews/weekly/vol5-4.html]

CHANDRASEKARAN, R. (1997). Brave new whorl: ID systems using the human body are here, but privacy issues persist, *Washington Post* (March 30): H1.

CHEN, H, (1988). *Medical Genetics Handbook.* St. Louis, MO: W.H. Green.

COLATOSTI, T. (1998, November 18). *Wisconsin Department of Corrections Chooses Viisage.* Viisage Technology, Inc. [Retrieved February 15, 2003, from http//www.viisage.com]

CRUELTY IN CONTROL? The stun belt and other electroshock weapons in law enforcement.

CUSAC, A. (1996). Stunning technology. *Progressive* 60(7): 18–22.

DAVIS, M. (1995, February 20). Hell factories in the field: A prison-industrial complex. *Nation.* 260(7): 229–234.

deGROOT, G. (1997). Hot new technologies. *Corrections Today* 59(4): 60–62.

DEMSKY, I. (2005). Prisons combat contraband cellular phones. Tennessean.com. [Retrieved March14, 2007 from http://tennessean.com/government/archives/05/03/67493825.shtml?Element_ID=67493825]

DESMARAIS, N. (2000). Biometrics and network security. *Information Technology Interest Group, New England Chapter* (November/December). [Retrieved February 15, 2003, from http://abacus.bates.edu/acrlnec/sigs/itig/tc_nov_dec2000.htm]

DIRECTIONS. (2001). ADC brings in the boss: 1, 8. [Retrieved February 20, 2003, from www.adc.state.az.us/Directions/2001/julydirections2001]. Publications of Arizona Department of Corrections.

ESSER, M. (2000). *Biometric Authentication* [Retrieved February 6, 2003, from http://faculty.ed.umuc.edu/-meinkej/inss690/messer/Paper]

FINGER-SCAN.COM. (1999). Finger scan technology [Retrieved February 16, 2003 http://au.fujitsu.com/FAL/CDA/Articles/0,1029,305~1063,00.htm]

FUJITSU AUSTRALIA. (2001). Fujitsu smart card solution for Australia's 21st Century prison. [Retrieved February 16, 2003, from http://www.au.fujitsu.com/FAL/CDA/Articles/0,1029,305~1063,00.htm]

GAILIUN, M. (1997). Telemedicine. *Corrections Today* 59(4): 68–70.

GASEAU, M. (1999). Corrections technology options are expanding. *Corrections Today* 61(6), 22–25.

GEO GROUP INC. (2006, July 26). GEO Group Inc. implements leading technology to combat hidden contraband cellular phones in correctional facilities. [Retrieved February 16, 2003, from http://www.reiusa.net/downloads/REI_GEO_July_06.pdf]

GUNNERSON, G. (1999). *Are you ready for biometrics?* [Retrieved February 16, 2003, from http://www.zdnet.com/products/stories/reviews/0,4161,386987-2,00.html]

ION TRACK. (2002). Prisons. [Retrieved *January 19, 2003,* from http://www.iontrack.com/applications/prisons/notes.html]

IOSOFTWARE. (2000). *Biometrics explained.* [Retrieved February 14, 2003, from http://www.iosoftware.com/biometrics/explained.htm]

ISAACS, L. (2002a). Emerging technologies use physical characteristics to verify identities of residents and employees. *American City and County* 117 (3): 22–27.

ISAACS, L. (2002b). Body language. *American City and County* 117(3): 22–27.

JACKSON, K. (1998a). Evaluating correctional technology. *Corrections Today* 60(4,): 58–67.

JACKSON, K. (1998b). The application of security measures. *Corrections Today* 60(4): 58–67.

JUSTICE TECHNOLOGY INFORMATION NETWORK. (1998). Ohio inmates get "carded". [Retrieved March 2, 2003 from http://www.nlectc.org/virlib/InfoDetail.asp?intInfoID=293]

KELLEY, D., and K. OIEN (2000, May 3). Implementing biometric technology to enhance correctional safety and security. [Retrieved February 12, 2003, from http://tunxis.commnet.edu/ccjci/futures/classviii/kelley_oien.html]

LAU, J. (2001, August 16). Inmates hide assortment of metallic items. 08/16/2001—NLECTC News Summary. [Retrieved February 11, 2003, from http://www.mail-archive.com/justnetnews_nlectc.org/msg00068.html]

McManus, K. (May 6, 1996). At banks of future, an eye for an ID. *Washington Post*, p. A3

Miller, B. (1996). Everything you need to know about automated biometric identification. CardTech/SecurTech (CTST) Government Conference Proceedings: 1.

Miller; M. (2002, March 20). Live video used in court case; keeps dangerous criminals in jail. *The Capital Times* (Madison, WI) (March 20): 3A.

NASCIO (2001). Ohio-telemedicine-innovative use of technology. [Retrieved February 16, 2003, from https://www.nascio.org/awards/1998awards/Innovative/ohio.cfm]

National Law Enforcement and Corrections Technology Center (2000). *TechBeat Fall 2000*. [Retrieved January 25, 2003 from http://www.nlectc.org/txtfiles/tbfall2000.html]

News Tribune Online Edition (2001). 5 of 6 Alabama escapees caught in Tennessee. [http://www.newstribune.com/stories/020101/wor0201010013.asphttp://www.new]

Pries, A. (2001). Looking into the future; Iris recognition: Could replace pins and passwords. *Bergen Record* (August 6): L6.

Prison Talk Online (2004, November 9). Ohio Prisons Pilot Facial Recognition Technology. Retrieved January 28, 2008 from http://prisontalk.com/forums/showthread.php?t=92796

Reid, K. (2001). Detection devices squelch escape tries in just a heartbeat: Prisons screen vehicles at gate. *Chicago Tribune* (September 10): B7.

Ritter, J. (1999). Eye scans help sheriff keep suspects in sight. *Chicago Sun-Times* (June 22): 18.

Roberti, M. (2002). Big brother goes behind bars. *Fortune* (September 30): 44.

Schulz, W. (1999). *Cruelty in Control? The Stun Belt and Other Electroshock Weapons in Law Enforcement*. Washington, DC: Amnesty International USA. [Retrieved February 9, 2003, from http://www.amnestyusa.org/rightsforall/stun/press-schulz.html]

Scolforo, M. (2005, July 1). Federal prisons install killer fences. *Associated Press*. [Retrieved April 10, 2007 from http://www.unknownnews.org/0507050701prisons.html]

Swedberg, C. (2005, May 15). L.A. County Jail to Track Inmates. [Retrieved April 10, 2007 from http://www.tsilink.com/assets/media/rfid journal_la.pdf]

Stewart, T. L. (2000). *Technology* and Security—Opportunities and Challenges. *Corrections Today* 62 (4): 8–9.

Strauss, S. (1997). Detecting stowaways. *Technology Review* 100(1): 14–15.

Sullivan, L. (2006, October 12). Inmates smuggle in cell phones with ease. NPR. [Retrieved April 13, 2007, from http://www.npr.org/templates/story/story.php?storyId=6248833]

The Associated Press State & Local Wire (2002, April 15). Prison inmates now make court appearances via TV. Retrieved February 16, 2003 from http://www.cor.state.mt.us/css/news/NewsRelease.asp

The Corrections Connection (2001). Florida DOC increases security with identification technology. [Retrieved March 2, 2003, from http://www.corrections.com/technetwork/thtml]

The Third Branch (2001, November 12). Video-conferencing in courts shows potential and possible problems. Vol. 33 (12). [Retrieved December 15, 2002, from http://www.uscourts.gov/ttb/dec01ttb/videoconferencing.html]

The ultimate scam (2002). Smart card 'n Microchips. [Retrieved February 16, 2003, http://www.members.shaw.ca/theultimatescam/Smart%20Card.htm]

Tierney, T. (1995). Eyes have it in future of law enforcement: Technology expands to identify suspects. *Chicago Tribrune* (June 27): 1.

Tugan, B. (2000). $100 million prison to open September 8. *Las Vegas Sun* (Nov. 12, 2001). [Retrieved February 13, 2003, from http://www.ndoc.state.nv.us/news/display.php?article_id=8]

Villa, J. (2005, October 31). Video screens edge out face-to-face visits in jail. *The Arizona Republic*. [Retrieved February 10, 2003, from http://www.azcentral.com/arizonarepublic/news/articles/1031videovisitation31.html]

Weed, W. S. (2001). Future tech: Iron bars, silicon chips: High-tech prison reform comes to America's state and federal inmates. Discover 22(5). [Retrieved February 20, 2003, from http://www.discover.com/may_01/feattech.html]

WEISS, D. (2003, May 2). Court teleconferencing a big money saver. *Times Leader.* [Retrieved February 20, 2003, from http://www.timesleader.com/mld/timesleader/news/5898553.htm]

WIRED NEWS (1997). Prisons aim to keep, and keep ahead of, convicts. [Retrieved February 23, 2003, from http://www.wired.com/news/technology/0,1282,8583,00.html]

WOOD, M. (2000). Overview of biometric encryption. *Information Security Reading Room.* [Retrieved February 23, 2003, from http://rr.sans.org/authentic/biometric3.php]

WOODWARD, J. D. (1997). Biometric scanning, law and policy: Identifying the concerns—Drafting the biometric blueprint. *University of Pittsburgh Law Review* 59: 97

WRIGHT. S, and R. F. BUTLER, (2001). Can drug detection technology stop drugs from entering prisons? *Corrections Today* 63(4): 66–69.

YEOMAN, B. (2000, March/April). Shocking discipline. *Mother Jones* 25(2): 17–18.

ZDNET. (1999). *How biometrics works.* [Retrieved February 23, 2003, from http://www.zdnet.com/products/stories/reviews/0,4161,2199371,00.html]

ZUNKEL, R. (1998). Hand geometry based verification. In *Biometrics: Personal Identification in Networked Society,* eds A. Jain, R. Bolle, and S. Pankanti, 87–102. Norwell, MA: Kluwer Academic Publishers.

DNA: the indispensable forensic science tool

From Chapter 11 of *Criminalistics: An Introduction to Forensic Science*, Tenth Edition. Richard Saferstein. Copyright © 2011 by Pearson Education, Inc. Published by Pearson Prentice Hall. All rights reserved.

O. J. Simpson—A Mountain of Evidence

On June 12, 1994, police arrived at the home of Nicole Simpson only to view a horrific scene. The bodies of O. J. Simpson's estranged wife and her friend Ron Goldman were found on the path leading to the front door of Nicole's home. Both bodies were covered in blood and had suffered deep knife wounds. Nicole's head was nearly severed from her body. This was not a well-planned murder. A trail of blood led away from the murder scene. Blood was found in O. J. Simpson's Bronco. Blood drops were on O. J.'s driveway and in the foyer of his home.

A blood-soaked sock was located in O. J. Simpson's bedroom, and a bloodstained glove rested outside his residence.

As DNA was extracted and profiled from each bloodstained article, a picture emerged that seemed to irrefutably link Simpson to the murders. A trail of DNA leaving the crime scene was consistent with O. J.'s profile, as was the DNA found entering Simpson's home.

Simpson's DNA profile was found in the Bronco along with that of both victims. The glove contained the DNA profiles of Nicole and Ron, and the sock had Nicole's DNA profile. At trial, the defense team valiantly fought back. Miscues in evidence collection were craftily exploited. The defense strategy was to paint a picture of not only an incompetent investigation, but one that was tinged with dishonest police planting evidence. The strategy worked. O. J. Simpson was acquitted of murder.

DNA: the indispensable forensic science tool

DNA
Abbreviation for deoxyribonucleic acid—the molecules carrying the body's genetic information; DNA is double stranded in the shape of a double helix

The discovery of **deoxyribonucleic acid (DNA)**, the deciphering of its structure, and the decoding of its genetic information were turning points in our understanding of the underlying concepts of inheritance. Now, with incredible speed, as molecular biologists unravel the basic structure of genes, we can create new products through genetic engineering and develop diagnostic tools and treatments for genetic disorders.

For a number of years, these developments were of seemingly peripheral interest to forensic scientists. All that changed when, in 1985, what started out as a more or less routine investigation into the structure of a human gene led to the discovery that portions of the DNA structure of certain genes are as unique to each individual as fingerprints. Alec Jeffreys and his colleagues at Leicester University, England, who were responsible for these revelations, named the process for isolating and reading these DNA markers *DNA fingerprinting*. As researchers uncovered new approaches and variations to the original Jeffreys technique, the terms *DNA profiling* and *DNA typing* came to be applied to describe this relatively new technology.

This discovery caught the imagination of the forensic science community because forensic scientists have long desired to link with certainty biological evidence such as blood, semen, hair, or tissue to a single individual. Although conventional testing procedures had gone a long way toward narrowing the source of biological materials, individualization remained an elusive goal. Now DNA typing has allowed forensic scientists to accomplish this goal. The technique is still relatively new, but in the few years since its introduction, DNA typing has become routine in public crime laboratories and has been made available to interested parties through the services of a number of skilled private laboratories. In the United States, courts have overwhelmingly admitted DNA evidence and accepted the reliability of its scientific underpinnings.

What Is DNA?

chromosome
A rodlike structure in the cell nucleus, along which the genes are located; it is composed of DNA surrounded by other material, mainly proteins

Inside each of 60 trillion cells in the human body are strands of genetic material called **chromosomes**. Arranged along the chromosomes, like beads on a thread, are nearly 25,000 genes. **The gene is the fundamental unit of heredity. It instructs the body cells to make proteins that determine everything from hair color to our susceptibility to diseases.** Each gene is actually composed of DNA specifically designed to carry out a single body function.

Interestingly, although DNA was first discovered in 1868, scientists were slow to understand and appreciate its fundamental role in inheritance. Painstakingly, researchers developed evidence that DNA was probably the substance by which genetic instructions are passed from one generation to the next. But the major breakthrough in comprehending how DNA works did not occur until the early 1950s, when two researchers, James Watson and Francis Crick, deduced the structure of DNA. It turns out that DNA is an extraordinary molecule skillfully designed to carry out the task of controlling the genetic traits of all living cells, plant and animal.

Structure of DNA

polymer
A substance composed of a large number of atoms; these atoms are usually arranged in repeating units, or monomers

Before examining the implications of Watson and Crick's discovery, let's see how DNA is constructed. DNA is a **polymer**. A polymer is a very large molecule made by linking a series of repeating units.

nucleotide
The unit of DNA consisting of one of four bases—adenine, guanine, cytosine, or thymine—attached to a phosphate–sugar group

NUCLEOTIDES In the case of DNA, the repeating units are known as **nucleotides**. A nucleotide is composed of a sugar molecule, a phosphorus-containing group, and a nitrogen-containing molecule called a *base*. Figure 1 shows how nucleotides can be strung together to form a DNA strand. In this figure, S designates the sugar component, which is joined with a phosphate group to form the backbone of the DNA strand. Projecting from the backbone are the bases.

The key to understanding how DNA works is to appreciate the fact that only four types of bases are associated with DNA: adenine, cytosine, guanine, and thymine. To simplify our discussion of DNA, we will designate each of these bases by the first letter of their names. Hence, *A* will stand for adenine, *C* will stand for cytosine, *G* will stand for guanine, and *T* will represent thymine.

Again, notice in Figure 1 how the bases project from the backbone of DNA. Also, although this figure shows a DNA strand of four bases, keep in mind that in theory there is no limit to the length of the DNA strand; in fact, a DNA strand can be composed of a long chain with millions of bases. The information just discussed was well known to Watson and Crick by the time they set about detailing the structure of DNA. Their efforts led to the discovery that the DNA molecule is actually composed of two DNA strands coiled into a *double helix*. This can be thought of as resembling two wires twisted around each other.

As these researchers manipulated scale models of DNA strands, they realized that the only way the bases on each strand could be properly aligned with each other in a double-helix configuration was to place base *A* opposite *T* and *G* opposite *C*. Watson and Crick had solved the puzzle of the double helix and presented the world with a simple but elegant picture of DNA (see Figure 2).

COMPLEMENTARY BASE PAIRING   The only arrangement possible in the double-helix configuration was the pairing of bases *A* to *T* and *G* to *C*, a concept that has become known as **complementary base pairing.** Although *A–T* and *G–C* pairs are always required, there are no restrictions on how the bases are to be sequenced on a DNA strand. Thus, one can observe the sequences *T–A–T–T* or *G–T–A–A* or *G–T–C–A*. When these sequences are joined with their complements in a double-helix configuration, they pair as follows:

```
T A T T        G T A A        G T C A
| | | |        | | | |        | | | |
A T A A        C A T T        C A G T
```

Any base can follow another on a DNA strand, which means that the possible number of different sequence combinations is staggering! Consider that the average human chromosome has DNA containing 100 million base pairs. All of the human chromosomes taken together contain

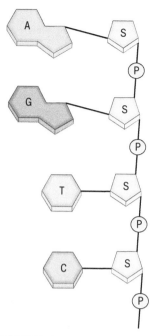

FIGURE 1

How nucleotides can be linked to form a DNA strand. S designates the sugar component, which is joined with phosphate groups (P) to form the backbone of DNA. Projecting from the backbone are four bases: *A*, adenine; *G*, guanine; *T*, thymine; and *C*, cytosine.

complementary base pairing
The specific pairing of base A with T and base C with G in double-stranded DNA

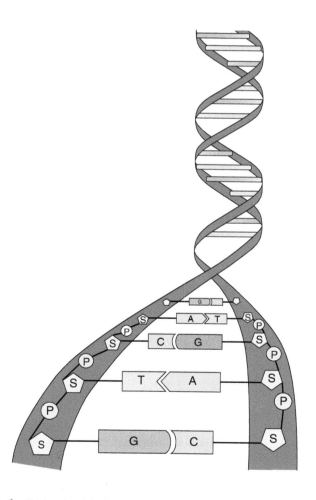

FIGURE 2

A representation of a DNA double helix. Notice how bases *G* and *C* pair with each other, as do bases *A* and *T*. This is the only arrangement in which two DNA strands can align with each other in a double-helix configuration.

proteins
Polymers of amino acids that play basic roles in the structures and functions of living things

amino acids
The building blocks of proteins; there are twenty common amino acids; amino acids are linked to form a protein; the types of amino acids and the order in which they're linked determine the character of each protein

about 3 billion base pairs. From these numbers, we can begin to appreciate the diversity of DNA and hence the diversity of living organisms. DNA is like a book of instructions. The alphabet used to create the book is simple enough: *A*, *T*, *G*, and *C*. The order in which these letters are arranged defines the role and function of a DNA molecule.

DNA at Work

The inheritable traits that are controlled by DNA arise out of its ability to direct the production of complex molecules called **proteins**. Proteins are actually made by linking a combination of **amino acids**. Although thousands of proteins exist, they can all be derived from a combination of up to 20 known amino acids. The sequence of amino acids in a protein chain determines the shape and function of the protein. Let's look at one example: The protein hemoglobin is found in our red blood cells. It carries oxygen to our body cells and removes carbon dioxide from these cells. One of the four amino acid chains of "normal" hemoglobin is shown in Figure 3(a). Studies of individuals with sickle-cell anemia show that this inheritable disorder arises from the presence of "abnormal" hemoglobin in their red blood cells. An amino acid chain for "abnormal" hemoglobin is shown in Figure 3(b). Note that the sole difference between "normal" and "abnormal" or sickle-cell hemoglobin arises from the substitution of one amino acid for another in the protein chain.

The genetic information that determines the amino acid sequence for every protein manufactured in the human body is stored in DNA in a genetic code that relies on the sequence of bases along the DNA strand. The alphabet of DNA is simple—*A*, *T*, *G*, and *C*—but the key to deciphering the genetic code is to know that each amino acid is coded by a sequence of three bases. Thus, the amino acid alanine is coded by the combination *C–G–T*; the amino acid aspartate is coded by the combination *C–T–A*; and the amino acid phenylalanine is coded by the combination *A–A–A*. With this code in hand, we can now see how the amino acid sequence in a protein chain is determined by the structure of DNA. Consider the DNA segment

$$-C–G–T–C–T–A–A–A–A–C–G–T-$$

The triplet code contained within this segment translates into

$$[C–G–T] – [C–T–A] – [A–A–T] – [C–G–T]$$
alanine   aspartate   phenylalanine alanine

or the protein chain

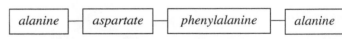

Interestingly, this code is not restricted to humans. Almost all living cells studied to date use the same genetic code as the language of protein synthesis.[1]

If we look at the difference between "normal" and sickle-cell hemoglobin (see Figure 3), we see that the latter is formed by substituting one amino acid (valine) for another (glutamate). Within the DNA segment that codes for the production of normal hemoglobin, the letter sequence is

$$-[C–C–T]–[G–A–G]–[G–A–G]-$$
proline glutamate glutamate

Individuals with sickle-cell disease carry the sequence

$$-[C–C–T]–[G–T–G]–[G–A–G]-$$
proline   valine   glutamate

Thus, we see that a single base or letter change (*T* has been substituted for *A* in valine) is the underlying cause of sickle-cell anemia, demonstrating the delicate chemical balance between health and disease in the human body.

As scientists unravel the base sequences of DNA, they obtain a greater appreciation for the roles that proteins play in the chemistry of life. Already the genes responsible for hemophilia,

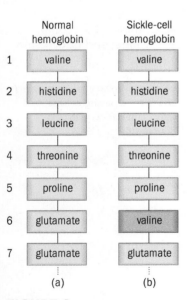

	Normal hemoglobin	Sickle-cell hemoglobin
1	valine	valine
2	histidine	histidine
3	leucine	leucine
4	threonine	threonine
5	proline	proline
6	glutamate	valine
7	glutamate	glutamate
	(a)	(b)

FIGURE 3

(a) A string of amino acids composes one of the protein chains of hemoglobin.
(b) Substitution of just one amino acid for another in the protein chain results in sickle-cell hemoglobin.

[1] Instructions for assembling proteins are actually carried from DNA to another region of the cell by ribonucleic acid (RNA). RNA is directly involved in the assembly of the protein using the genetic code it received from DNA.

Duchenne muscular dystrophy, and Huntington's disease have been located. Once scientists have isolated a disease-causing gene, they can determine the protein that the gene has directed the cell to manufacture. By studying these proteins—or the absence of them—scientists will be able to devise a treatment for genetic disorders.

A 13-year project to determine the order of bases on all 23 pairs of human chromosomes (also called the **human genome**) is now complete. Knowing where on a specific chromosome DNA codes for the production of a particular protein is useful for diagnosing and treating genetic diseases. This information is crucial for understanding the underlying causes of cancer. Also, comparing the human genome with that of other organisms will help us understand the role and implications of evolution.

human genome
The total DNA content found within the nucleus of a human cell; it is composed of approximately three billion base pairs of genetic information

Polymerase Chain Reaction (PCR)

Once the double-helix structure of DNA was discovered, how DNA duplicated itself before cell division became apparent. The concept of base pairing in DNA suggests the analogy of positive and negative photographic film. Each strand of DNA in the double helix has the same information; one can make a positive print from a negative or a negative from a positive.

DNA Replication

The synthesis of new DNA from existing DNA begins with the unwinding of the DNA strands in the double helix. Each strand is then exposed to a collection of free nucleotides. Letter by letter, the double helix is re-created as the nucleotides are assembled in the proper order, as dictated by the principle of base pairing (A with T and G with C). The result is the emergence of two identical copies of DNA where before there was only one (see Figure 4). A cell can now pass on its genetic identity when it divides.

Many enzymes and proteins are involved in unwinding the DNA strands, keeping the two DNA strands apart, and assembling the new DNA strands. For example, DNA *polymerases* are enzymes that assemble a new DNA strand in the proper base sequence determined by the original or parent DNA strand. DNA polymerases also "proofread" the growing DNA double helices for mismatched base pairs, which are replaced with correct bases.

Until recently, the phenomenon of DNA **replication** appeared to be only of academic interest to forensic scientists interested in DNA for identification. However, this changed when researchers perfected the technology of using DNA polymerases to copy a DNA strand located outside a living cell. This relatively new laboratory technique is known as **polymerase chain reaction (PCR)**. Put simply, PCR is a technique designed to copy or multiply DNA strands.

replication
The synthesis of new DNA from existing DNA

polymerase chain reaction (PCR)
A technique for replicating or copying a portion of a DNA strand outside a living cell; this technique leads to millions of copies of the DNA strand

The PCR Process

In PCR, small quantities of DNA or broken pieces of DNA found in crime-scene evidence can be copied with the aid of a DNA polymerase. The copying process can be accomplished in an automated fashion using a DNA Thermal Cycler (see Figure 5). Each cycle of the PCR technique results in a doubling of the DNA, as shown in Figure 4. Within a few hours, 30 cycles can multiply DNA a billionfold. Once DNA copies are in hand, they can be analyzed by any of the methods of modern molecular biology. The ability to multiply small bits of DNA opens new and exciting avenues for forensic scientists to explore. It means that sample size is no longer a limitation in characterizing DNA recovered from crime-scene evidence.

PCR is the outgrowth of knowledge gained from an understanding of how DNA strands naturally replicate within a cell. The most important feature of PCR is knowing that an enzyme called *DNA polymerase* can be directed to synthesize a specific region of DNA. In a relatively straightforward manner, PCR can be used to repeatedly duplicate or amplify a strand of DNA millions of times. As an example, let's consider a segment of DNA that we want to duplicate by PCR:

$$-G{-}T{-}C{-}T{-}C{-}A{-}G{-}C{-}T{-}T{-}\mathbf{C}{-}\mathbf{C}{-}\mathbf{A}{-}\mathbf{G}{-}$$

$$-\mathbf{C}{-}\mathbf{A}{-}\mathbf{G}{-}\mathbf{A}{-}G{-}T{-}C{-}G{-}A{-}A{-}G{-}G{-}T{-}C{-}$$

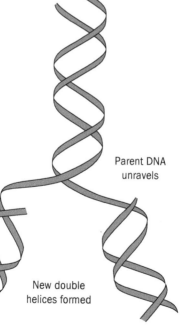

Parent DNA unravels

New double helices formed

FIGURE 4

Replication of DNA. The strands of the original DNA molecule are separated, and two new strands are assembled.

FIGURE 5

The DNA Thermal Cycler, an instrument that automates the rapid and precise temperature changes required to copy a DNA strand. Within a matter of hours, DNA can be multiplied a millionfold.
Courtesy Applied Biosystems, Foster City, Calif.

primer

A short strand of DNA used to target a region of DNA for replication by PCR

hybridization

The process of joining two complementary strands of DNA to form a double-stranded molecule

mycrimekit

WEBEXTRA 11.2
Polymerase Chain Reaction
www.mycrimekit.com

tandem repeat

A region of a chromosome that contains multiple copies of a core DNA sequence that are arranged in a repeating fashion

To perform PCR on this DNA segment, short sequences of DNA on each side of the region of interest must be identified. In the example shown here, the short sequences are designated by boldface letters in the DNA segment. These short DNA segments must be available in a pure form known as a **primer** if the PCR technique is going to work.

The first step in the PCR process is to heat the DNA strands to about 94°C. At this temperature, the double-stranded DNA molecules separate completely:

$$-G-T-C-T-C-A-G-C-T-T-C-C-A-G-$$

$$-C-A-G-A-G-T-C-G-A-A-G-G-T-C-$$

The second step is to add the primers to the separated strands and allow the primers to combine or **hybridize** with the strands by lowering the test-tube temperature to about 60°C.

$$-G-T-C-T-C-A-G-C-T-T-C-C-A-G-$$

$$C-A-G-A$$

$$C-C-A-G$$

$$-C-A-G-A-G-T-C-G-A-A-G-G-T-C-$$

The third step is to add the DNA polymerase and a mixture of free nucleotides (G, A, T, C) to the separated strands. When the test tube is heated to 72°C, the polymerase enzyme directs the rebuilding of a double-stranded DNA molecule, extending the primers by adding the appropriate bases, one at a time, resulting in the production of two complete pairs of double-stranded DNA segments.

$$-G-T-C-T-C-A-G-C-T-T-C-C-A-G-$$

$$C-A-G-A-G-T-C-G-A-A-G-G-T-C-$$

$$-G-T-C-T-C-A-G-C-T-T-C-C-A-G$$

$$-C-A-G-A-G-T-C-G-A-A-G-G-T-C-$$

This completes the first cycle of the PCR technique, and the outcome is a doubling of the number of DNA strands—that is, from one to two. The cycle of heating, cooling, and strand rebuilding is then repeated, resulting again in a doubling of the DNA strands. On completion of the second cycle, four double-stranded DNA molecules will have been created from the original double-stranded DNA sample. Typically, 28 to 32 cycles are carried out to yield almost a billion copies of the original DNA molecule. Each cycle takes less than two minutes to perform.

From the forensic scientist's viewpoint, PCR offers another distinct advantage in that it can amplify minute quantities of DNA, thus overcoming the limited sample-size problem often associated with crime-scene evidence. With PCR, less than one-billionth of a gram of DNA is required for analysis. Consequently, PCR can characterize DNA extracted from small quantities of blood, semen, and saliva.

DNA Typing

Geneticists have discovered that portions of the DNA molecule contain sequences of letters that are repeated numerous times. In fact, more than 30 percent of the human genome is composed of repeating segments of DNA. These repeating sequences, or **tandem repeats,** seem to act as filler or spacers between the coding regions of DNA. Although these repeating segments do not seem to affect our outward appearance or control any other basic genetic function, they are nevertheless part of our genetic makeup, inherited from our parents in the manner illustrated by the Punnett square. The origin and significance of these tandem repeats is a mystery, but to forensic scientists they offer a means of distinguishing one individual from another through DNA typing.

Forensic scientists first began applying DNA technology to human identity in 1985. From the beginning, attention has focused on the tandem repeats of the genome. These repeats can be visualized as a string of connected boxes with each box having the same core sequence of DNA

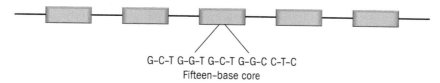

G-C-T G-G-T G-C-T G-G-C C-T-C
Fifteen-base core

FIGURE 6

A DNA segment consisting of a series of repeating DNA units. In this illustration, the 15-base core can repeat itself hundreds of times. The entire DNA segment is typically hundreds to thousands of bases long.

bases (see Figure 6). All humans have the same type of repeats, but there is tremendous variation in the number of repeats that each of us has.

Restriction Fragment Length Polymorphisms (RFLPs)

Up until the mid-1990s, the forensic community aimed its efforts at characterizing repeat segments known as **restriction fragment length polymorphisms (RFLPs).** These repeats are cut out of the DNA double helix by a restriction enzyme that acts like a pair of scissors. A number of different RFLPs were selected by the forensic science community for performing DNA typing. Typically a core sequence is 15 to 35 bases long and repeats itself up to one thousand times.

RFLP DNA typing has the distinction of being the first scientifically accepted protocol in the United States used for the forensic characterization of DNA. However, its utility has been short lived. New technology incorporating PCR has supplanted RFLP. In its short history, perhaps RFLP's most startling impact related to the impeachment trial of President Bill Clinton. The whole complexion of the investigation regarding the relationship of the president with a White House intern, Monica Lewinsky, changed when it was revealed that Ms. Lewinsky possessed a dress that she claimed was stained with the president's semen. The FBI Laboratory was asked to compare the DNA extracted from the dress stain with that of the president. An RFLP match was obtained between the president's DNA and the stain. The combined frequency of occurrence for the seven DNA types found was nearly one in eight trillion, an undeniable link. The dress and a copy of the FBI DNA report are shown in Figure 7.

Why couldn't the PCR technology be applied to RFLP DNA typing? Simply put, the RFLP strands are too long, often containing thousands of bases. PCR is best used with DNA strands that are no longer than a couple of hundred bases. The obvious solution to this problem is to characterize DNA strands that are much shorter than RFLPs. Another advantage in moving to shorter DNA strands is that they would be expected to be more stable and less subject to degradation brought about by adverse environmental conditions. The long RFLP strands tend to break apart under adverse conditions not uncommon at crime scenes.

restriction fragment length polymorphisms (RFLPs)
Different fragment lengths of base pairs that result from cutting a DNA molecule with restriction enzymes

Short Tandem Repeats (STRs)

Currently, **short tandem repeat (STR)** analysis has emerged as the most successful and widely used DNA-profiling procedure. STRs are locations (loci) on the chromosome that contain short sequence elements that repeat themselves within the DNA molecule. They serve as helpful markers for identification because they are found in great abundance throughout the human genome.

STRs normally consist of repeating sequences of three to seven bases; the entire strand of an STR is also very short, less than 450 bases long. These strands are significantly shorter than those encountered in other DNA-typing procedures. This means that STRs are much less susceptible to degradation and are often recovered from bodies or stains that have been subject to extreme decomposition. Also, because of their shortness, STRs are an ideal candidate for multiplication by PCR, thus overcoming the limited-sample-size problem often associated with crime-scene evidence. Only the equivalent of 18 DNA-containing cells is needed to obtain a DNA profile. For instance, STR has been used to identify the origin of saliva residue on envelopes, stamps, soda cans, and cigarette butts.

To understand the utility of STRs in forensic science, let's look at one commonly used STR known as TH01. This DNA segment contains the repeating sequence A–A–T–G. Seven TH01 variants have been identified in the human genome. These variants contain five to eleven repeats of A–A–T–G. Figure 8 illustrates two such TH01 variants, one containing six repeats and the other containing eight repeats of A–A–T–G.

short tandem repeat (STR)
A region of a DNA molecule that contains short segments consisting of three to seven repeating base pairs

FEDERAL BUREAU OF INVESTIGATION
WASHINGTON, D. C. 20535

Report of Examination

Examiner Name:	Date:	08/17/98
Unit: DNA Analysis 1	Phone No.:	202-324-4409
FBI File No.: 29D-OIC-LR-35063	Lab No.:	980730002 S BO
		980803100 S BO

Results of Examinations:

Deoxyribonucleic acid (DNA) profiles for the genetic loci
D2S44, D17S79, D1S7, D4S139, D10S28, D5S110 and D7S467 were
developed from HaeIII-digested high molecular weight DNA
extracted from specimens K39 and Q3243-1(a semen stain removed
from specimen Q3243). Based on the results of these seven
genetic loci, specimen K39 (CLINTON) is the source of the DNA
obtained from specimen Q3243-1, to a reasonable degree of
scientific certainty.

No DNA-RFLP examinations were conducted on specimen Q3243-
2 (a semen stain removed from specimen Q3243).

BLACK — 1,440,000,000,000
CAUC — 7,870,000,000,000
SEH — 3,140,000,000,000
S&H — 943,000,000,000

DNAU1 - Page 1 of 1

This Report Is Furnished For Official Use Only

Q3243

FIGURE 7

The dress and the FBI Report of Examination for a semen stain located on the dress.

During a forensic examination, TH01 is extracted from biological materials and amplified by PCR as described earlier. The ability to copy an STR means that extremely small amounts of the molecule can be detected and analyzed. Once the STRs have been copied or amplified, they are separated by **electrophoresis**. By examining the distance the STR has migrated on the electrophoretic plate, one can determine the number of *A–A–T–G* repeats in the STR. Every person has two STR types for TH01, one inherited from each parent. Thus, for example, one may find in a semen stain TH01 with six repeats and eight repeats. This combination of TH01 is found in approximately 3.5 percent of the population.

When examining an STR DNA pattern, one merely needs to look for a match between band sets. For example in, Figure 9, DNA extracted from a crime-scene stain matches the DNA

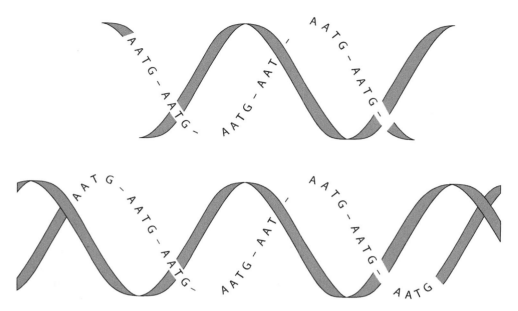

FIGURE 8

Variants of the short tandem repeat TH01. The upper DNA strand contains six repeats of the sequence *A–A–T–G*; the lower DNA strand contains eight repeats of the sequence *A–A–T–G*. This DNA type is designated as TH01 6,8.

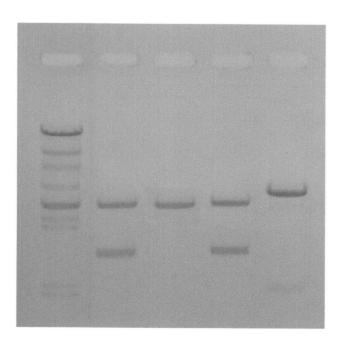

FIGURE 9

A DNA profile pattern of a suspect and its match to crime-scene DNA. From left to right, lane 1 is a DNA standard marker; lane 2 is the crime-scene DNA; and lanes 3 to 5 are control samples from suspects 1, 2, and 3, respectively. Crime-scene DNA matches suspect 2.

Courtesy Edvotek, The Biotechnology Education Company www.edvotek.com

recovered from one of three suspects. When comparing only one STR, only a limited number of people in a population would have the same STR fragment pattern as the suspect. However, by using additional STRs, a high degree of discrimination or complete individualization can be achieved.

Multiplexing

What makes STRs so attractive to forensic scientists is that hundreds of different types of STRs are found in human genes. The more STRs one can characterize, the smaller the percentage of the population from which these STRs can emanate. This gives rise to the concept of **multiplexing.** Using PCR technology, one can simultaneously extract and amplify a combination of different STRs.

multiplexing
A technique that simultaneously detects more than one DNA marker in a single analysis

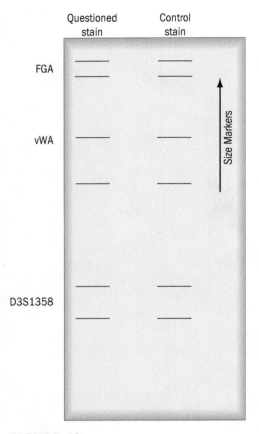

FIGURE 10

A triplex system containing three loci: FGA, vWA, and D3S1358, indicating a match between the questioned and the standard/reference stains.

One STR system on the commercial market is the STR Blue Kit.[2] This kit provides the necessary materials for amplifying and detecting three STRs (a process called *triplexing*)—D3S1358, vWA, and FGA. The design of the system ensures that the size of the STRs does not overlap, thereby allowing each marker to be viewed clearly on an electrophoretic gel, as shown in Figure 10. In the United States, the forensic science community has standardized on thirteen STRs for entry into a national database known as the Combined DNA Index System (CODIS).

When an STR is selected for analysis, not only must the identity and number of core repeats be defined, but the sequence of bases flanking the repeats must also be known. This knowledge allows commercial manufacturers of STR-typing kits to prepare the correct primers to delineate the STR segment to be amplified by PCR. Also, a mix of different primers aimed at different STRs will be used to simultaneously amplify a multitude of STRs (multiplexing). In fact, one STR kit on the commercial market can simultaneously make copies of 15 different STRs (see Figure 11).

DNA Typing with STRs

The thirteen CODIS STRs are listed in Table 1 along with their probabilities of identity. The probability of identity is a measure of the likelihood that two individuals selected at random will have an identical STR type. The smaller the value of this probability, the more discriminating the STR. A high degree of discrimination and even individualization can be attained by analyzing a combination of STRs (multiplexing). Because STRs occur independently of each other, the probability of biological evidence having a particular combination of STR types is determined by the product of their frequency of occurrence in a population. This combination is referred to as the *product rule*. Hence, the greater the number of STRs characterized, the smaller the frequency of occurrence of the analyzed sample in the general population.

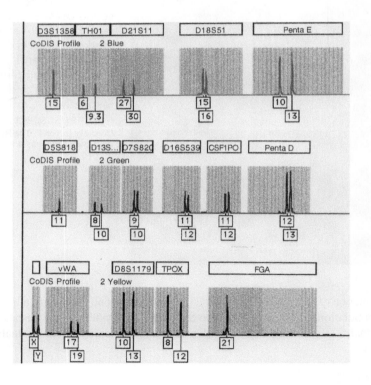

FIGURE 11

STR profile for 15 loci.

Courtesy H. Edward Grotjan, Ph.D.

[2] Applied Biosystems, 850 Lincoln Centre Drive, Foster City, Calif. 94404.

TABLE 1
The Thirteen CODIS STRs and Their Probability of Identities

STR	African American	U.S. Caucasian
D3S1358	0.094	0.075
vWA	0.063	0.062
FGA	0.033	0.036
TH01	0.109	0.081
TPOX	0.090	0.195
CSF1PO	0.081	0.112
D5S818	0.112	0.158
D13S317	0.136	0.085
D7S820	0.080	0.065
D8S1179	0.082	0.067
D21S11	0.034	0.039
D18S51	0.029	0.028
D16S539	0.070	0.089

Source: The Future of Forensic DNA Testing: Predictions of the Research and Development Working Group. Washington, D.C.: National Institute of Justice, Department of Justice, 2000, p. 41.

The combination of the first three STRs shown in Table 1 typically produces a frequency of occurrence of about 1 in 5,000. A combination of the first six STRs typically yields a frequency of occurrence in the range of 1 in two million for the Caucasian population, and if the top nine STRs are determined in combination, this frequency declines to about 1 in one billion. The combination of all 13 STRs shown in Table 1 typically produces frequencies of occurrence that measure in the range of 1 in 575 trillion for Caucasian Americans and 1 in 900 trillion for African Americans. Importantly, several commercially available kits allow forensic scientists to profile STRs in the kinds of combinations cited here.

Capillary Electrophoresis

The separation of STRs can typically be carried out on a flat gel-coated electrophoretic plate, as described earlier. However, the need to reduce analysis time and to automate sampling and data collection has led to the emergence of *capillary electrophoresis* as the preferred technology for characterization of STRs. Capillary electrophoresis is carried out in a thin glass column rather than on the surface of a coated-glass plate.

As illustrated in Figure 12, each end of the column is immersed in a reservoir of buffer liquid that also holds electrodes (coated with platinum) to supply high-voltage energy. The column is coated with a gel polymer, and the DNA-containing sample solution is injected into one end of the column by applying a high voltage to an electrode immersed in the DNA solution. The STR fragments then move through the column under the influence of an electrical potential at a speed that is related to the length of the STR fragments. The other end of the column is connected to a detector that tracks the separated STRs as they emerge from the column. As the DNA peaks pass through the detector, they are recorded on a display known as an *electropherogram*, as shown in Figure 11.

Sex Identification Using STRs

Manufacturers of commercial STR kits typically used by crime laboratories provide one additional piece of useful information along with STR types: the sex of the DNA contributor. The focus of attention here is the **amelogenin gene** located on both the X and Y chromosomes. This gene, which is actually the gene for tooth pulp, has an interesting characteristic in that it is shorter by six bases in the X chromosome than in the Y chromosome. Hence, when the amelogenin gene is amplified by PCR and separated by electrophoresis, males, who have an X and a Y chromosome, show two bands; females, who have two X chromosomes, have just one band. Typically, these results are obtained in conjunction with STR types.

Another tool in the arsenal of the DNA analyst is the ability to type STRs located on the Y chromosome. The Y chromosome is male specific and is always paired with the X chromosome.

amelogenin gene
A genetic locus useful for determining gender

forensic brief

MiniSTRs

The forensic science community turned to STRs when it became apparent that short segments of DNA would be required to meet the requirements of PCR. Commercial manufacturers of DNA-typing kits prepared a series of 13 STRs for compatibility with the CODIS DNA database that ranged in length from 100 to 450 bases. One obvious benefit in working with short DNA segments was the likelihood that useful information could be extracted even from fragmented DNA. This often proved to be the case, but not always. On occasion, degraded DNA is encountered that is so badly damaged that traditional STR analysis is not possible. Prolonged exposure of DNA to extreme environmental elements, such as temperature extremes, humidity, or microbial activity, can lead to such degradation. An approach to dealing with this problem is to further shorten the STR strands that emerge form the PCR process.

The approach that has been taken to accomplish this task is to create new primers that can be positioned closer to the STR repeat region (see Figure 1). The shorter STR products (called *amplicons*) that now emerge from PCR increase the chances of char-

acterizing badly fragmented strands of DNA. These smaller amplicons are called "miniSTRs." One manufacturer of STR kits has produced a miniSTR kit designed to amplify eight miniSTRs, seven of which are totally compatible with the CODIS database. The miniSTRs range in size from 71 to 250 bases. A DNA analyst suspecting a degraded sample now has the option, if sample size permits, of running both traditional STR and miniSTR determinations, or just the latter.

The advent of miniSTRs means that forensic scientists can now analyze samples that were once thought to be of no value. One of the first benefactors of miniSTR technology was the identification of a number of victims from the Waco Branch Davidian fire. Also, a number of World Trade Center victims were identified by miniSTR technology. Another focus of attention has been human hair. In the past, extracting nuclear DNA out of the hair shaft has been enormously difficult; the number of STRs in hair has been found to be very low as well as highly degraded. However, one study has demonstrated that miniSTRs may overcome some of the difficulties in obtaining partial profiles from the degraded DNA present in shed hair.[3]

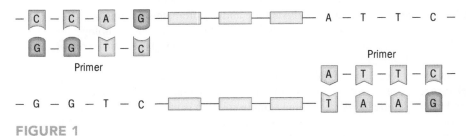

FIGURE 1

Appropriate primers are positioned close to the repeat units of a DNA segment in order to initiate the PCR process that will create short or miniSTRs.

Y-STRs
Short tandem repeats located on the human Y chromosome

Although more than 400 **Y-STRs** have been identified, only a small number of them are being used for forensic applications. One commercial kit allows for the characterization of 17 Y chromosome STRs. When can it be advantageous to seek out Y-STR types? Generally, Y-STRs are useful for analyzing blood, saliva, or a vaginal swab that is a mix originating from more than one male. For example, Y-STRs prove useful when multiple males are involved in a sexual assault. Further simplifying the analysis is that any DNA in the mixture that originates from a female will not show.

[3] K. E. Opel et al., "Evaluation and Quantification of Nuclear DNA from Human Telogen Hairs," *Journal of Forensic Sciences* 53 (2008): 853.

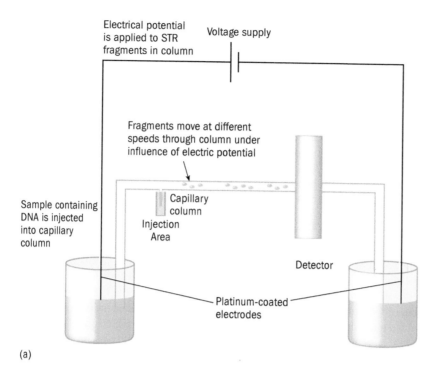

Electrical potential is applied to STR fragments in column

Voltage supply

Fragments move at different speeds through column under influence of electric potential

Capillary column

Injection Area

Sample containing DNA is injected into capillary column

Detector

Platinum-coated electrodes

(a)

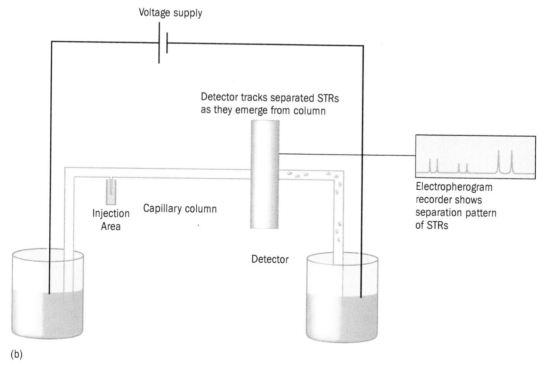

Voltage supply

Detector tracks separated STRs as they emerge from column

Electropherogram recorder shows separation pattern of STRs

Injection Area

Capillary column

Detector

(b)

FIGURE 12

Capillary electrophoresis technology has evolved from the traditional flat gel electrophoresis approach. The separation of DNA segments is carried out on the interior wall of a glass capillary tube that is kept at a constant voltage. The size of the DNA fragments determines the speed at which they move through the column. This figure illustrates the separation of three sets of STRs (triplexing).

mycrimekit

WEBEXTRA 11.3
See the 13 CODIS STRs and Their
Chromosomal Positions
www.mycrimekit.com

mycrimekit

WEBEXTRA 11.4
See How to Calculate the Frequency
of Occurrence of a DNA Profile
www.mycrimekit.com

mycrimekit

WEBEXTRA 11.5
Understand the Operational Principles of Capillary Electrophoresis
www.mycrimekit.com

mycrimekit

WEBEXTRA 11.6
See the Electropherogram Record
from One Individual's DNA
www.mycrimekit.com

mycrimekit

WEBEXTRA 11.7
An Animation Depicting Y-STRs
www.mycrimekit.com

Keep in mind that STR types derived from the Y chromosome originate only from this single male chromosome. A female subject, or one with an XX chromosome pattern, does not contribute any DNA information. Also, unlike a conventional STR type that is derived from two chromosomes and typically shows two bands or peaks, a Y-STR has only one band or peak for each STR type.

For example, the traditional STR DNA pattern may prove to be overly complex in the case of a vaginal swab containing the semen of two males. Each STR type would be expected to show four bands, two from each male. Also complicating the appearance of the DNA profile may be the presence of DNA from skin cells emanating from the walls of the vagina. In this circumstance, homing in on the Y chromosome greatly simplifies the appearance and interpretation of the DNA profile. Thus, when presented with a DNA mixture of two males and one female, each STR type would be expected to show six bands. However, the same mixture subjected to Y-STR analysis would show only two bands (one band for each male) for each Y-STR type.

Significance of DNA Typing

STR DNA typing has become an essential and basic investigative tool in the law enforcement community. The technology has progressed at a rapid rate and in only a few years has surmounted numerous legal challenges to become vital evidence for resolving violent crimes and sex offenses. DNA evidence is impartial, implicating the guilty and exonerating the innocent.

In a number of well-publicized cases, DNA evidence has exonerated individuals who have been wrongly convicted and imprisoned. The importance of DNA analyses in criminal investigations has also placed added burdens on crime laboratories to improve their quality-assurance procedures and to ensure the correctness of their results. In several well-publicized instances, the accuracy of DNA tests conducted by government-funded laboratories has been called into question.

The Combined DNA Index System (CODIS)

Perhaps the most significant investigative tool to arise from a DNA-typing program allows crime laboratories to compare DNA types recovered from crime-scene evidence to those of convicted sex offenders and other convicted criminals. This capability is of tremendous value to investigators in cases in which the police have not been able to identify a suspect. All 50 states have legislatively mandated collection of DNA samples from convicted offenders of particular crimes and establishment of DNA databases for law enforcement purposes. CODIS (Combined DNA Index System) is a computer software program developed by the FBI that maintains local, state, and national databases of DNA profiles from convicted offenders, unsolved crime-scene evidence, arrestees, and profiles of missing people. CODIS software enables local, state, and national crime laboratories to compare DNA profiles electronically. Thousands of matches have linked serial crimes to each other and have solved crimes by allowing investigators to match crime-scene evidence to known convicted offenders. As mentioned earlier, in the United States the forensic science community has currently standard-ized on 13 STRs for entry into CODIS.

Currently, more than 170 public law enforcement laboratories across the United States participate in CODIS. In addition, CODIS is used by more than 40 law enforcement laboratories in more than 25 countries for their own DNA database inquiries. As previously mentioned, state laws now require the acquisition of DNA profiles from all convicted offenders. These profiles are continually added to state and national DNA data banks and have proven to be invaluable investigative resources for law enforcement. CODIS has produced more than 95,000 hits.

Mitochondrial DNA

Typically, when one describes DNA in the context of a criminal investigation, the subject is assumed to be the DNA in the nucleus of a cell. Actually, a human cell contains two types of DNA—nuclear and mitochondrial. The first constitutes the 23 pairs of chromosomes in the nuclei of our

>>>>>>>>>>>>>>>>>>>>

forensic brief

Familial DNA—Expanding the DNA Database

In 1984, Deborah Sykes was raped and stabbed to death as she walked to work in Winston-Salem, North Carolina. A month later, Darryl Hunt, then 19 years old, was arrested and eventually convicted of the crime. Hunt insisted that he was innocent, and by 1990, DNA testing of semen found on Sykes proved that he was not its source. Nevertheless, North Carolina prosecutors ignored this new evidence and he remained in jail. Finally, a search against Darryl Hunt's STR profile in the North Carolina DNA database revealed a close but not perfect match to a genetic profile already in the database, that of his brother. Upon further investigation, that man, Willard Brown, confessed to Sykes's murder in 2003, and Hunt was finally freed from prison.

In this case, DNA profiling exonerated an innocent man and helped lead the police to the real culprit. The Sykes case illustrates how the contents of a criminal DNA database can be dramatically expanded to aid the police in identifying criminals by searching the database for near matches.

Typically, the CODIS database is used to find exact matches with crime-scene DNA. However, taking into account the facts that the 13 STR loci that constitute U.S. offender DNA databases are genetically inherited and that each individual's DNA profile is genetically determined by one's parents creates opportunities to use the database's raw data to search out close relatives. DNA profiles of related individuals are likely to show a higher proportion of shared STR loci as compared to unrelated individuals. Hence, searching the database for profiles that have a high degree of commonality may lead to the identification of a close relative of the perpetrator. Interestingly, studies have shown that a person's chances of committing a crime increase if a parent or sibling had previously done so. A 1999 U.S. Department of Justice survey found that 46 percent of jail inmates had at least one close relative who had also been incarcerated.

The potential for improving the effectiveness of DNA database searches is considerable. Familial searches of a DNA database would dramatically increase the size of the database by three or more times because every profile that is entered would, in effect, contain genetic information about the STR alleles of the donor's parents, siblings, and children. One study estimates that using familial DNA searches could increase the "cold hit" rates by 40 percent. Considering the fact that there have been about 95,000 cold hits in the United States, familial DNA has the potential for identifying thousands of additional criminal suspects.

The concept of familial DNA searching has been routinely adopted in the United Kingdom. In the United States, the FBI notifies investigators about close matches it finds using its current software, but the agency has no current plans to modify its search algorithms to optimize the database's capacity to ferret out near or close matches. This leaves it up to the states to decide whether to release identifying information about an offender whose DNA closely matches a crime scene sample from another state. Challengers to familial database searching have cited it as a violation of constitutional protections against unreasonable search and seizure. A number of mixed state court decisions have failed to produce a consensus on the constitutionality of familial DNA database searches.

cells. Each parent contributes to the genetic makeup of these chromosomes. Mitochondrial DNA (mtDNA), on the other hand, is found outside the nucleus of the cell and is inherited solely from the mother.

MITOCHONDRIA **Mitochondria** are cell structures found in all human cells. They are the power plants of the body, providing about 90 percent of the energy that the body needs to function. A single mitochondrion contains several loops of DNA, all of which are involved in energy generation. Further, because each cell in our bodies contains hundreds to thousands of mitochondria, there are hundreds to thousands of mtDNA copies in a human cell. This compares to just one set of nuclear DNA located in that same cell. Thus, forensic scientists are offered enhanced sensitivity and the opportunity to characterize mtDNA when nuclear DNA is significantly degraded, such as

mitochondria
Small structures located outside the nucleus of a cell; these structures supply energy to the cell; maternally inherited DNA is found in each mitochondrion

WEBEXTRA 11.8
See How We Inherit Our Mitochondrial DNA

www.mycrimekit.com

in charred remains, or when nuclear DNA may be present in a small quantity (such as in a hair shaft). Interestingly, when authorities cannot obtain a reference sample from an individual who may be long deceased or missing, an mtDNA reference sample can be obtained from any maternally related relative. However, all individuals of the same maternal lineage will be indistinguishable by mtDNA analysis.

Although mtDNA analysis is significantly more sensitive than nuclear DNA profiling, forensic analysis of mtDNA is more rigorous, time consuming, and costly than nuclear DNA profiling. For this reason, only a handful of public and private forensic laboratories receive evidence for this type of determination. The FBI Laboratory has imposed strict limitations on the type of cases in which it will apply mtDNA technology.

sequencing
A procedure used to determine the order of the base pairs that constitute DNA

SEQUENCING As was previously discussed, nuclear DNA is composed of a continuous linear strand of nucleotides (*A*, *T*, *G*, and *C*). On the other hand, mtDNA is constructed in a circular or loop configuration. Each loop contains enough (approximately 16,569) *A*, *T*, *G*, and *C* to make up 37 genes involved in mitochondrial energy generation. Two regions of mtDNA have been found to be highly variable in the human population. These two regions have been designated hypervariable region I (HV1) and hypervariable region II (HV2), as shown in Figure 13. As indicated previously, the process for analyzing HV1 and HV2 is tedious. It involves generating many copies of these DNA hypervariable regions by PCR and then determining the order of the *A*–*T*–*G*–*C* bases constituting the hypervariable regions. This process is known as **sequencing.** The FBI Laboratory, the Armed Forces DNA Identification Laboratory, and other laboratories have collaborated to compile an mtDNA population database containing the base sequences from HV1 and HV2.

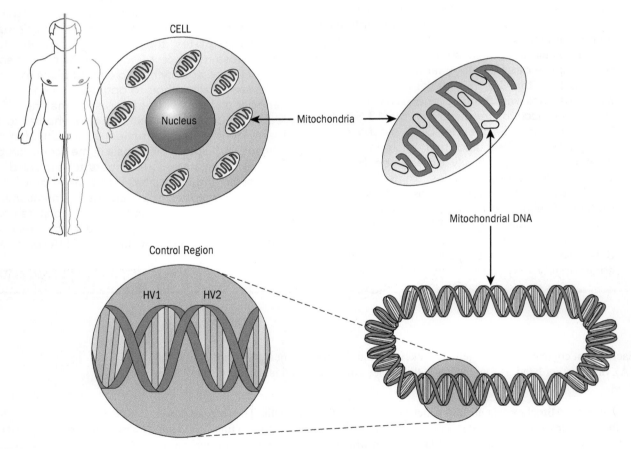

FIGURE 13

Every cell in the body contains hundreds of mitochondria, which provide energy to the cell. Each mitochondrion contains numerous copies of DNA shaped in the form of a loop. Distinctive differences between individuals in their mitochondrial DNA makeup are found in two specific segments of the control region on the DNA loop known as HV1 and HV2.

Once the sequences of the hypervariable regions from a case sample are obtained, most laboratories simply report the number of times these sequences appear in the mtDNA database maintained by the FBI. The mtDNA database contains about five thousand sequences. This approach permits an assessment of how common or rare an observed mtDNA sequence is in the database. Interestingly, many of the sequences that have been determined in casework are unique to the existing database, and many types are present at frequencies no greater than 1 percent in the database. Thus it is often possible to demonstrate how uncommon a particular mitochondrial DNA sequence is. However, even under the best circumstances, mtDNA typing does not approach STR analysis in its discrimination power. Thus, mtDNA analysis is best reserved for samples for which nuclear DNA typing is simply not possible.

The first time mtDNA was admitted as evidence in a U.S. court was in 1996 in the case of *State of Tennessee* v. *Paul Ware*. Here, mtDNA was used to link two hairs recovered from the crime scene to the defendant. Interestingly, in this case, blood and semen evidence was absent. Mitochondrial DNA analysis also plays a key role in the identification of human remains. An abundant amount of mtDNA is generally found in skeletal remains. Importantly, mtDNA reference samples are available from family members sharing the same mother, grandmother, great-grandmother, and so on. One of the most publicized cases performed on human remains was the identification of the individual buried in the tomb of the Vietnam War's unknown soldier. The remains lying in the tomb were believed to belong to First Lt. Michael J. Blassie, whose A-37 warplane was shot down near An Loc, South Vietnam, in 1972. In 1984, the U.S. Army Central Identification Laboratory failed to identify the remains by physical characteristics, personal artifacts, or blood-typing results from hairs. The remains were subsequently placed in the tomb. In 1998, at the insistence of the Blassie family, the remains were disinterred for the purpose of performing mtDNA analysis and comparing the results to references from seven families thought to be associated with the case. The remains in the tomb were subsequently analyzed and confirmed to be consistent with DNA from Lt. Blassie's family.

mycrimekit

WEBEXTRA 11.9
Look into the Structure of Mitochondrial DNA and See How It Is Used for DNA Typing
www.mycrimekit.com

Collection and Preservation of Biological Evidence for DNA Analysis

Since the early 1990s, the advent of DNA profiling has vaulted biological crime-scene evidence to a stature of importance that is eclipsed only by the fingerprint. In fact, the high sensitivity of DNA determinations has even changed the way police investigators define biological evidence.

forensic brief

In the fall of 1979, a 61-year-old patient wandered away from a U.S. Department of Veterans Affairs medical facility. Despite an extensive search, authorities never located the missing man. More than ten years later, a dog discovered a human skull in a wooded area near the facility. DNA Analysis Unit II of the FBI Laboratory received the case in the winter of 1999. The laboratory determined that the mitochondrial DNA profile from the missing patient's brother matched the mitochondrial DNA profile from the recovered skull and provided the information to the local medical examiner. Subsequently, the remains were declared to be those of the missing patient and returned to the family for burial.

Source: FBI Law Enforcement Bulletin 78 (2002): 21.

The JonBenét Ramsey Murder Case

Point–Counterpoint
Point
July 9, 2008

Boulder District Attorney Mary T. Lacy issues the following announcement with regard to the investigation of the murder of JonBenét Ramsey.

On December 25–26, 1996, JonBenét Ramsey was murdered in the home where she lived with her mother, father and brother. Despite a long and intensive investigation, the death of JonBenét remains unsolved.

The murder has received unprecedented publicity and has been shrouded in controversy. That publicity has led to many theories over the years in which suspicion has focused on one family member or another. However, there has been at least one persistent stumbling block to the possibility of prosecuting any Ramsey family members for the death of JonBenét—DNA.

As part of its investigation of the JonBenét Ramsey homicide, the Boulder Police identified genetic material with apparent evidentiary value. Over time, the police continued to investigate DNA, including taking advantage of advances in the science and methodology. One of the results of their efforts was that they identified genetic material and a DNA profile from drops of JonBenét's blood located in the crotch of the underwear she was wearing at the time her body was discovered. That genetic profile belongs to a male and does not belong to anyone in the Ramsey family.

The police department diligently compared that profile to a very large number of people associated with the victim, with her family, and with the investigation, and has not identified the source, innocent or otherwise, of this DNA. The Boulder Police and prosecutors assigned to this investigation in the past also worked conscientiously with laboratory analysts to obtain better results through new approaches and additional tests as they became available. Those efforts ultimately led to the discovery of sufficient genetic markers from this male profile to enter it into the national DNA data bank.

In December of 2002, the Boulder District Attorney's Office, under Mary T. Lacy, assumed responsibility for the investigation of the JonBenét Ramsey homicide. Since then, this office has worked with the Boulder Police Department to continue the investigation of this crime.

In early August of 2007, District Attorney Lacy attended a Continuing Education Program in West Virginia sponsored by the National Institute of Justice on Forensic Biology and DNA. The presenters discussed successful outcomes from a new methodology described as "touch DNA." One method for sampling for touch DNA is the "scraping method." In this process, forensic scientists scrape a surface where there is no observable stain or other indication of possible DNA in an effort to recover for analysis any genetic material that might nonetheless be present. This methodology was not well known in this country until recently and is still used infrequently.

In October of 2007, we decided to pursue the possibility of submitting additional items from the JonBenét Ramsey homicide to be examined using this methodology. We checked with a number of Colorado sources regarding which private laboratory to use for this work. Based upon multiple recommendations, including that of the Boulder Police Department, we contacted the Bode Technology Group located near Washington, D.C., and initiated discussions with the professionals at that laboratory. First Assistant District Attorney Peter Maguire and Investigator Andy Horita spent a full day with staff members at the Bode facility in early December of 2007.

The Bode Technology laboratory applied the "touch DNA" scraping method to both sides of the waist area of the long johns that JonBenét Ramsey was wearing over her underwear when her body was discovered. These sites were chosen because evidence supports the likelihood that the perpetrator removed and/or replaced the long johns, perhaps by handling them on the sides near the waist.

On March 24, 2008, Bode informed us that they had recovered and identified genetic material from both sides of the waist area of the long johns. The unknown male profile previously identified from the inside crotch area of the underwear matched the DNA recovered from the long johns at Bode.

We consulted with a DNA expert from a different laboratory, who recommended additional investigation into the remote possibility that the DNA might have come from sources at the autopsy when this clothing was removed. Additional samples were obtained and then analyzed by the Colorado Bureau of Investigation to assist us in this effort. We received those results on June 27th of this year and are, as a result, confidant that this DNA did not come from innocent sources at the autopsy. As mentioned above, extensive DNA testing had previously excluded people connected to the family and to the investigation as possible innocent sources.

I want to acknowledge my appreciation for the efforts of the Boulder Police Department, Bode Technology

Group, the Colorado Bureau of Investigation, and the Denver Police Department Forensic Laboratory for the great work and assistance they have contributed to this investigation.

The unexplained third party DNA on the clothing of the victim is very significant and powerful evidence. It is very unlikely that there would be an innocent explanation for DNA found at three different locations on two separate items of clothing worn by the victim at the time of her murder. This is particularly true in this case because the matching DNA profiles were found on genetic material from inside the crotch of the victim's underwear and near the waist on both sides of her long johns, and because concerted efforts that might identify a source, and perhaps an innocent explanation, were unsuccessful.

It is therefore the position of the Boulder District Attorney's Office that this profile belongs to the perpetrator of the homicide.

DNA is very often the most reliable forensic evidence we can hope to find during a criminal investigation. We rely on it often to bring to justice those who have committed crimes. It can likewise be reliable evidence upon which to remove people from suspicion in appropriate cases.

The Boulder District Attorney's Office does not consider any member of the Ramsey family, including John, Patsy, or Burke Ramsey, as suspects in this case. We make this announcement now because we have recently obtained this new scientific evidence that adds significantly to the exculpatory value of the previous scientific evidence. We do so with full appreciation for the other evidence in this case.

Local, national, and even international publicity has focused on the murder of JonBenét Ramsey. Many members of the public came to believe that one or more of the Ramseys, including her mother or her father or even her brother, were responsible for this brutal homicide. Those suspicions were not based on evidence that had been tested in court; rather, they were based on evidence reported by the media.

It is the responsibility of every prosecutor to seek justice. That responsibility includes seeking justice for people whose reputations and lives can be damaged irreparably by the lingering specter of suspicion. In a highly publicized case, the detrimental impact of publicity and suspicion on people's lives can be extreme. The suspicions about the Ramseys in this case created an ongoing living hell for the Ramsey family and their friends, which added to their suffering from the unexplained and devastating loss of JonBenét.

For reasons including those discussed above, we believe that justice dictates that the Ramseys be treated only as victims of this very serious crime. We will accord them all the rights guaranteed to the victims of violent crimes under the law in Colorado and all the respect and sympathy due from one human being to another. To the extent that this office has added to the distress suffered by the Ramsey family at any time or to any degree, I offer my deepest apology.

We prefer that any tips related to this ongoing investigation be submitted in writing or via electronic mail to BoulderDA.org, but they can also be submitted to our tip line at (303) 441–1636.

This office will make no further statements.

Counterpoint

Last year, then–Boulder, Colorado, District Attorney Mary Keenan Lacy, who had been "investigating" the Ramsey case for the last few years, wrote a letter to JonBenét's father John, apologizing for having believed he or his wife, the late Patsy, or their son Burke (then nine) had anything to do with their daughter's 1996 death. Lacy indicated that recent tests from the Bode Laboratory of Virginia revealed that their "new methodology" of touch DNA found a match that proves an intruder was culpable of the slaying in which the six-year-old was molested, strangled and given a fractured skull.

There has always been unmatched, unknown male DNA—likely from saliva—in the inside crotch of the child's underpants. A minute amount, too degraded to get a proper DNA profile, was mixed with her blood when someone stuck her oh-so-slightly with the pointed end of a broken paintbrush on the night of her death. Because the DNA was so insignificant, it was theorized to have come from someone coughing during the manufacturing process, then the blood drops on top rehydrated it. If the DNA and blood were deposited at the same time, they would have degraded at the same rate—but here the blood sample was robust.

Lacy wrote that the lab discovered that sloughed-off skin cells on the waist area of the long johns JonBenét wore over her underpants can be matched to the underpants' DNA.

That was great news for people who want to believe there was an intruder with no link to the family members. No one imagines a parent could harm a child in such a brutal and horrendous fashion. Only problem is, adults—including parents—kill kids all the time. While

(Continued)

The JonBenét Ramsey Murder Case (continued)

this murder is unique in its application and renown, from an investigative point of view it's just another homicide that has to be dissected to be understood. Anyone looking rationally at the evidence here, and assessing it as a whole, cannot be pleased with Lacy's letter to Ramsey or the fact that she cleared the most credible suspects in the case. At the least it sets a terrible precedent where other people "under the umbrella of suspicion" in other cases will demand the same treatment if their investigations take a long time to reach a courtroom. Just because someone isn't on trial, or a case has gone cold, doesn't mean that the right people aren't firmly under the microscope of authorities.

Mary Lacy left office in January, 2009, and the new DA, or any in the future, can retract her pronouncement. Frankly it will take a brave person to go against the sea of public opinion by individuals who want to blame a bogeyman. One note of encouragement is the case has been returned to the Boulder police, who are better equipped to investigate than the DA's office ever was. The case had been moved to Lacy's predecessor when the Ramsey family complained that the police spotlight on them was unfair. As we all know, there's no statute of limitations on homicide.

This doesn't take Lacy off the hook, as I see it. Here are some facts of the case which were ignored by her reckless decision. . . .

Touch DNA is nothing new to law enforcement, although Bode has only tested for it for about three years. For some ten years, the FBI lab at Quantico and other labs have used it to capture skin cells from inside masks or gloves, and from guns or knives.

Neither Lacy nor Bode will make available their test results so independent experts can critically review the information. If scientific evidence is to be used to make an argument, proof should be offered. Perhaps some media outlet will file a lawsuit to compel the documents.

What Lacy and Bode have said is that the mystery man's DNA is on the waist area, and that the DNA doesn't match any Ramsey family member. Nothing is stated about where and how much Ramsey DNA was discovered. Patsy dressed the child in those long johns before putting her to bed, and the waistband is precisely what John's two hands touched when he carried his daughter's stiff body in a vertical position upstairs from the basement where she was found deceased. And since DNA can survive multiple launderings, we can't pinpoint when that touch DNA was left on the waistband.

Boulder County Coroner Dr. John Meyer's autopsy report is the Rosetta Stone to this case. It explains the type and order of JonBenét's injuries—asphyxiation by a ligature, then a head blow. It does not reveal who killed the girl. Due to the three-page phony ransom note that many analysts believe was penned by Patsy, the working strategy was to consider Mrs. Ramsey as the perpetrator of all the insults inflicted upon the tot. But while there might have been enough evidence for an arrest, there was not enough for a conviction—and among insiders there was debate about who—if anyone in the household—did what. Without a clear through-line that police and prosecutors could agree upon, what chance would a jury have to find its way to a guilty verdict?

What the autopsy report states without equivocation is that the child suffered vaginal injuries that were "chronic," meaning they predated the murder by days or weeks. We're talking repeated digital penetration that eroded—not ruptured—her hymen. Also, the opening of her vagina was twice the size of a similar aged child's. These factors would have been testified to by at least three pediatric gynecological physicians, had the case gone to trial. This unknown pedophile would have needed on-going intimate access to JonBenét before the night she died. Mary Lacy's early prosecutorial career was as a sex crimes expert, so why didn't she recognize the nature of this little girl's injuries?

If some accident led to JonBenét being strangled, then hit violently in the head, a normal reaction would have been for her caretakers to rush her to a hospital.

---

picogram
One-trillionth of a gram, or 0.000000000001 gram

low copy number
Fewer than 18 DNA-bearing cells

Just how sensitive is STR profiling? Forensic analysts using currently accepted protocols can reach sensitivity levels as low as 125 **picograms.** Interestingly, a human cell has an estimated 7 picograms of DNA, which means that only 18 DNA-bearing cells are needed to obtain an STR profile. However, modifications in the technology can readily extend the level of detection down to 9 cells. A quantity of DNA that is below the normal level of detection is defined as a **low copy number.** With this technology in hand, the horizon of the criminal investigator extends beyond the traditional dried blood or semen stain to include stamps and envelopes licked with saliva, a cup or can that has touched a person's lips, chewing gum, the sweat band of a hat, or a bedsheet

But that didn't happen, I surmise, because her pre-existing genital injuries would have been noticed. And so, a ridiculous—and sadly, effective—cover-up ensued.

Mary Lacy was responsible for the 2006 debacle where she had arrested and brought back from Thailand a false confessor named John Mark Karr. When the underpants' DNA excluded him from being the perpetrator she let him go and publicly stated: "The DNA could be an artifact. It isn't necessarily the killer's. There's a probability that it's the killer's. But it could be something else."

She added: "No one is really cleared of a homicide until there's a conviction in court, beyond a reasonable doubt. And I don't think you will get any prosecutor, unless they were present with the person at the time of the crime, to clear someone."

What made her change her thinking when she cleared the Ramseys?

More to the point, where are the intruder's skin cells from the rope around the child's neck, the paintbrush, the spoon and bowl of pineapple she ate from just before she died, the white blanket that covered her, the flashlight believed to have hit her head, and the pen and paper used in the bogus ransom note? And where is the intruder's touch DNA on the waistband of JonBenét's underpants? Did the stranger pull down her long johns, then command her to pull down her own panties? Are we to believe he then put on gloves—or maybe a whole scuba suit, since there were no unidentified footprints, finger- or handprints, hairs or fibers?

Woven inside the rope around the neck, which was wrapped around a piece of a broken paintbrush, were fibers from the distinctive jacket Patsy wore that evening—and, allegedly, inside the underpants were fibers from the wool sweater John had on. Patsy's fibers were also in the tote where the paintbrush came from and on the sticky side of the piece of duct tape that covered JonBenét's mouth—a length of tape so small it could have been easily flicked aside by her

tongue if it had been placed on her mouth while she was alive.

Lacy wrote that autopsy personnel were swabbed and tested for a DNA match, and thus excluded. But what about crime scene workers or lab technicians? And how many markers are in the touch DNA profile? The underpants' DNA was not enough to get a proper match through CODIS, the federal database. That didn't stop Lacy from sending it through on a regular basis—such busywork has little prospect of ending with a match, but it makes it seem as if something is being done.

Years ago, there was a civil suit in this case wherein a federal judge issued a statement that said, based on her reading of the material submitted to her, there was a higher likelihood of an intruder being the killer than a family member. At that time, Mary Lacy read a statement that suggested the Ramseys were innocent, based on the judicial ruling—though not clearing them. That statement was reportedly dictated to her by a Ramsey associate. What only those close to the case know is that one side of the civil suit completely abandoned its case, never offering paperwork, so the only information the judge had was that which came from the Ramsey camp. Ergo, an easy decision for the judge to make. Since then, Ramsey advisers have pummeled Lacy to clear the family entirely and eventually it happened. The Ramsey case isn't alone. The parents of a missing and presumed dead British three-year-old have used the media and spinmeisters that include members of the Ramseys' own team, and a duped public which has contributed millions of bucks, to petition for their names to be cleared.

It's egregious when an officer of the court misrepresents scientific evidence to win political favor. Mary Lacy was right to offer up an apology. But it should have been to JonBenét and not her family.

Source: Dawna Kaufmann, investigative journalist Co-author with Cyril H. Wecht, MD, JD, of *A Question of Murder.*

---

containing dead skin cells. Likewise, skin or **epithelial cells** transferred onto the surface of a weapon, the interior of a glove, or a pen have yielded DNA results.[4]

The phenomenon of transferring DNA via skin cells onto the surface of an object has come to be called **touch DNA.** Again, keep in mind that, in theory, only 18 skin cells deposited on an object are required to obtain a DNA profile.

The ultimate sensitivity goal in forensic DNA analysis is profiling DNA extracted from one human cell. Such an accomplishment seems close to fruition. Researchers have reported obtaining

epithelial cells

The outer layer of skin cells; these DNA-bearing cells often fall off or are rubbed off onto objects retrieved from crime scenes

touch DNA

DNA from skin cells transferred onto the surface of an object by simple contact

[4] R. A. Wickenheiser, "Trace DNA: A Review, Discussion of Theory, and Application of the Transfer of Trace Qualities through Skin Contact," *Journal of Forensic Sciences* 47 (2002): 442.

STR profiles from one or two cells and have successfully profiled DNA from single dermal-ridge fingerprints.[5] Although it's premature to imply that this technology, or a comparable one, is eligible for admission in criminal trials, one cannot exclude its use in criminal and forensic intelligence investigations. Table 2 illustrates the power of DNA as a creator of physical evidence.

Collection of Biological Evidence

However, before investigators become enamored with the wonders of DNA, they should first realize that the crime scene must be treated in the traditional manner. Before the collection of evidence begins, biological evidence should be photographed close up and its location relative to the entire crime scene recorded through notes, sketches, and photographs. If the shape and position of bloodstains may provide information about the circumstances of the crime, an expert must immediately conduct an on-the-spot evaluation of the blood evidence. The significance of the position and shape of bloodstains can best be ascertained when the expert has an on-site overview of the entire crime scene and can better reconstruct the movement of the individuals involved. No attempt should be made to disturb the blood pattern before this phase of the investigation is completed.

The evidence collector must handle all body fluids and biologically stained materials with a minimum amount of personal contact. All body fluids must be assumed to be infectious; hence, wearing disposable latex gloves while handling the evidence is required. Latex gloves also significantly reduce the possibility that the evidence collector will contaminate the evidence. These gloves should be changed frequently during the evidence-collection phase of the investigation. Safety considerations and avoidance of contamination also call for the wearing of face masks, shoe covers, and possibly coveralls.

Blood has great evidential value when a transfer between a victim and suspect can be demonstrated. For this reason, all clothing from both victim and suspect should be collected and sent to the laboratory for examination. This procedure must be followed even when the presence of blood on a garment does not appear obvious to the investigator. Laboratory search procedures are far

TABLE 2

Location and Sources of DNA at Crime Scenes

Evidence	Possible Location of DNA on the Evidence	Source of DNA
Baseball bat or similar weapon	Handle, end	Sweat, skin, blood, tissue
Hat, bandanna or mask	Inside	Sweat, hair, dandruff
Eyeglasses	Nose or ear pieces, lens	Sweat, skin
Facial tissue, cotton swab	Surface area	Mucus, blood, sweat, semen, ear wax
Dirty laundry	Surface area	Blood, sweat, semen
Toothpick	Tips	Saliva
Used cigarette	Cigarette butt	Saliva
Stamp or envelope	Licked area	Saliva
Tape or ligature	Inside/outside surface	Skin, sweat
Bottle, can, or glass	Sides, mouthpiece	Saliva, sweat
Used condom	Inside/outside surface	Semen, vaginal or rectal cells
Blanket, pillow, sheet	Surface area	Sweat, hair, semen, urine, saliva
"Through and through" bullet	Outside surface	Blood, tissue
Bite mark	Person's skin or clothing	Saliva
Fingernail, partial fingernail	Scrapings	Blood, sweat, tissue

Source: National Institute of Justice, U.S. Department of Justice.

---

[5] E. K. Hanson and J. Ballantyne, "Whole Genome Amplification Strategy for Forensic Genetic Analysis Using Single or Few Cell Equivalents of Genomic DNA," *Analytical Biochemistry* 346 (2005): 246.

more revealing and sensitive than any that can be conducted at the crime scene. In addition, blood should also be searched for in less-than-obvious places. For example, the criminal may have wiped his or her hands on materials not readily apparent to the investigator. Investigators should look for towels, handkerchiefs, or rags that may have been used and then hidden, and should also examine floor cracks or other crevices that may have trapped blood.

Packaging of Biological Evidence

Biological evidence should not be packaged in plastic or airtight containers because accumulation of residual moisture could contribute to the growth of DNA-destroying bacteria and fungi. **Each stained article should be packaged separately in a paper bag or a well-ventilated box.** If feasible, the entire stained article should be packaged and submitted for examination. If this is not possible, dried blood is best removed from a surface with a sterile cotton-tipped swab lightly moistened with distilled water from a dropper bottle. A portion of the unstained surface material near the recovered stain must likewise be removed or swabbed and placed in a separate package. This is known as a **substrate control**. The forensic examiner may use the substrate swab to confirm that the results of the tests performed were brought about by the stain and not by the material on which it was deposited. However, this practice is normally not necessary when DNA determinations are carried out in the laboratory. One point is critical, and that is that the collected swabs must not be packaged in a wet state. After the collection is made, the swab must be air-dried for approximately five to ten minutes. Then it is best to place it in a swab box (see Figure 14), which has a circular hole to allow air circulation. The swab box can then be placed in a paper or manila envelope.

All packages containing biological evidence should be refrigerated or stored in a cool location out of direct sunlight until delivery to the laboratory. However, one common exception is blood mixed with soil. Microbes present in soil rapidly degrade DNA. Therefore, blood in soil must be stored in a clean glass or plastic container and immediately frozen.

substrate control
An unstained object adjacent to an area on which biological material has been deposited

buccal cells
Cells derived from the inner cheek lining

Obtaining DNA Reference Specimens

Biological evidence attains its full forensic value only when an analyst can compare each of its DNA types to known DNA samples collected from victims and suspects. For this purpose, at least 7 milliliters (7 cc) of whole blood should be drawn from individuals by a qualified medical person. The blood sample should be collected in a sterile vacuum tube containing the preservative *EDTA* (ethylenediamine tetraacetic acid). In addition to serving as a preservative, EDTA inhibits the activity of enzymes that degrade DNA. The tubes must be kept refrigerated (not frozen) while awaiting transportation to the laboratory. In addition to blood, other options exist for obtaining standard/reference DNA specimens. The least intrusive method for obtaining a DNA standard/reference, one that nonmedical personnel can readily use, is the *buccal swab*. Cotton swabs are placed in the subject's mouth and the inside of the cheek is vigorously swabbed, resulting in the transfer of **buccal cells** onto the swab.

With the increasing need for collection and analysis of DNA samples in forensic investigations, collection and long-term storage of DNA has become an important consideration. FTA paper is a type of commercially available filter paper loaded with a mix of reagents on which DNA samples can be stored. The card has been impregnated with a chemical that protects DNA from bacterial enzyme breakdown. The fibers of the paper can entrap the DNA for more than ten years without refrigeration. Figure 15 illustrates the collection of a buccal swab and its transfer onto an FTA card for storage.

If an individual is not available to give a DNA standard/reference sample, some interesting alternatives are available to evidence collectors, including a toothbrush, combs and hairbrushes, a razor, soiled laundry, used cigarette butts, and earplugs. Any of these items may contain a sufficient quantity of DNA for typing purposes. Interestingly, as investigators worked to identify the remains of victims of the World Trade Center attack on September 11, 2001, the families of the missing were requested to supply the New York City DNA Laboratory with these types of items in an effort to match recovered DNA with human remains.

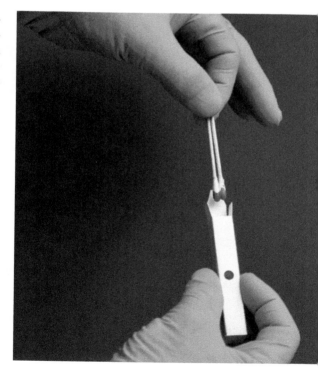

FIGURE 14

Air-dried swabs are placed in a swab box for delivery to the forensic laboratory.
Courtesy Tri-Tech, Inc., Southport, N.C., www.tritechusa.com

(1)

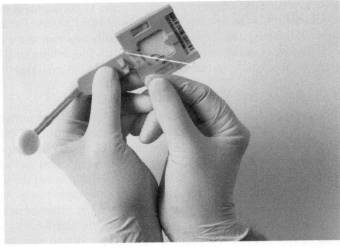
(2)

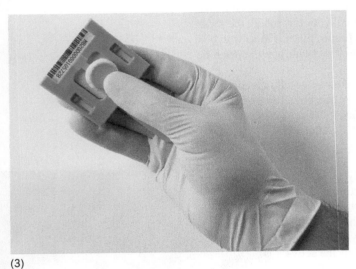
(3)

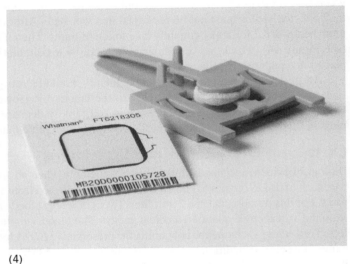
(4)

FIGURE 15

(1) A buccal swab is collected by rubbing each cheek for 15 seconds. (2) A protective film is peeled off the FTA card. (3) The swab is snapped in place against the FTA paper. (4) The FTA card is removed from the collection device and stored.

Courtesy GE Healthcare Bio-Sciences Corp. (GEHC), Piscataway, N.J., www.whatman.com

Contamination of DNA Evidence

One key concern during the collection of a DNA-containing specimen is contamination. Contamination can occur by introducing foreign DNA through coughing or sneezing onto a stain during the collection process, or there can be a transfer of DNA when items of evidence are incorrectly placed in contact with each other during packaging. Fortunately, an examination of DNA band patterns in the laboratory readily reveals the presence of contamination. For example, with an STR, one will expect to see a two-band pattern. More than two bands suggest a mixture of DNA from more than one source.

Crime-scene investigators can take some relatively simple steps to minimize contamination of biological evidence:

1. Change gloves before handling each new piece of evidence.
2. Collect a substrate control for possible subsequent laboratory examination.

3. Pick up small items of evidence such as cigarette butts and stamps with clean forceps. Disposable forceps are to be used so that they can be discarded after a single evidence collection.

4. Always package each item of evidence in its own well-ventilated container.

A common occurrence at crime scenes is to suspect the presence of blood but not be able to observe any with the naked eye. In these situations, the common test of choice is luminol. Interestingly, luminol does not inhibit the ability to detect and characterize STRs.[6] Therefore, luminol can be used to locate traces of blood and areas that have been washed nearly free of blood without compromising the potential for DNA typing.

mycrimekit

WEBEXTRA 11.12
Assume the Duties of an Evidence Collection Technician at a Burglary Scene
www.mycrimekit.com

forensic brief

> > > > > > > > > >

A woman alleged that she had been held against her will and sexually assaulted by a male friend in an apartment. During the course of the assault, a contact lens was knocked from the victim's eye. After the assault, she escaped, but because she was afraid of the threats made by her attacker, she did not report the assault to the police for three days. When the police examined the apartment, they noted that it had been thoroughly cleaned. A vacuum cleaner bag was seized for examination, and several pieces of material resembling fragments of a contact lens were discovered within the bag.

In the laboratory, approximately 20 nanograms of human DNA was recovered from the contact lens fragments. Cells from both the eyeball and the interior of the eyelids are naturally replaced every 6 to 24 hours. Therefore, both are potential sources for the DNA found. The DNA profile originating from the fragments matched the victim, thus corroborating the victim's account of the crime. The estimated population frequency of occurrence for the nine matching STRs are approximately 1 in 850 million. The suspect subsequently pleaded guilty to the offense.

STR Locus	Victim's DNA Type	Contact Lens
D3S1358	15,18	15,18
FGA	24, 25	24, 25
vWA	17,17	17,17
TH01	6, 7	6, 7
F13A1	5, 6	5, 6
fes/fps	11,12	11,12
D5S818	11,12	11,12
D13S317	11,12	11,12
D7S820	10,12	10,12

Source: R. A. Wickenheiser and R. M. Jobin, "Comparison of DNA Recovered from a Contact Lens Using PCR DNA Typing," *Canadian Society of Forensic Science Journal* 32 (1999): 67.

[6] A. M. Gross et al., "The Effect of Luminol on Presumptive Tests and DNA Analysis Using the Polymerase Chain Reaction," *Journal of Forensic Sciences* 44 (1999): 837.

chapter summary

> > > > > > > > > > >

Portions of the DNA structure are as unique to each individual as fingerprints. The gene is the fundamental unit of heredity. Each gene is actually composed of DNA specifically designed to control the genetic traits of our cells. DNA is constructed as a very large molecule made by linking a series of repeating units called nucleotides. Four types of bases are associated with the DNA structure: adenine (*A*), guanine (*G*), cytosine (*C*), and thymine (*T*). The bases on each strand are properly aligned in a double-helix configuration. As a result, adenine pairs with thymine and guanine pairs with cytosine. This concept is known as base pairing. The order of the bases is what distinguishes different DNA strands.

Portions of the DNA molecule contain sequences of bases that are repeated numerous times. To a forensic scientist, these tandem repeats offer a means of distinguishing one individual from another through DNA typing. Length differences associated with relatively short repeating DNA strands are called short tandem repeats (STRs) and form the basis for the current DNA-typing procedure. They serve as useful markers for identification because they are found in great abundance throughout the human genome. STRs normally consist of repeating sequences 3 to 7 bases long, and the entire strand of an STR is also very short, less than 450 bases long. This means that STRs are much less susceptible to degradation and may often be

recovered from bodies or stains that have been subjected to decomposition. Also, because of their shortness, STRs are ideal candidates for multiplication by PCR, in which STR strands are multiplied over a billionfold. PCR is responsible for the ability of STR typing to detect the genetic material of as few as 18 DNA-bearing cells. The more STRs one can characterize, the smaller the percentage of the population from which a particular combination of STRs can emanate. This gives rise to the concept of multiplexing. Using the technology of PCR, one can simultaneously extract and amplify a combination of different STRs. Currently, U.S. crime laboratories have standardized on 13 STRs. With STR analysis, as few as 125 picograms of DNA are required.

Another type of DNA used for individual characterization is mitochondrial DNA. Mitochondrial DNA is located outside the cell's nucleus and is inherited from the mother. However, mitochondrial DNA typing does not approach STR analysis in its discrimination power and thus is best reserved for samples, such as hair, for which STR analysis may not be possible.

Bloodstained evidence should not be packaged in plastic or airtight containers because accumulation of residual moisture could contribute to the growth of blood-destroying bacteria and fungi. Each stained article should be packaged separately in a paper bag or in a well-ventilated box.

review questions

1. The fundamental unit of heredity is the _____.

2. Each gene is actually composed of _____, specifically designed to carry out a single body function.

3. A(n) _____ is a very large molecule made by linking a series of repeating units.

4. A(n) _____ is composed of a sugar molecule, a phosphorus-containing group, and a nitrogen-containing molecule called a base.

5. DNA is actually a very large molecule made by linking a series of _____ to form a natural polymer.

6. _____ different bases are associated with the makeup of DNA.

7. Watson and Crick demonstrated that DNA is composed of two strands coiled into the shape of a(n) _____.

8. The structure of DNA requires the pairing of base A to _____ and base G to _____.

9. The base sequence *T–G–C–A* can be paired with the base sequence _____ in a double-helix configuration.

10. The inheritable traits that are controlled by DNA arise out of DNA's ability to direct the production of _____.

11. _____ are derived from a combination of up to 20 known amino acids.

12. The production of an amino acid is controlled by a sequence of _____ bases on the DNA molecule.

13. True or False: Enzymes known as DNA polymerase assemble new DNA strands into a proper base sequence during replication. _____

14. True or False: DNA can be copied outside a living cell. _____

15. True or False: All of the letter sequences in DNA code for the production of proteins. _____

16. In STR DNA typing, a typical DNA pattern shows (two, three) bands.

17. True or False: Specimens amenable to DNA typing are blood, semen, body tissues, and hair. _____

18. Short DNA segments containing repeating sequences of three to seven bases are called _____.

19. True or False: The longer the DNA strand, the less susceptible it is to degradation. _____

20. The short length of STRs allows them to be replicated by _____.

21. True or False: Enzymes known as DNA polymerases assemble new DNA strands into a proper base sequence based off the template strand during replication. _____

22. DNA evidence at a crime scene can be copied by the processes of the _____ with the aid of a DNA polymerase and specific primers.

23. Used as markers for identification purposes, _____ are locations on the chromosome that contain short sequences that repeat themselves within the DNA molecule and in great abundance throughout the human genome.

24. (CODIS, AFIS) maintains local, state, and national databases of DNA profiles from convicted offenders, unsolved crime-scene evidence, and profiles of missing people.

25. Amazingly, the sensitivity of STR profiling requires only _____ DNA-bearing cells to obtain an STR profile.

26. During evidence collection, all body fluids must be assumed to be _____ and handled with latex-gloved hands.

27. The concept of (CODIS, multiplexing) involves simultaneous detection of more than one DNA marker.

28. DNA fragments can be separated and identified by (gas chromatography, capillary electrophoresis).

29. The amelogenin gene shows two bands for a (male, female) and one band for a (male, female).

30. Y-STR typing is useful when one is confronted with a DNA mixture containing more than one (male, female) contributor.

31. Mitochondrial DNA is inherited from the (mother, father).

32. True or False: Mitochondrial DNA is more plentiful in the human cell than is nuclear DNA. _____

33. (Two, Four) regions of mitochondrial DNA have been found to be highly variable in the human population.

34. True or False: Polymerase chain reaction is a part of the process used in the forensic analysis of RFLP, STRs, and mitochondrial DNA. _____

35. The national DNA database in the United States has standardized on _____ STRs for entry into the database.

36. True or False: Y-STR data is normally entered into the CODIS database collection. _____.

37. Small amounts of blood are best submitted to a crime laboratory in a (wet, dry) condition.

38. True or False: Airtight packages make the best containers for blood-containing evidence. _____

39. Whole blood collected for DNA-typing purposes must be placed in a vacuum containing the preservative _____.

40. A typical STR DNA type emanating from a single individual shows a (one, two, three)-band pattern.

application and critical thinking

1. The following sequence of bases is located on one strand of a DNA molecule:

   C–G–A–A–T–C–G–C–A–A–T–C–G–A–C–C–T–G

   List the sequence of bases that will form complementary pairs on the other strand of the DNA molecule.

2. A woman reports being mugged by a masked assailant, whom she scratched on the arm during a brief struggle. The victim gives the police a good description of her attacker, but she is not sure whether the attacker was male or female. Describe the steps and procedures you would use to determine the sex of the attacker. How will you know whether the attacker is male or female?

3. Police discover a badly decomposed body buried in an area where a man disappeared some years before. The case was never solved, nor was the victim's body ever recovered. As the lead investigator, you suspect that the newly discovered body is that of the victim. What is your main challenge in using DNA typing to determine whether your suspicion is correct? How would you go about using DNA technology to test your theory?

4. You are a forensic scientist performing DNA typing on a blood sample sent to your laboratory. While performing an STR analysis on the sample, you notice a four-band pattern. What conclusion should you draw? Why?

further references

Butler, J. M., *Forensic DNA Typing*, 3rd ed. Burlington, Mass.: Elsevier Academic Press, 2010.

Inman, K., and N. Rudin, *An Introduction to Forensic DNA Analysis*, 2nd ed. Boca Raton, Fla.: Taylor & Francis, 2002.

Isenberg, A. R., "Forensic Mitochondrial DNA Analysis," in R. Saferstein, ed., *Forensic Science Handbook*, vol. 2, 2nd ed. Upper Saddle River, N.J.: Prentice Hall, 2005.

Isenberg, A. R., and J. M. Moore, "Mitochondrial DNA Analysis at the FBI Laboratory," *Forensic Science Communications* 1, no. 2 (1999), http://www.fbi.gov/hq/lab/fsc/backissu/july1999/dnalist.htm.

Kobilinsky, L., "Deoxyribonucleic Acid Structure and Function—A Review," in R. Saferstein, ed., *Forensic Science Handbook*, vol. 3, 2nd ed.., Upper Saddle River, N.J.: Prentice Hall, 2010.

The Forensic Community's Response to September 11

On September 11, Brion Smith was home in Frederick, Md., enjoying a vacation day when the news flashed across his television screen—the World Trade Center (WTC) buildings had been struck by two hijacked airplanes. Minutes later, a third plane struck the Pentagon while a fourth later crashed in a field in Somerset County, Pa. Acting on impulse, Smith, chief deputy medical examiner for the DNA Division of the Office of the Armed Forces Medical Examiner (OAFME), immediately gathered his things and headed in to work. "Your first inclination, of course, is to go to the crash site," he says, "however, a DNA person has little utility outside of the laboratory.". . .

Wilder Damian Smith
Staff editor for *Analytical Chemistry*

World Trade Center

Marie Samples, an assistant director in the Department of Forensic Biology in the Office of Chief Medical Examiner (OCME) in New York, was sitting in a management meeting when a co-worker poked his head in and delivered the horrific news. "When someone tells you that the WTCs have just collapsed, you don't ever fathom that happening," says Samples. "I don't think it sunk in with me until I got home."

Overseeing mass tragedies is nothing new to the OCME. In 1990, the lab handled the Happy Land Social Club fire in which 87 people died; then in 1993, they handled the *Golden Venture* tragedy in which 286 Chinese immigrants drowned when their boat went aground off the coast of New Jersey. The OCME has about 90 experienced technicians on staff who perform various tasks, including examining physical evidence; conducting DNA extractions; and overseeing DNA quantitation, amplification, and finally, DNA typing.

"Our first thought was that we would be able to handle the samples in-house," says Samples. But as the estimates of the number of bodies at the WTC site continued to pile up—initial reports were as high as 7000—those plans quickly changed. "We've handled big disasters in the past, but this was nothing like we've ever seen," exclaims Samples. Although the OCME has the largest DNA analysis lab in the country, the thought of tackling a project with that many unknown and presumed dead presented other problems for Samples and her lab. "We had two big responsibilities that were clashing," she says,

United Flight 175, hijacked by terrorists, crashes into 2 World Trade Center. *Courtesy Robert Clark, Aurora Photos Inc.*

"our commitment to serve the criminal justice system in New York for the cases we normally handle—sexual assaults, homicides, etc.—and our role as a support lab for the medical examiners in determining the cause of death." She goes on to say, "We knew we couldn't do both of them well at the same time, so we decided to contract out the DNA typing work."

As the search and rescue mission for the victims of the WTC collapse became a recovery mission, more problems faced the forensic community. At Ground Zero—the name given to the site of the collapsed WTC buildings—literally millions of human remains were lying scattered deep beneath the tons of twisted metal and shattered cement. "We have to remember that when those towers fell, they turned into giant shredders," says Kevin McElfresh, a senior scientist with BODE Technologies. The smoldering fires, the exposure to the outside weather, and the estimated amount of time it would take to remove the debris—a year, by some calculations—also presented problems for the chemists. "At least in the [1999] Swiss Air crash, the remains were in the water at the bottom of the ocean in four degree water; even though they were down there for three months, we were still able to extract DNA to generate full profiles," says Benoit Leclair, senior scientist with Myriad Genetics. . . .

Some 7 months later, remains were still being collected and taken to Fresh Kills, an abandoned 3000-acre landfill on Staten Island, N.Y., that has been reincarnated as the country's largest "rake-and-sift" DNA lab. There, workers meticulously pick through bits of concrete, rocks, and other rubble in search of the tiniest remnants of human tissue, teeth, and even hair to aid in the identification process. The OCME extracts the DNA from each of the remains recovered, and those extracts are then shipped off to the respective companies for DNA typing and profiling.

To handle the profiling, the OCME contracted the services of three companies: Myriad Genetics, Celera Genomics, and BODE Technologies. Blood and tissue samples recovered from the site are being sent to Myriad Genetics, based in Salt Lake City, Utah. The company is using the technique of short tandem repeats (STR) on the recovered tissues. "I would refer to this as data mining," says Leclair. STR is a technique that focuses on 13 loci found over the 23 pairs of chromosomes that make up a human's genome. After polymerase chain reaction (PCR) amplification, the newly formed DNA fragments are separated by capillary electrophoresis. Myriad had worked with the New York State Police prior to September 11, performing similar analysis on New York's rape kits.

When blood and tissue samples are not available from the WTC site for DNA typing, forensic scientists often have to turn to another source: bones. BODE Technical Group, a Virginia-based company, is overseeing the bone analysis of the victims. Its lab has about 70 employees, and one of its two specialized units is devoted to forensic analysis. The company participated in the forensic identification of the 88 victims in the Alaska Air crash in 2000. Currently, it has received over 7000 samples from the WTC site.

When the tissue samples are severely burned or degraded, a process called mitochondrial DNA (mtDNA) analysis often has to be done; because this was the case with some of the recovered remains from Ground Zero, the OCME contracted the Rockville, Md., company Celera Genomics to oversee the mtDNA analyses of the WTC victims. However, Celera, a business under the Applera Corp., was an unusual choice. "Unlike BODE and Myriad," says Heather Kowalski, Celera's director of corporate communications, "[Celera] didn't have a forensic part to our business before this tragedy

occurred." Celera is known mainly for its work on the Human Genome Project and as a high-throughput sequencing company.

In preparation for the incoming samples, Celera built four new forensic laboratories in the span of two months and hired Rhonda Roby to oversee the forensics program. Before that, Roby worked as a forensic scientist for Applied Biosystems (AB), which is also a business unit of Applera, and which has a Human Identification Group and experience working with the forensic community. Despite the novelty of the project, Roby wasn't intimidated. "As scientists, we knew we had something to offer, and Applera wanted to do it right," says Roby. "Celera offers expertise in high-throughput sequencing and bioinformatics capabilities, and Applied Biosystems offers expertise as the inventors of the sequencing chemistry, software and instruments, and a team of forensic scientists from the Human Identification Group."

Quality Control

After DNA profiles are obtained, the results are then shipped back to the New York State Police Laboratory in Albany, N.Y. There, the information is stored in a specially modified version of the FBI's Combined DNA Index System (CODIS) database.

The original CODIS database stores the DNA information of convicted felons and is used to match that information in prosecution cases. This new version of the database uses the same DNA comparison software, but only for purposes of matching the September 11 DNA profiles to those of the recovered victims' blood samples submitted by their relatives, and to the DNA information obtained from the victims' toothbrushes, hair, soiled laundry, and used cigarette butts. Also, as part of the OCME's quality control efforts, BODE is also repeating 5% of the mtDNA analysis that Celera conducts.

Sample Analysis

Medical and legal issues have to be considered when determining how much of a sample is needed to yield identifying information.

Ground Zero. *Courtesy AP/Wide World Photos*

The condition of the recovered body parts determines which type of analysis—nuclear (nucDNA) or mtDNA—is performed.

NucDNA analysis is the most commonly used because it's faster, the genome is found in the cell's nucleus, and the DNA has alleles from each parent. In nucDNA analysis, the DNA fragments are analyzed and amplified using PCR. The profile from the nucDNA is then obtained and used to match and verify a victim. However, this type of analysis usually requires a lot of sample. "The problem," says Smith, "is that despite having a large amount of sample, sometimes there are only three grams of usable tissue available for analysis; and that is often totally exhausted during analysis."

MtDNA analysis is somewhat different. Mitochondria are abundant in the cell's cytoplasm, but the mtDNA only comes from the mother. The high number of mtDNA genomes in the cell increases the likelihood of successful PCR amplification. However, mtDNA analysis is more difficult to perform than nucDNA, more time consuming, and very expensive.

The second issue facing analysts is more humanitarian. "We can't tell someone, 'The good news was that it was him; the bad news is that he's all gone,'" says Smith. Most families would rather have some remains of their loved one to take home, even if it is just a small piece. "There isn't one of our people that doesn't understand that there is a family in dire need to know what happened to their loved one," says McElfresh. The scientists use every piece of information they can to find answers. "What gets to me the most is that when it's late and you have a set of records in front of you and what you are looking at is the reconstruction of a person's life through the eyes and the contributions of their family," he says. The resolve of the scientists, says Smith, is evident every day. "With this project, I've seen people so driven that they are standing with their eyes shut and you have to tell them to go home," he says.

The Pentagon and Somerset

Civilian plane crashes are normally assigned to the Federal Aviation Administration (FAA) and the National Transportation Safety Board (NTSB). However, the DNA Division of the OAFME—a federal lab based in Rockville, Md., with two forensic facilities—handled the remains from the Pentagon and the Somerset County, Pa., sites. "We [NTSB] don't have DNA analysis capability," says Frank Ciaccio, chief of forensic sciences and a forensic anthropologist for the NTSB.

In 1996, the NTSB established a memorandum of understanding with the Department of Defense that recommends to local coroners that they use the services of the Armed Forces DNA Identification Laboratory (AFDIL)—the first facility of the OAFME—for DNA analysis. Under the terms of that agreement, the Armed Forces Institute of Pathology (AFIP) simply had to be invited to perform the DNA identifications of the crash victims by the local coroner, and that is what happened in the Pentagon and Somerset cases.

Previously, the AFDIL had performed DNA casework on the victims of the 1999 Egypt Air and the 2000 Alaska Air plane crashes. The AFDIL has 30 technicians divided into 6 teams that specialize in mtDNA analysis and a smaller group that handles all the nucDNA casework. The mtDNA section of the AFDIL was created in 1991 and has been instrumental in the identification of the recovered remains of American servicemen from the Korean War. To date, the AFDIL has received over 2000 samples for typing from the Pentagon and Somerset crashes.

The second OAFME facility, called the Armed Forces Repository of Specimen Samples for the Identification of Remains, houses blood-stained cards for all active duty, reserve, and National Guard military personnel. These filter paper cards are refrigerated and contain each person's name, social security number, date of birth, and two quarter-size spots of blood. In the Pentagon and Somerset crashes, about 50 of the victims were active duty American servicemen.

Were They Prepared?

"We have the largest DNA lab in the country, and even we couldn't handle [the WTC] caseload," says Samples. "It's hard for a lab to try to prepare for something along the lines of New York when it isn't likely to happen." (Samples's lab also had 12 new lab technicians start work on September 10.)

Learning from previous crashes, Smith's lab implemented a few critical changes. "We found that by having a DNA collection team [at the crash site], they could collect the tissue sample after it has been taken from the body and tag it with a number and bar code onsite before it gets back to the lab," he says. Creating better software in the chain of custody was also important. "For the Pentagon and Somerset crashes we set up two computer systems, one at the Dover Air Force Base and the other in Somerset County for the Pennsylvania crash."

Smith believes experience is the best teacher. "The thing we were missing in the Egypt and Alaska Air crashes was how to compare hundreds of DNA profiles obtained from the evidence with hundreds of DNA reference profiles," he says. "The hardest part of the project was sorting, comparing, matching, and reporting the data, so there was clearly a role for automation."

Need for New Technology

Although forensic technology has advanced, Leclair believes it still is always a step behind the last disaster. "We have the DNA typing tools to tackle a disaster such as Swiss Air only as a result of the TWA 800 disaster," states Leclair. Back in the late 1980s, DNA analysis was all done using a variable number of tandem repeats or restriction fragment-length polymorphisms, which required an enormous amount of sample and analysis time.

Today, most labs are using PCR to analyze DNA. "PCR has been the biggest addition to forensic technology," says McElfresh. "I can't imagine dealing with something the magnitude of this [WTC buildings and Pentagon] with that old technology."

But the tragedies of September 11, say some forensic scientists, should be a wake-up call to the community. "Considering the magnitude of the New York disaster, one can readily see the need for powerful bioinformatics tools," states Leclair.

Roby believes that robotics and more advanced automation are the technologies of the future for forensics. "What may come out of [September 11] is that we are using robotic systems and automation, and we may be able to advance forensic sciences with the scientific technology that is available in other areas with these systems," she says. Samples agrees. "We had thought about using the robotics system before, but our caseload had never justified using them."

Justifying new technology, and finding the time to develop it, seem to be the biggest obstacles. "I think the forensic community could have handled the caseload of the WTC buildings without robotics and automation," says Roby, "but the question is how long would it have taken?"

answers to review questions

Odd-Numbered Review Questions

1. gene
3. polymer
5. nucleotides
7. double helix
9. *A–C–G–T*
11. Proteins
13. True
15. False
17. True
19. False
21. True
23. tandem repeats
25. 18
27. multiplexing
29. male; female
31. mother
33. Two
35. 13
37. dry
39. EDTA (ethylenedi-
    amine tetraacetic acid)

Application and Critical Thinking

1. *G–C–T–T–A–G–C–G–T–T–A–G–C–T–G–G–A–C*
2. You would first collect any blood or skin scrapings under the victim's fingernails because these may contain DNA. You would then amplify the DNA in the sample using PCR and separate the fragments using electrophoresis. Finally, you would look for the bands of separated DNA that correspond to the amelogenin gene. If the sample contains two bands, the attacker is male; if the sample contains only one band, the attacker is female.
3. Investigators use mtDNA to determine whether the body is that of the victim of the unsolved murder. To do so, you would collect mtDNA from one of the victim's maternal relatives and compare it to the mtDNA recovered from the body. If the samples match, the body is that of the victim.
4. With an STR, you should expect to see a two-band pattern. The presence of more than two bands suggests a mixture of DNA from more than one source.

fingerprints

James Earl Ray: Conspirator or Lone Gunman?

Since his arrest in 1968 for the assassination of Dr. Martin Luther King, Jr., endless speculation has swirled around the motives and connections of James Earl Ray. Ray was a career criminal who was serving time for armed robbery when he escaped from the Missouri State Prison almost one year before the assassination. On April 3, 1968, Ray arrived in Memphis, Tennessee. The next day he rented a room at Bessie Brewer's Rooming House, across the street from the Lorraine Motel where Dr. King was staying.

At 6:00 p.m., Dr. King left his second-story motel room and stepped onto the balcony of the Lorraine Motel. As King turned toward his room, a shot rang out, striking the civil rights activist. Nothing could be done to revive him, and Dr. King was pronounced dead at 7:05 p.m. As the assailant ran on foot from Bessie Brewer's, he left a blanket-covered package in front of a nearby building and then drove off in a white Mustang. The package was later shown to contain a high-powered rifle equipped with a scope, a radio, some clothes, a pair of binoculars, a couple of beer cans, and a receipt for the binoculars. Almost a week after the shooting, the white Mustang was found abandoned in Atlanta, Georgia.

Fingerprints later identified as James Earl Ray's were found in the Mustang, on the rifle, on the binoculars, and on a beer can. In 1969, Ray entered a guilty plea in return for a sentence of ninety-nine years. Although a variety of conspiracy theories surround this crime, the indisputable fact is that a fingerprint put the rifle that killed Martin Luther King, Jr., in the hands of James Earl Ray.

fingerprints

Learning Objectives

After studying this chapter you should be able to:

- Know the common ridge characteristics of a fingerprint
- List the three major fingerprint patterns and their respective subclasses
- Distinguish visible, plastic, and latent fingerprints
- Describe the concept of an automated fingerprint identification system (AFIS)
- List the techniques for developing latent fingerprints on porous and nonporous objects
- Describe the proper procedures for preserving a developed latent fingerprint

History of Fingerprinting

Since the beginnings of criminal investigation, police have sought an infallible means of human identification. The first systematic attempt at personal identification was devised and introduced by a French police expert, Alphonse Bertillon, in 1883. The Bertillon system relied on a detailed description (**portrait parlé**) of the subject, combined with full-length and profile photographs and a system of precise body measurements known as **anthropometry**.

The use of anthropometry as a method of identification rested on the premise that the dimensions of the human bone system remained fixed from age 20 until death. Skeleton sizes were thought to be so extremely diverse that no two individuals could have exactly the same measurements. Bertillon recommended routine taking of eleven measurements of the human anatomy. These included height, reach, width of head, and length of the left foot.

For two decades, this system was considered the most accurate method of identification. But in the first years of the new century, police began to appreciate and accept a system of identification based on the classification of finger ridge patterns known as *fingerprints*. Today, the fingerprint is the pillar of modern criminal identification.

Early Use of Fingerprints

Evidence exists that the Chinese used the fingerprint to sign legal documents as far back as three thousand years ago. However, whether this practice was performed for ceremonial custom or as a means of personal identity remains a point of conjecture lost to history. In any case, the examples of fingerprinting in ancient history are ambiguous, and the few that exist did not contribute to the development of fingerprinting techniques as we know them today.

Several years before Bertillon began work on his system, William Herschel, an English civil servant stationed in India, started the practice of requiring Indian citizens to sign contracts with the imprint of their right hand, which was pressed against a stamp pad for the purpose. The motives for Herschel's requirement remain unclear; he may have envisioned fingerprinting as a means of personal identification or just as a form of the Hindu custom that a trace of bodily contact was more binding than a signature on a contract. In any case, he did not publish anything about his activities until after a Scottish physician, Henry Fauld, working in a hospital in Japan, published his views on the potential application of fingerprinting to personal identification.

In 1880, Fauld suggested that skin ridge patterns could be important for the identification of criminals. He told about a thief who left his fingerprint on a whitewashed wall, and how in comparing these prints with those of a suspect, he found that they were quite different. A few days later another suspect was found whose fingerprints compared with those on the wall. When confronted with this evidence, the individual confessed to the crime.

Fauld was convinced that fingerprints furnished infallible proof of identification. He even offered to set up, at his own expense, a fingerprint bureau at Scotland Yard to test the practicality of the method. But his offer was rejected in favor of the Bertillon system. This decision was reversed less than two decades later.

Early Classification of Fingerprints

The extensive research into fingerprinting conducted by another Englishman, Francis Galton, provided the needed impetus that made police agencies aware of its potential application. In 1892, Galton published his classic textbook *Finger Prints*, the first book of its kind on the subject. In his book, he discussed the anatomy of fingerprints and suggested methods for recording them. Galton also proposed assigning fingerprints to three pattern types—loops, arches, and whorls. Most important, the book demonstrated that no two prints were identical and that an individual's prints remained unchanged from year to year. At Galton's insistence, the British government adopted fingerprinting as a supplement to the Bertillon system.

The next step in the development of fingerprint technology was the creation of classification systems capable of filing thousands of prints in a logical and searchable sequence. Dr. Juan Vucetich, an Argentinian police officer fascinated by Galton's work, devised a workable concept in 1891. His classification system has been refined over the years and is still widely used today in most Spanish-speaking countries. In 1897, another classification system was proposed by an Englishman, Sir Edward Richard Henry. Four years later, Henry's system was adopted by Scotland

portrait parlé
A verbal description of a perpetrator's physical characteristics and dress provided by an eyewitness

anthropometry
A system of identification of individuals by measurement of parts of the body, developed by Alphonse Bertillon

Yard. Today, most English-speaking countries, including the United States, use some version of Henry's classification system to file fingerprints.

Adoption of Fingerprinting

Early in the 20th century, Bertillon's measurement system began to fall into disfavor. Its results were highly susceptible to error, particularly when the measurements were taken by people who were not thoroughly trained. The method was dealt its most severe and notable setback in 1903 when a convict, Will West, arrived at Fort Leavenworth prison. A routine check of the prison files startlingly revealed that a William West, already in the prison, could not be distinguished from the new prisoner by body measurements or even by photographs. In fact, the two men looked just like twins, and their measurements were practically the same. Subsequently, fingerprints of the prisoners clearly distinguished them.

In the United States, the first systematic and official use of fingerprints for personal identification was adopted by the New York City Civil Service Commission in 1901. The method was used for certifying all civil service applications. Several American police officials received instruction in fingerprint identification at the 1904 World's Fair in St. Louis from representatives of Scotland Yard. After the fair and the Will West incident, fingerprinting began to be used in earnest in all major cities of the United States. In 1924, the fingerprint records of the Bureau of Investigation and Leavenworth were merged to form the nucleus of the identification records of the new Federal Bureau of Investigation. The FBI has the largest collection of fingerprints in the world. By the beginning of World War I, England and practically all of Europe had adopted fingerprinting as their primary method of identifying criminals.

In 1999, the admissibility of fingerprint evidence was challenged in the case of *United States* v. *Byron C. Mitchell* in the Eastern District of Pennsylvania. The defendant's attorneys argued that fingerprints could not be proven unique under the guidelines cited in *Daubert*. Government experts vigorously disputed this claim. After a four-and-a-half-day *Daubert* hearing, the judge upheld the admissibility of fingerprints as scientific evidence and ruled that (1) human friction ridges are unique and permanent and (2) human friction ridge skin arrangements are unique and permanent.

Fundamental Principles of Fingerprints

First Principle: A Fingerprint Is an Individual Characteristic; No Two Fingers Have Yet Been Found to Possess Identical Ridge Characteristics

The acceptance of fingerprint evidence by the courts has always been predicated on the assumption that no two individuals have identical fingerprints. Early fingerprint experts consistently referred to Galton's calculation, showing the possible existence of 64 billion different fingerprints, to support this contention. Later, researchers questioned the validity of Galton's figures and attempted to devise mathematical models to better approximate this value. However, no matter what mathematical model one refers to, the conclusions are always the same: the probability for the existence of two identical fingerprint patterns in the world's population is extremely small.

Not only is this principle supported by theoretical calculations, but just as important, it is verified by the millions of individuals who have had their prints classified during the past 110 years—no two have ever been found to be identical. The FBI has nearly 50 million fingerprint records in its computer database and has yet to find an identical image belonging to two different people.

RIDGE CHARACTERISTICS   The individuality of a fingerprint is not determined by its general shape or pattern but by a careful study of its **ridge characteristics** (also known as **minutiae**). The identity, number, and relative location of characteristics such as those illustrated in Figure 1 impart individuality to a fingerprint. If two prints are to match, they must reveal characteristics that not only are identical but have the same relative location to one another in a print. In a judicial proceeding, a point-by-point comparison must be demonstrated by the expert, using charts similar to the one shown in Figure 2, in order to prove the identity of an individual.

If an expert were asked to compare the characteristics of the complete fingerprint, no difficulty would be encountered in completing such an assignment; the average fingerprint has as

ridge characteristics (minutiae)
Ridge endings, bifurcations, enclosures, and other ridge details, which must match in two fingerprints in order for their common origin to be established

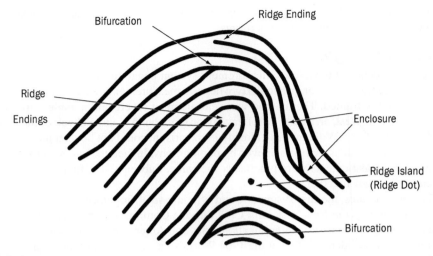

FIGURE 1

Fingerprint ridge characteristics.
Courtesy Sirchie Finger Print Laboratories, Inc., Youngsville, N.C., www.sirchie.com

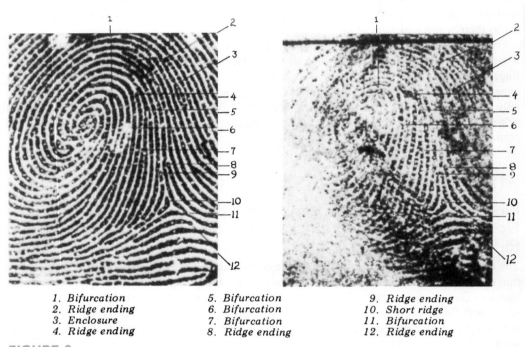

1. *Bifurcation*	5. *Bifurcation*	9. *Ridge ending*
2. *Ridge ending*	6. *Bifurcation*	10. *Short ridge*
3. *Enclosure*	7. *Bifurcation*	11. *Bifurcation*
4. *Ridge ending*	8. *Ridge ending*	12. *Ridge ending*

FIGURE 2

A fingerprint exhibit illustrating the matching ridge characteristics between the crime-scene print and an inked impression of one of the suspect's fingers.

many as 150 individual ridge characteristics. However, most prints recovered at crime scenes are partial impressions, showing only a segment of the entire print. Under these circumstances, the expert can compare only a small number of ridge characteristics from the recovered print to a known recorded print.

RIDGE COMPARISONS For years, experts have debated how many ridge comparisons are necessary to identify two fingerprints as the same. Numbers that range from 8 to 16 have been suggested as being sufficient to meet the criteria of individuality. However, the difficulty in establishing such a minimum is that no comprehensive statistical study has ever been undertaken to determine the frequency of occurrence of different ridge characteristics and their relative locations. Until such a study is undertaken and completed, no meaningful guidelines can be established for defining the uniqueness of a fingerprint.

In 1973, the International Association for Identification, after a three-year study of this question, concluded that "no valid basis exists for requiring a predetermined minimum number of friction ridge characteristics which must be present in two impressions in order to establish positive identification." Hence, the final determination must be based on the experience and knowledge of the expert, with the understanding that others may profess honest differences of opinion on the uniqueness of a fingerprint if the question of minimal number of ridge characteristics exists. In 1995, members of the international fingerprint community at a conference in Israel issued the Ne'urim Declaration, which supported the 1973 International Association for Identification resolution.

Second Principle: A Fingerprint Remains Unchanged During an Individual's Lifetime

Fingerprints are a reproduction of friction skin ridges found on the palm side of the fingers and thumbs. Similar friction skin can also be found on the surface of the palms and soles of the feet. Apparently, these skin surfaces have been designed by nature to provide our bodies with a firmer grasp and a resistance to slippage. A visual inspection of friction skin reveals a series of lines corresponding to hills (ridges) and valleys (grooves). The shape and form of the skin ridges are what one sees as the black lines of an inked fingerprint impression.

STRUCTURE OF THE SKIN   Skin is composed of layers of cells. Those nearest the surface make up the outer portion of the skin known as the *epidermis*, and the inner skin is known as the *dermis*. A cross section of skin (see Figure 3) reveals a boundary of cells separating the epidermis and dermis. The shape of this boundary, made up of *dermal papillae*, determines the form and pattern of the ridges on the surface of the skin. Once the dermal papillae develop in the human fetus, the ridge patterns remain unchanged throughout life except to enlarge during growth.

Each skin ridge is populated by a single row of pores that are the openings for ducts leading from the sweat glands. Through these pores, perspiration is discharged and deposited on the surface of the skin. Once the finger touches a surface, perspiration, along with oils that may have been picked up by touching the hairy portions of the body, is transferred onto that surface, thereby leaving an impression of the finger's ridge pattern (a fingerprint). Prints deposited in this manner are invisible to the eye and are commonly referred to as **latent fingerprints**.

CHANGING FINGERPRINTS   Although it is impossible to change one's fingerprints, there has been no lack of effort on the part of some criminals to obscure them. If an injury reaches deeply

latent fingerprint
A fingerprint made by the deposit of oils and/or perspiration; it is invisible to the naked eye

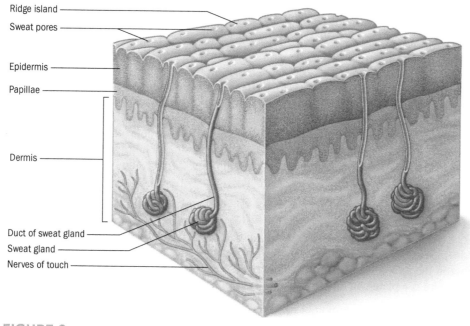

Ridge island
Sweat pores
Epidermis
Papillae
Dermis
Duct of sweat gland
Sweat gland
Nerves of touch

FIGURE 3

Cross-section of human skin.

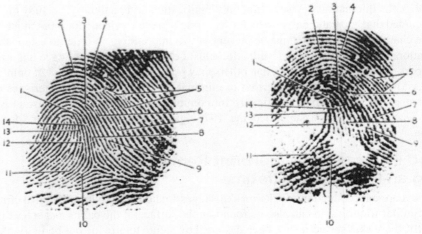

FIGURE 4

The right index finger impression of John Dillinger, before scarification on the left and afterward on the right. Comparison is proved by the 14 matching ridge characteristics.
Courtesy Institute of Applied Science, Youngsville, N.C.

enough into the skin and damages the dermal papillae, a permanent scar will form. However, for this to happen, such a wound would have to penetrate 1 to 2 millimeters beneath the skin's surface. Indeed, efforts at intentionally scarring the skin can only be self-defeating, for it would be totally impossible to obliterate all of the ridge characteristics on the hand, and the presence of permanent scars merely provides new characteristics for identification.

Perhaps the most publicized attempt at obliteration was that of the notorious gangster John Dillinger, who tried to destroy his own fingerprints by applying a corrosive acid to them. Prints taken at the morgue after he was shot to death, compared with fingerprints recorded at the time of a previous arrest, proved that his efforts had been fruitless (see Figure 4).

Third Principle: Fingerprints Have General Ridge Patterns That Permit Them to Be Systematically Classified

All fingerprints are divided into three classes on the basis of their general pattern: **loops, whorls,** and **arches**. Sixty to 65 percent of the population have loops, 30 to 35 percent have whorls, and about 5 percent have arches. These three classes form the basis for all ten-finger classification systems presently in use.

LOOPS   A typical loop pattern is illustrated in Figure 5. A loop must have one or more ridges entering from one side of the print, recurving, and exiting from the same side. If the loop opens toward the little finger, it is called an *ulnar loop*; if it opens toward the thumb, it is a *radial loop*. The pattern area of the loop is surrounded by two diverging ridges known as *type lines*. The ridge point at or nearest the type-line divergence and located at or directly in front of the point of divergence is known as the *delta*. To many, a fingerprint delta resembles the silt formation that builds up as a river flows into the entrance of a lake—hence, the analogy to the geological formation known as a delta. All loops must have one delta. The *core*, as the name suggests, is the approximate center of the pattern.

WHORLS   Whorls are actually divided into four distinct groups, as shown in Figure 6: plain, central pocket loop, double loop, and accidental. All whorl patterns must have type lines and at least two deltas. A plain whorl and a central pocket loop have at least one ridge that makes a complete circuit. This ridge may be in the form of a spiral, oval, or any variant of a circle. If an imaginary line drawn between the two deltas contained within these two patterns touches any one of the spiral ridges, the pattern is a plain whorl. If no such ridge is touched, the pattern is a central pocket loop.

ARCHES   Arches, the least common of the three general patterns, are subdivided into two distinct groups: plain arches and tented arches, as shown in Figure 7. The plain arch is the simplest of all fingerprint patterns; it is formed by ridges entering from one side of the print and

loop
A class of fingerprints characterized by ridge lines that enter from one side of the pattern and curve around to exit from the same side of the pattern

whorl
A class of fingerprints that includes ridge patterns that are generally rounded or circular in shape and have two deltas

arch
A class of fingerprints characterized by ridge lines that enter the print from one side and flow out the other side

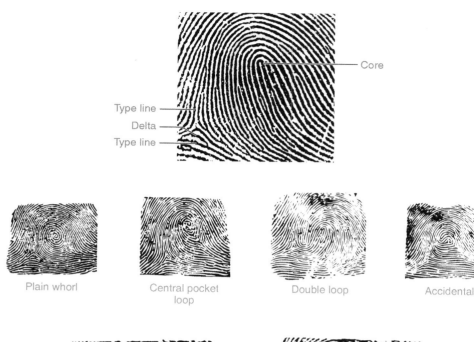

FIGURE 5
Loop pattern.

FIGURE 6
Whorl patterns.

Plain whorl · Central pocket loop · Double loop · Accidental

FIGURE 7
Arch patterns.

Plain · Tented

exiting on the opposite side. Generally, these ridges tend to rise in the center of the pattern, forming a wavelike pattern. The tented arch is similar to the plain arch except that instead of rising smoothly at the center, there is a sharp upthrust or spike, or the ridges meet at an angle that is less than 90 degrees.[1] Arches do not have type lines, deltas, or cores.

OTHER PATTERNS   As the name implies, the double loop is made up of two loops combined into one fingerprint. Any whorl classified as an accidental either contains two or more patterns (not including the plain arch) or is a pattern not covered by other categories. Hence, an accidental may consist of a combination loop and plain whorl or loop and tented arch.

With a knowledge of basic fingerprint pattern classes, we can now begin to develop an appreciation for fingerprint classification systems. However, the subject is far more complex than can be described in a textbook of this nature. The student seeking a more detailed treatment of the subject would do well to consult the references cited at the end of the chapter.

Classification of Fingerprints

The original Henry system, as it was adopted by Scotland Yard in 1901, converted ridge patterns on all ten fingers into a series of letters and numbers arranged in the form of a fraction. However, the system as it was originally designed could accommodate files of up to only 100,000 sets of

---

[1] A tented arch is also any pattern that resembles a loop but lacks one of the essential requirements for classification as a loop.

prints; thus, as collections grew in size, it became necessary to expand the capacity of the classification system. In the United States, the FBI, faced with the problem of filing ever-increasing numbers of prints, expanded its classification capacity by modifying and extending the original Henry system. These modifications are collectively known as the *FBI system* and are used by most agencies in the United States today.

The Primary Classification

Although we will not discuss all of the different divisions of the FBI system, a description of just one part, the primary classification, will provide an interesting insight into the process of fingerprint classification.

The primary classification is part of the original Henry system and provides the first classification step in the FBI system. Using this classification alone, all of the fingerprint cards in the world could be divided into 1,024 groups. The first step in obtaining the primary classification is to pair up fingers, placing one finger in the numerator of a fraction, the other in the denominator. The fingers are paired in the following sequence:

$$\frac{\text{R. Index}}{\text{R. Thumb}} \quad \frac{\text{R. Ring}}{\text{R. Middle}} \quad \frac{\text{L. Thumb}}{\text{R. Little}} \quad \frac{\text{L. Middle}}{\text{L. Index}} \quad \frac{\text{L. Little}}{\text{L. Ring}}$$

The presence or absence of the whorl pattern is the basis for determination of the primary classification. If a whorl pattern is found on any finger of the first pair, it is assigned a value of 16; on the second pair, a value of 8; on the third pair, a value of 4; on the fourth pair, a value of 2; and on the last pair, a value of 1. Any finger with an arch or loop pattern is assigned a value of 0.

After values for all ten fingers are obtained in this manner, they are totaled, and 1 is added to both the numerator and denominator. The fraction thus obtained is the primary classification. For example, if the right index and right middle fingers are whorls and all the others are loops, the primary classification is

$$\frac{16 + 0 + 0 + 0 + 0 + 1}{0 + 8 + 0 + 0 + 0 + 1} = \frac{17}{8}$$

Approximately 25 percent of the population falls into the 1/1 category; that is, all their fingers have either loops or arches.

A fingerprint classification system cannot in itself unequivocally identify an individual; it merely provides the fingerprint examiner with a number of candidates, all of whom have an indistinguishable set of prints in the system's file. The identification must always be made by a final visual comparison of the suspect print's and file print's ridge characteristics; only these features can impart individuality to a fingerprint. Although ridge patterns impart class characteristics to the print, the type and position of ridge characteristics give it its individual character.

Automated Fingerprint Identification Systems

The Henry system and its subclassifications have proven to be a cumbersome system for storing, retrieving, and searching for fingerprints, particularly as fingerprint collections grow in size. Nevertheless, until the emergence of fingerprint computer technology, this manual approach was the only viable method for the maintenance of fingerprint collections. Since 1970, technological advances have made possible the classification and retrieval of fingerprints by computers. Automated Fingerprint Identification Systems (AFISs) have proliferated throughout the law enforcement community.

In 1999, the FBI initiated full operation of the Integrated Automated Fingerprint Identification System (IAFIS), the largest AFIS in the United States, which links state AFIS computers with the FBI database. This database contains nearly 50 million fingerprint records. However, an AFIS can come in all sizes ranging from the FBI's to independent systems operated by cities, counties, and other agencies of local government (see Figure 8). Unfortunately, these local systems often are not linked to the state's AFIS system because of differences in software configurations.

How AFIS Works

The heart of AFIS technology is the ability of a computer to scan and digitally encode fingerprints so that they can be subject to high-speed computer processing. **The AFIS uses automatic scanning devices that convert the image of a fingerprint into digital minutiae that contain data showing ridges at their points of termination (ridge endings) and the branching of ridges into two ridges (bifurcations).** The relative position and orientation of the minutiae are also determined, allowing the computer to store each fingerprint in the form of a digitally recorded geometric pattern.

The computer's search algorithm determines the degree of correlation between the location and relationship of the minutiae for both the search and file prints. In this manner, a computer can make thousands of fingerprint comparisons in a second; for example, a set of ten fingerprints can be searched against a file of 500,000 ten-finger prints (ten-prints) in about eight-tenths of a second. During the search for a match, the computer uses a scoring system that assigns prints to each of the criteria set by an operator. When the search is complete, the computer produces a list of file prints that have the closest correlation to the search prints. All of the selected prints are then examined by a trained fingerprint expert, who makes the final verification of the print's identity. Thus, the AFIS makes no final decisions on the identity of a fingerprint, leaving this function to the eyes of a trained examiner.

The speed and accuracy of ten-print processing by AFIS have made possible the search of single latent crime-scene fingerprints against an entire file's print collection. Before the AFIS, police were usually restricted to comparing crime-scene fingerprints against those of known suspects. The impact of the AFIS on no-suspect cases has been dramatic. Minutes after California's AFIS network received its first assignment, the computer scored a direct hit by identifying an individual who had committed 15 murders, terrorizing the city of Los Angeles. Police estimate that it would have taken a single technician, manually searching the city's 1.7 million print cards,

FIGURE 8

An AFIS system designed for use by local law enforcement agencies.
Courtesy AFIX Technologies Inc., Pittsburg, KS 66762, www.afix.net

FIGURE 9

A side-by-side comparison of a latent print against a file fingerprint is conducted in seconds, and their similarity rating (SIM) is displayed on the upper-left portion of the screen.
Courtesy Sirchie Finger Print Laboratories, Inc., Youngsville, N.C., www.sirchie.com

67 years to come up with the perpetrator's prints. With the AFIS, the search took approximately 20 minutes. In its first year of operation, San Francisco's AFIS computer conducted 5,514 latent fingerprint searches and achieved 1,001 identifications—a hit rate of 18 percent. This compares to the previous year's average of 8 percent for manual latent-print searches.

As an example of how an AFIS computer operates, one system has been designed to automatically filter out imperfections in a latent print, enhance its image, and create a graphic representation of the fingerprint's ridge endings and bifurcations and their direction. The print is then computer searched against file prints. The image of the latent print and a matching file print are then displayed side by side on a high-resolution video monitor, as shown in Figure 9. The matching latent and file prints are then verified and charted by a fingerprint examiner at a video workstation.

The stereotypical image of a booking officer rolling inked fingers onto a standard ten-print card for ultimate transmission to a database has, for the most part, been replaced with digital-capture devices (**livescan**) that eliminate ink and paper. The livescan captures the image on each finger and the palms as they are lightly pressed against a glass platen. These livescan images can then be sent to the AFIS database electronically, so that within minutes the booking agency can enter the fingerprint record into the AFIS database and search the database for previous entries of the same individual. See Figure 10.

livescan
An inkless device that captures the digital images of fingerprints and palm prints and electronically transmits the images to an AFIS

FIGURE 10
Livescan technology enables law enforcement to print and compare a subject's fingerprints rapidly, without inking the fingerprints.
Courtesy MorphoTrak, Inc.

Considerations with AFIS

AFIS has fundamentally changed the way criminal investigators operate, allowing them to spend less time developing suspect lists and more time investigating the suspects generated by the computer. However, investigators must be cautioned against overreliance on a computer. Sometimes a latent print does not make a hit because of the poor quality of the file print. To avoid these potential problems, investigators must still print all known suspects in a case and manually search these prints against the crime-scene prints.

AFIS computers are available from several different suppliers. Each system scans fingerprint images and detects and records information about minutiae (ridge endings and bifurcations); however, they do not all incorporate exactly the same features, coordinate systems, or units of measure to record fingerprint information. These software incompatibilities often mean that, although state systems can communicate with the FBI's IAFIS, they may not communicate with each other directly. Likewise, local and state systems frequently cannot share information with each other. Many of these technical problems will be resolved as more agencies follow transmission standards developed by the National Institute of Standards and Technology and the FBI.

forensic brief

The Night Stalker

Richard Ramirez committed his first murder in June 1984. His victim was a 79-year-old woman who was stabbed repeatedly and sexually assaulted and then had her throat slashed. It would be eight months before Ramirez murdered again. In the spring, Ramirez began a murderous rampage that resulted in 13 additional killings and 5 rapes.

His modus operandi was to enter a home through an open window, shoot the male residents, and savagely rape his female victims. He scribed a pentagram on the wall of one of his victims and the words *Jack the Knife*, and was reported by another to force her to "swear to Satan" during the assault. His identity still unknown, the news media dubbed him the "Night Stalker." As the body count continued to rise, public hysteria and a media frenzy prevailed.

The break in the case came when the license plate of what seemed to be a suspicious car related to a sighting of the Night Stalker was reported to the police. The police determined that the car had been stolen and eventually located it, abandoned in a parking lot. After processing the car for prints, police found one usable partial fingerprint. This fingerprint was entered into the Los Angeles Police Department's brand-new AFIS computerized fingerprint system.

The Night Stalker was identified as Richard Ramirez, who had been fingerprinted following a traffic violation some years before. Police searching the home of one of his friends found the gun used

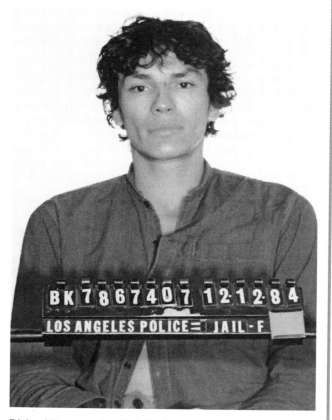

Richard Ramirez, the Night Stalker.
© Bettmann/CORBIS. All Rights Reserved

to commit the murders, and jewelry belonging to his victims was found in the possession of Ramirez's sister. Ramirez was convicted of murder and sentenced to death in 1989. He remains on death row.

forensics at work

The Mayfield Affair

On March 11, 2004, a series of ten explosions at four sites occurred on commuter trains traveling to or near the Atocha train station in Madrid, Spain. The death toll from these explosions was nearly 200, with more than 1,500 injured. On the day of the attack, a plastic bag was found in a van previously reported as stolen. The bag contained copper detonators like those used on the train bombs. On March 17, the FBI received electronic images of latent fingerprints that were recovered from the plastic bag. A search was initiated on the FBI's IAFIS. A senior fingerprint examiner encoded seven minutiae points from the high-resolution image of one suspect latent fingerprint and initiated an IAFIS search matching the print to Brandon Mayfield.

Mayfield's prints were in the FBI's central database because they had been taken when he joined the military, where he served for eight years before being honorably discharged as a second lieutenant. After a visual comparison of the suspect and file prints, the examiner concluded a "100 percent match." The identification was verified by a retired FBI fingerprint examiner with more than 30 years of experience who was under contract with the bureau, as well as by a court-appointed independent fingerprint examiner (see Figure 11).

Mayfield, age 37, a Muslim convert, was arrested on May 6 on a material witness warrant. The U.S. Attorney's Office came up with a list of Mayfield's potential ties to Muslim terrorists, which they included in the affidavit they presented to the federal judge who ordered his arrest and detention. The document also said that, although no travel records were found for Mayfield, "It is believed that Mayfield may have traveled under a false or fictitious name." On May 24, after the Spaniards had linked the print from the plastic bag to an Algerian national, Mayfield's case was thrown out. The FBI issued him a highly unusual official apology, and his ordeal became a stunning embarrassment to the U.S. government.

As part of its corrective-action process, the FBI formed an international committee of distinguished latent-print examiners and forensic experts. Their task was to review the analysis performed by the FBI Laboratory and make recommendations that would help prevent this type of error in the future. The committee came up with some startling findings and observations (available at www.fbi.gov/hq/lab/fsc/backissu/jan2005/special_report/2005_special_report.htm).

The committee members agreed that "the quality of the images that were used to make the erroneous identification was not a factor. . . . [T]he identification is filled with dissimilarities that were easily observed when a detailed analysis of the latent print was conducted."

They further stated,

> the power of the IAFIS match, coupled with the inherent pressure of working an extremely high-profile case, was thought to have influenced the initial examiner's judgment and subsequent examination. . . . The apparent mindset of the initial examiner after reviewing the results of the IAFIS search was that a match did exist; therefore, it would be reasonable to assume that the other characteristics must match as well. In the absence of a detailed analysis of the print, it can be a short distance from finding only seven characteristics sufficient for plotting, prior to the automated search, to the position of 12 or 13 matching characteristics once the mind-set of identification has become dominant. . . .

> Once the mind-set occurred with the initial examiner, the subsequent examinations were tainted. . . . because of the inherent pressure of such a high-profile case, the power of an IAFIS match in conjunction with the similarities in the candidate's print, and the knowledge of the previous examiners' conclusions (especially since the initial examiner was a highly respected supervisor with many years of experience), it was concluded that subsequent examinations were incomplete and inaccurate. To disagree was not an expected response. . . . when the individualization had been made by the examiner, it

Methods of Detecting Fingerprints

Through common usage, the term *latent fingerprint* has come to be associated with any fingerprint discovered at a crime scene. Sometimes, however, prints found at the scene of a crime are quite visible to the eye, and the word *latent* is a misnomer. Actually, there are three kinds of crime-scene prints: **visible prints** are made by fingers touching a surface after the ridges have been in contact with a colored material such as blood, paint, grease, or ink; **plastic prints** are ridge impressions left on a soft material such as putty, wax, soap, or dust; and *latent* or *invisible prints* are impressions caused by the transfer of body perspiration or oils present on finger ridges to the surface of an object.

forensics at work

(a)

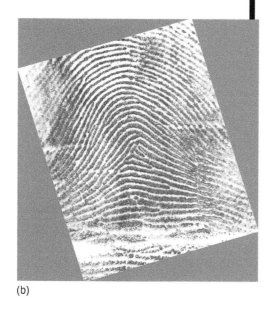

(b)

FIGURE 11

(a) Questioned print recovered in connection with the Madrid bombing investigation. (b) File print of Brandon Mayfield.
Courtesy U.S. Department of Justice

became increasingly difficult for others in the agency to disagree.

The committee went on to make a number of quality-assurance recommendations to help avoid a recurrence of this type of error.

The Mayfield incident has also been the subject of an investigation by the Office of the Inspector General (OIG), U.S. Department of Justice (www.usdoj.gov/oig/special/s0601/final.pdf). The OIG investigation concluded that a "series of systemic issues" in the FBI Laboratory contributed to the Mayfield misidentification. The report noted that the FBI has made significant procedural modifications to help prevent similar errors in the future and strongly supported the FBI's

decision to undertake research to develop more objective standards for fingerprint identification.

An internal review of the FBI Latent Print Unit conducted in the aftermath of the Mayfield affair has resulted in the implementation of revisions in training, as well as in the decision-making process when determining the comparative value of a latent print, along with more stringent verification policies and procedures (M. A. Smrz et al., *Journal of Forensic Identification* 56 [2006]: 402–34).

The impact of the Mayfield affair on fingerprint technology as currently practiced and the weight courts will assign to fingerprint matches remain open questions.

Locating Fingerprints

Locating visible or plastic prints at the crime scene normally presents little problem to the investigator because these prints are usually distinct and visible to the eye. Locating latent or invisible prints is obviously much more difficult and requires the use of techniques to make the print visible. Although the investigator can choose from several methods for visualizing a latent print, the choice depends on the type of surface being examined.

Hard and nonabsorbent surfaces (such as glass, mirror, tile, and painted wood) require different development procedures from surfaces that are soft and porous (such as papers, cardboard, and cloth). Prints on the former are preferably developed by the application of a powder or treatment with superglue, whereas prints on the latter generally require treatment with one or more chemicals.

Sometimes the most difficult aspect of fingerprint examination is the location of prints. Recent advances in fingerprint technology have led to the development of an ultraviolet image converter for the purpose of detecting latent fingerprints. This device, called the Reflected Ultraviolet Imaging System (RUVIS), can locate prints on most nonabsorbent surfaces without the aid of chemical or powder treatments (see Figure 12).

RUVIS detects the print in its natural state by aiming UV light at the surface suspected of containing prints. When the UV light strikes the fingerprint, the light is reflected back to the viewer, differentiating the print from its background surface. The transmitted UV light is then converted into visible light by an image intensifier. Once the print is located in this manner, the crime-scene investigator can develop it in the most appropriate fashion. See Figure 13.

FIGURE 12

A Reflected Ultraviolet Imaging System allows an investigator to directly view surfaces for the presence of untreated latent fingerprints.
Courtesy Sirchie Finger Print Laboratories, Inc., Youngsville, N.C., www.sirchie.com

FIGURE 13

Using a Reflected Ultraviolet Imaging System with the aid of a UV lamp to search for latent fingerprints.
Courtesy Sirchie Finger Print Laboratories, Inc., Youngsville, N.C., www.sirchie.com

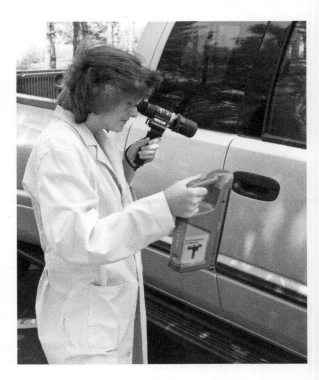

Developing Latent Prints

FINGERPRINT POWDERS Fingerprint powders are commercially available in a variety of compositions and colors. These powders, when applied lightly to a nonabsorbent surface with a camel's-hair or fiberglass brush, readily adhere to perspiration residues and/or deposits of body oils left on the surface (see Figure 14).

Experienced examiners find that gray and black powders are adequate for most latent-print work; the examiner selects the powder that affords the best color contrast with the surface being dusted. Hence, the gray powder, composed of an aluminum dust, is used on dark-colored surfaces. It is also applied to mirrors and metal surfaces that are polished to a mirrorlike finish because these surfaces photograph as black. The black powder, composed basically of black carbon or charcoal, is applied to white or light-colored surfaces.

Other types of powders are available for developing latent prints. A magnetic-sensitive powder can be spread over a surface with a magnet in the form of a Magna Brush. A Magna Brush does not have any bristles to come in contact with the surface, so there is less chance that the print will be destroyed or damaged. The magnetic-sensitive powder comes in black and gray and is especially useful on such items as finished leather and rough plastics, where the minute texture of the surface tends to hold particles of ordinary powder. Fluorescent powders are also used to develop latent fingerprints. These powders fluoresce under ultraviolet light. By photographing the fluorescence pattern of the developing print under UV light, it is possible to avoid having the color of the surface obscure the print.

IODINE FUMING Of the several chemical methods used for visualizing latent prints, **iodine fuming** is the oldest. Iodine is a solid crystal that, when heated, is transformed into a vapor without passing through a liquid phase; such a transformation is called **sublimation**. Most often, the suspect material is placed in an enclosed cabinet along with iodine crystals (see Figure 15). As the crystals are heated, the resultant vapors fill the chamber and combine with constituents of the latent print to make it visible. The reasons why latent prints are visualized by iodine vapors are not yet fully understood. Many believe that the iodine fumes combine with fatty oils; however, there is also convincing evidence that the iodine may actually interact with residual water left on a print from perspiration.[2]

Unfortunately, iodine prints are not permanent and begin to fade once the fuming process is stopped. Therefore, the examiner must photograph the prints immediately on development in order to retain a permanent record. Also, iodine-developed prints can be fixed with a 1 percent solution of starch in water, applied by spraying. The print turns blue and lasts for several weeks to several months.

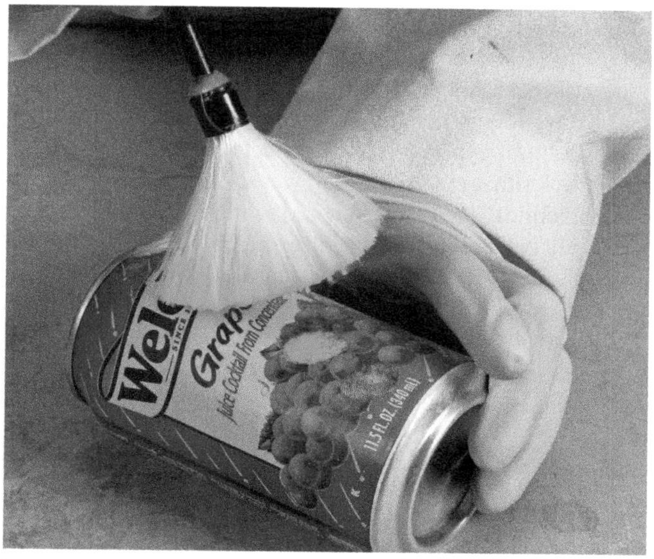

iodine fuming
A technique for visualizing latent fingerprints by exposing them to iodine vapors

sublimation
A physical change from the solid directly into the gaseous state

FIGURE 14

Developing a latent fingerprint on a surface by applying a fingerprint powder with a fiberglass brush.
Courtesy Sirchie Finger Print Laboratories, Inc., Youngsville, N.C., www.sirchie.com

[2] J. Almag, Y. Sasson, and A. Anati, "Chemical Reagents for the Development of Latent Fingerprints II: Controlled Addition of Water Vapor to Iodine Fumes—A Solution to the Aging Problem," *Journal of Forensic Sciences* 24 (1979): 431.

FIGURE 15

A heated fuming cabinet.
Courtesy Sirchie Finger Print Laboratories, Inc.,
Youngsville, N.C., www.sirchie.com

ninhydrin

A chemical reagent used to develop latent fingerprints on porous materials by reacting with amino acids in perspiration

NINHYDRIN   Another chemical used for visualizing latent prints is **ninhydrin**. The development of latent prints with ninhydrin depends on its chemical reaction to form a purple-blue color with amino acids present in trace amounts in perspiration. Ninhydrin (triketohydrindene hydrate) is commonly sprayed onto the porous surface from an aerosol can. A solution is prepared by mixing the ninhydrin powder with a suitable solvent, such as acetone or ethyl alcohol; a 0.6 percent solution appears to be effective for most applications.

Generally, prints begin to appear within an hour or two after ninhydrin application; however, weaker prints may be visualized after 24 to 48 hours. The development can be hastened if the treated specimen is heated in an oven or on a hot plate at a temperature of 80–100°C. The ninhydrin method has developed latent prints on paper as old as 15 years.

Physical Developer

A silver nitrate–based reagent formulated to develop latent fingerprints on porous surfaces

PHYSICAL DEVELOPER   **Physical Developer** is a third chemical mixture used for visualizing latent prints. Physical Developer is a silver nitrate–based liquid reagent. The procedure for preparing and using Physical Developer is described in Appendix IV. This method has gained wide acceptance by fingerprint examiners, who have found it effective for visualizing latent prints that remain undetected by the previously described methods. Also, this technique is effective for developing latent fingerprints on porous articles that may have been wet at one time.

For most fingerprint examiners, the chemical method of choice is ninhydrin. Its extreme sensitivity and ease of application have all but eliminated the use of iodine for latent-print visualization. However, when ninhydrin fails, development with Physical Developer may provide identifiable results. Application of Physical Developer washes away any traces of proteins from an object's surface; **hence, if one wishes to use all of the previously mentioned chemical development methods on the same surface, it is necessary to first fume with iodine, follow this treatment with ninhydrin, and then apply Physical Developer to the object.**

superglue fuming

A technique for visualizing latent fingerprints on nonporous surfaces by exposing them to cyanoacrylate vapors; named for the commercial product Super Glue.

SUPERGLUE FUMING   In the past, chemical treatment for fingerprint development was reserved for porous surfaces such as paper and cardboard. However, since 1982, a chemical technique known as **superglue fuming** has gained wide popularity for developing latent prints on nonporous surfaces such as metals, electrical tape, leather, and plastic bags.[3] See Figure 16.

[3] F. G. Kendall and B. W. Rehn, "Rapid Method of Superglue Fuming Application for the Development of Latent Fingerprints," *Journal of Forensic Sciences* 28 (1983): 777.

FIGURE 16

Superglue fuming a nonporous metallic surface in the search for latent fingerprints.
Courtesy Sirchie Finger Print Laboratories, Inc., Youngsville, N.C., www.sirchie.com

(a)

(b)

FIGURE 17

(a) A handheld fuming wand uses disposable cartridges containing cyanoacrylate. The wand is used to develop prints at the crime scene and (b) in the laboratory.
Courtesy Sirchie Finger Print Laboratories, Inc., Youngsville, N.C., www.sirchie.com

Superglue is approximately 98–99 percent cyanoacrylate ester, a chemical that interacts with and visualizes a latent fingerprint. Cyanoacrylate ester fumes can be created when superglue is placed on absorbent cotton treated with sodium hydroxide. The fumes can also be created by heating the glue. The fumes and the evidential object are contained within an enclosed chamber for up to six hours. Development occurs when fumes from the glue adhere to the latent print, usually producing a white-appearing latent print. Interestingly, small enclosed areas, such as the interior of an automobile, have been successfully processed for latent prints with fumes from superglue.

Through the use of a small handheld wand, cyanoacrylate fuming is now easily done at a crime scene or in a laboratory setting. The wand heats a small cartridge containing cyanoacrylate. Once heated, the cyanoacrylate vaporizes, allowing the operator to direct the fumes onto the suspect area (see Figure 17).

OTHER TECHNIQUES FOR VISUALIZATION   One of the most exciting and dynamic areas of research in forensic science today is the application of chemical techniques to the visualization of latent fingerprints. Changes are occurring rapidly as researchers uncover a variety of processes applicable to the visualization of latent fingerprints. Interestingly, for many years progress in this field was minimal, and fingerprint specialists traditionally relied on three chemical techniques—iodine, ninhydrin, and silver nitrate—to reveal a hidden fingerprint. Then superglue fuming extended chemical development to prints deposited on nonporous surfaces.

Fluorescence   The first hint of things to come was the discovery that latent fingerprints could be visualized by exposure to laser light. This laser method took advantage of the fact that perspiration contains a variety of components that **fluoresce** when illuminated by laser light. Fluorescence occurs when a substance absorbs light and reemits the light in wavelengths longer than the illuminating source. Importantly, substances that emit light or fluoresce are more readily seen with either the naked eye or through photography than are non-light-emitting materials. The high sensitivity of fluorescence serves as the underlying principle of many of the new chemical techniques used to visualize latent fingerprints.

The earliest use of fluorescence to visualize fingerprints came with the direct illumination of a fingerprint with argon–ion lasers. This laser type was chosen because its blue-green light output induced some of the perspiration components of a fingerprint to fluoresce (see Figure 18). The major drawback of this approach is that the perspiration components of a fingerprint are often present in quantities too minute to observe even with the aid of fluorescence. The fingerprint examiner, wearing safety goggles containing optical filters, visually examines the specimen being exposed to the laser light. The filters absorb the laser light and permit the wavelengths at which latent-print residues fluoresce to pass through to the eyes of the wearer. The filter also protects the operator against eye damage from scattered or reflected laser light. Likewise, latent-print residue producing sufficient fluorescence can be photographed by placing this same filter across the lens of the camera. Examination of specimens and photography of the fluorescing latent prints are carried out in a darkened room.

Chemically Induced Fluorescence   The next advancement in latent-fingerprint development occurred with the discovery that fingerprints could be treated with chemicals that would induce fluorescence when exposed to laser illumination. For example, the application of zinc chloride after ninhydrin treatment or the application of the dye rhodamine 6G after superglue fuming caused fluorescence and increased the sensitivity of detection on exposure to laser illumination. The discovery of numerous chemical developers for visualizing fingerprints through fluorescence quickly followed. This knowledge set the stage for the next advance in latent-fingerprint development—the *alternate light source*.

With the advent of chemically induced fluorescence, lasers were no longer needed to induce fingerprints to fluoresce through their perspiration residues. High-intensity light sources or alternate light sources have proliferated and all but replaced laser lights. See Figure 19. High-intensity quartz halogen or xenon-arc light sources can be focused on a suspect area through a

fluoresce
To emit visible light when exposed to light of a shorter wavelength

FIGURE 18

Schematic depicting latent-print detection with the aid of a laser. A fingerprint examiner, wearing safety goggles containing optical filters, examines the specimen being exposed to the laser light. The filter absorbs the laser light and permits the wavelengths at which latent-print residues fluoresce to pass through to the eyes of the wearer.
Courtesy Federal Bureau of Investigation, Washington, D.C.

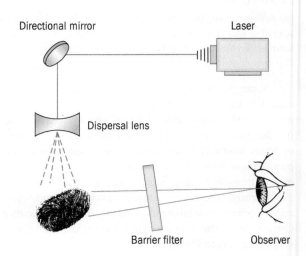

Directional mirror

Laser

Dispersal lens

Barrier filter

Observer

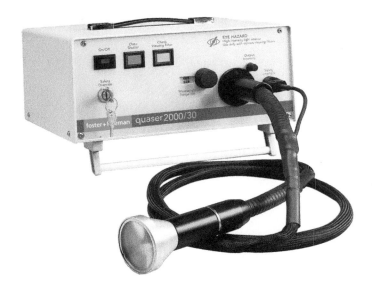

FIGURE 19

An alternate light source system incorporating a high-intensity light source.
Courtesy Foster & Freeman Limited, Worcestershire, U.K., www.fosterfreeman.co.uk

FIGURE 20

Lightweight handheld alternate light source that uses an LED light source.
Courtesy Foster & Freeman Limited, Worcestershire, U.K., www.fosterfreeman.co.uk

fiber-optic cable. This light can be passed through several filters, giving the user more flexibility in selecting the wavelength of light to be aimed at the latent print. Alternatively, lightweight, portable alternate light sources that use light-emitting diodes (LEDs) are also commercially available (see Figure 20). In most cases, these light sources have proven to be as effective as laser light in developing latent prints, and they are commercially available at costs significantly less than those of laser illuminators. Furthermore, these light sources are portable and can be readily taken to any crime scene.

NEWER CHEMICAL PROCESSES   A large number of chemical treatment processes are available to the fingerprint examiner (see Figure 21), and the field is in a constant state of flux. Selection of an appropriate procedure is best left to technicians who have developed their skills through casework experience.

Newer chemical processes include a substitute for ninhydrin called DFO (1,8-diazafluoren-9-one). This chemical visualizes latent prints on porous materials when exposed to an alternate light source. DFO has been shown to develop 2.5 times more latent prints on paper than ninhydrin. A chemical called 1,2-indanedione is also emerging as a potential reagent for the development of latent fingerprints on porous surfaces. 1,2-indanedione gives both good initial color and

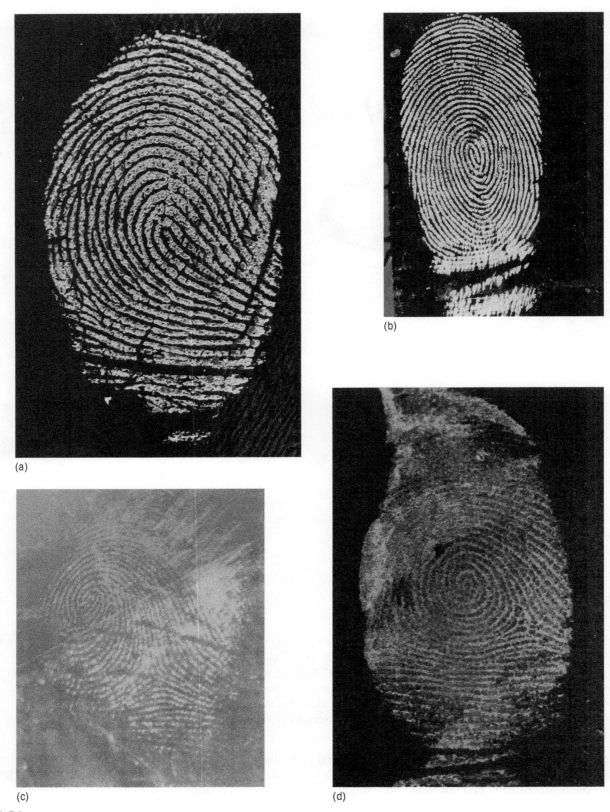

FIGURE 21

(a) Latent fingerprint visualized by cyanoacrylate fuming. (b) Fingerprint treated with cyanoacrylate and rhodamine 6G fluorescent dye. (c) Fingerprint treated with cyanoacrylate and the fluorescent dye combination RAM. (d) A bloody fingerprint detected by laser light after spraying with merbromin and hydrogen peroxide.

strong fluorescence when reacted with amino acids derived from prints and thus has the potential to provide in one process what ninhydrin and DFO can do in two different steps.

Dye combinations known as RAM, RAY, and MRM 10, when used in conjunction with superglue fuming, have been effective in visualizing latent fingerprints by fluorescence. A number of chemical formulas useful for latent-print development are listed in Appendix IV.

Studies have demonstrated that common fingerprint-developing agents do not interfere with DNA-testing methods used for characterizing bloodstains.[4] Nonetheless, in cases involving items with material adhering to their surfaces and/or items that will require further laboratory examinations, fingerprint processing should not be performed at the crime scene. Rather, the items should be submitted to the laboratory, where they can be processed for fingerprints in conjunction with other necessary examinations.

Preservation of Developed Prints

Once the latent print has been visualized, it must be permanently preserved for future comparison and possible use in court as evidence. A photograph must be taken before any further attempts at preservation. Any camera equipped with a close-up lens will do; however, many investigators prefer to use a camera specially designed for fingerprint photography. Such a camera comes equipped with a fixed focus to take photographs on a 1:1 scale when the camera's open eye is held exactly flush against the print's surface (see Figure 22). In addition, photographs must be taken to provide an overall view of the print's location with respect to other evidential items at the crime scene.

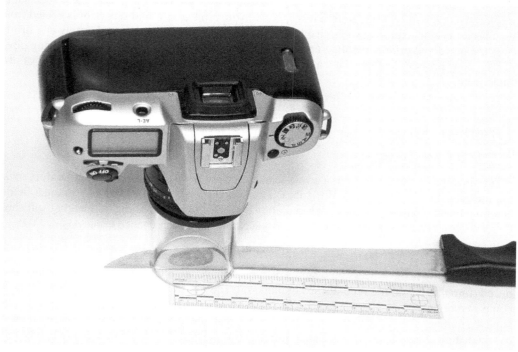

FIGURE 22

Camera fitted with an adapter designed to give an approximate 1:1 photograph of a fingerprint.
Courtesy Sirchie Finger Print Laboratories, Inc., Youngsville, N.C., www.sirchie.com

[4] C. Roux et al., "A Further Study to Investigate the Effect of Fingerprint Enhancement Techniques on the DNA Analysis of Bloodstains," *Journal of Forensic Identification* 49 (1999): 357; C. J. Frégeau et al., "Fingerprint Enhancement Revisited and the Effects of Blood Enhancement Chemicals on Subsequent Profiler Plus™ Fluorescent Short Tandem Repeat DNA Analysis of Fresh and Aged Bloody Fingerprints," *Journal of Forensic Sciences* 45 (2000): 354; and P. Grubwieser et al., "Systematic Study on STR Profiling on Blood and Saliva Traces after Visualization of Fingerprints," *Journal of Forensic Sciences* 48 (2003): 733.

Once photographs have been secured, one of two procedures is to be followed. If the object is small enough to be transported without destroying the print, it should be preserved in its entirety; the print should be covered with cellophane so it will be protected from damage. On the other hand, prints on large immovable objects that have been developed with a powder can best be preserved by "lifting." The most popular type of lifter is a broad adhesive tape similar to clear adhesive tape. When the powdered surface is covered with the adhesive side of the tape and pulled up, the powder is transferred to the tape. Then the tape is placed on a properly labeled card that provides a good background contrast with the powder.

A variation of this procedure is the use of an adhesive-backed clear plastic sheet attached to a colored cardboard backing. Before it is applied to the print, a celluloid separator is peeled from the plastic sheet to expose the adhesive lifting surface. The tape is then pressed evenly and firmly over the powdered print and pulled up (see Figure 23). The sheet containing the adhering powder is now pressed against the cardboard backing to provide a permanent record of the fingerprint.

Digital Imaging for Fingerprint Enhancement

When fingerprints are lifted from a crime scene, they are not usually in perfect condition, making the analysis that much more difficult. Computers have advanced technology in most fields, and fingerprint identification has not been left behind. With the help of digital imaging software, fingerprints can now be enhanced for the most accurate and comprehensive analysis.

Creating Digital Images

digital imaging
A process through which a picture is converted into a series of square electronic dots known as pixels; the picture is manipulated by computer software that changes the numerical value of each pixel

pixel
A square electronic dot that is used to compose a digital image

Digital imaging is the process by which a picture is converted into a digital file. The image produced from this digital file is composed of numerous square electronic dots called **pixels**. Images composed of only black and white elements are referred to as *grayscale images*. Each pixel is assigned a number according to its intensity. The grayscale image is made from the set of numbers to which a pixel may be assigned, ranging from 0 (black) to 255 (white). Once an image is digitally stored, it is manipulated by computer software that changes the numerical value of each pixel, thus altering the image as directed by the user. *Resolution* reveals the degree of detail that can be seen in an image. It is defined in terms of dimensions, such as 800 × 600 pixels. The larger the numbers, the more closely the digital image resembles the real-world image.

The input of pictures into a digital imaging system is usually done through the use of scanners, digital cameras, and video cameras. After the picture is changed to its digital image, several methods can be employed to enhance the image. The overall brightness of an image, as well as the contrast between the image and the background, can be adjusted through contrast-enhancement methods. One approach used to enhance an image is *spatial filtering*. Several types of filters produce various effects. A low-pass filter is used to eliminate harsh edges by reducing the intensity difference between pixels. A second filter, the high-pass filter, operates by modifying a pixel's numerical value to exaggerate its intensity difference from that of its neighbor. The resulting effect increases the contrast of the edges, thus providing a high contrast between the elements and the background.

Analyzing Digital Images

Frequency analysis, also referred to as *frequency Fourier transform* (FFT), is used to identify periodic or repetitive patterns such as lines or dots that interfere with the interpretation of the image. These patterns are diminished or eliminated to enhance the appearance of the image. Interestingly, the spacings between fingerprint ridges are themselves periodic. Therefore, the contribution of the fingerprint can be identified in FFT mode and then enhanced. Likewise, if ridges from overlapping prints are positioned in different directions, their corresponding frequency information is at different locations in FFT mode. The ridges of one latent print can then be enhanced while the ridges of the other are suppressed.

Color interferences also pose a problem when analyzing an image. For example, a latent fingerprint found on paper currency or a check may be difficult to analyze because of the distracting colored background. With the imaging software, the colored background can simply be removed to make the image stand out (see Figure 24). If the image itself is a particular color, such as a ninhydrin-developed print, the color can be isolated and enhanced to distinguish it from the background.

Digital imaging software also provides functions in which portions of the image can be examined individually. With a scaling and resizing tool, the user can select a part of an image and resize it for a closer look. This function operates much like a magnifying glass, helping the examiner view fine details of an image.

An important and useful tool, especially for fingerprint identification, is the compare function. This specialized feature places two images side by side and allows the examiner to chart the common features on both images simultaneously (see Figure 25). The zoom function is used in conjunction with the compare tool. As the examiner zooms into a portion of one image, the software automatically zooms into the second image for comparison.

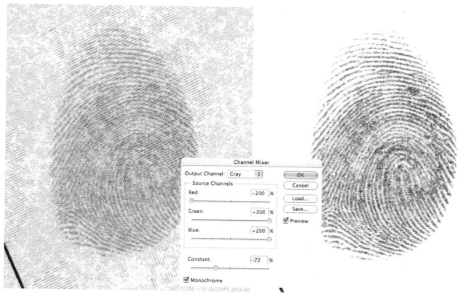

FIGURE 24

A fingerprint being enhanced in Adobe Photoshop. In this example, on the left is the original scan of an inked fingerprint on a check. On the right is the same image after using Adobe Photoshop's Channel Mixer to eliminate the green security background.
Courtesy Imaging Forensics, Fountain Valley, Calif., www.imagingforensics.com

Although digital imaging is undoubtedly an effective tool for enhancing and analyzing images, it is only as useful as the images it has to work with. If the details do not exist on the original images, the enhancement procedures are not going to work. The benefits of digital enhancement methods are apparent when weak images are made more distinguishable.

Case # 05-01234

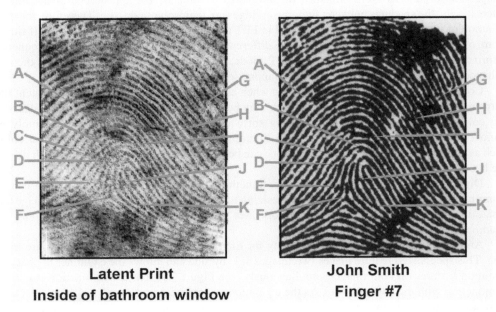

Latent Print

Inside of bathroom window

John Smith

Finger #7

FIGURE 25

Current imaging software allows fingerprint analysts to prepare a fingerprint comparison chart. The fingerprint examiner can compare prints side by side and display important features that are consistent between the fingerprints. The time needed to create a display of this sort digitally is about 30 to 60 minutes.
Courtesy Imaging Forensics, Fountain Valley, Calif., www.imagingforensics.com

chapter summary

> > > > > > > > > > >

Fingerprints are a reproduction of friction skin ridges found on the palm side of the fingers and thumbs. The basic principles underlying the use of fingerprints in criminal investigations are that (1) a fingerprint is an individual characteristic because no two fingers have yet been found to possess identical ridge characteristics, (2) a fingerprint remains unchanged during an individual's lifetime, and (3) fingerprints have general ridge patterns that permit them to be systematically classified. All fingerprints are divided into three classes on the basis of their general pattern: loops, whorls, and arches.

Fingerprint classification systems are based on knowledge of fingerprint pattern classes. The individuality of a fingerprint is not determined by its general shape or pattern, but by a careful study of its ridge characteristics. The expert must demonstrate a point-by-point comparison in order to prove the identity of an individual. AFIS aids this process by converting the image of a fingerprint into digital minutiae that contain data showing ridges at their points of termination (ridge endings) and their branching into two ridges (bifurcations). A single fingerprint can be searched against the FBI AFIS digital database of 50 million fingerprint records in a matter of minutes.

Once the finger touches a surface, perspiration, along with oils that may have been picked up by touching the hairy portions of the body, is transferred onto that surface, thereby leaving an impression of the finger's ridge pattern (a fingerprint). Prints deposited in this manner are invisible to the eye and are commonly referred to as latent or invisible fingerprints.

Visible prints are made when fingers touch a surface after the ridges have been in contact with a colored material such as blood, paint, grease, or ink. Plastic prints are ridge impressions left on a soft material, such as putty, wax, soap, or dust. Latent prints deposited on hard and nonabsorbent surfaces (such as glass, mirror, tile, and painted wood) are preferably developed by the application of a powder; prints on porous surfaces (such as paper and cardboard) generally require treatment with a chemical. Examiners use various chemical methods to visualize latent prints, such as iodine fuming, ninhydrin, and Physical Developer. Superglue fuming develops latent prints on nonporous surfaces, such as metals, electrical tape, leather, and plastic bags. Development occurs when fumes from the glue adhere to the print, usually producing a white latent print.

The high sensitivity of fluorescence serves as the underlying principle of many of the new chemical techniques used to visualize latent fingerprints. Fingerprints are treated with chemicals that induce fluorescence when exposed to a high-intensity light or an alternate light source.

Once the latent print has been visualized, it must be permanently preserved for future comparison and for possible use as court evidence. A photograph must be taken before any further attempts at preservation are made. If the object is small enough to be transported without destroying the print, it should be preserved in its entirety. Prints on large immovable objects that have been developed with a powder are best preserved by "lifting" with a broad adhesive tape.

review questions

1. The first systematic attempt at personal identification was devised and introduced by _____.

2. A system of identification relying on precise body measurements is known as _____.

3. The fingerprint classification system used in most English-speaking countries was devised by _____.

4. True or False: The first systematic and official use of fingerprints for personal identification in the United States was adopted by the New York City Civil Service Commission. _____

5. The individuality of a fingerprint (is, is not) determined by its pattern.

6. A point-by-point comparison of a fingerprint's _____ must be demonstrated in order to prove identity.

7. _____ are a reproduction of friction skin ridges.

8. The form and pattern of skin ridges are determined by the (epidermis, dermal papillae).

9. A permanent scar forms in the skin only when an injury damages the _____.

10. Fingerprints (can, cannot) be changed during a person's lifetime.

11. The three general patterns into which fingerprints are divided are _____, _____, and _____.

12. The most common fingerprint pattern is the _____.

13. Approximately 5 percent of the population has the _____ fingerprint pattern.

14. A loop pattern that opens toward the thumb is known as a(n) (radial, ulnar) loop.

15. The pattern area of the loop is enclosed by two diverging ridges known as _____.

16. The ridge point nearest the type-line divergence is known as the _____.

17. All loops must have (one, two) delta(s).

18. The approximate center of a loop pattern is called the _____.

19. If an imaginary line drawn between the two deltas of a whorl pattern touches any of the spiral ridges, the pattern is classified as a (plain whorl, central pocket loop).

20. The simplest of all fingerprint patterns is the _____.

21. Arches (have, do not have) type lines, deltas, and cores.

22. The presence or absence of the _____ pattern is used as a basis for determining the primary classification in the Henry system.

23. The largest category (25 percent) in the primary classification system is (1/1, 1/2).

24. A fingerprint classification system (can, cannot) unequivocally identify an individual.

25. True or False: Computerized fingerprint search systems match prints by comparing the position of bifurcations and ridge endings. _____

26. A fingerprint left by a person with soiled or stained fingertips is called a(n) _____.

27. _____ fingerprints are impressions left on a soft material.

28. Fingerprint impressions that are not readily visible are called _____.

29. Fingerprints on hard and nonabsorbent surfaces are best developed by the application of a(n) _____.

30. Fingerprints on porous surfaces are best developed with _____ treatment.

31. _____ vapors chemically combine with fatty oils or residual water to visualize a fingerprint.

32. The chemical _____ visualizes fingerprints by its reaction with amino acids.

33. Chemical treatment with _____ visualizes fingerprints on porous articles that may have been wet at one time.

34. True or False: A latent fingerprint is first treated with Physical Developer followed by ninhydrin. _____

35. A chemical technique known as _____ is used to develop latent prints on nonporous surfaces such as metal and plastic.

36. _____ occurs when a substance absorbs light and reemits the light in wavelengths longer than the illuminating source.

37. High-intensity light sources known as _____ are effective in developing latent fingerprints.

38. Once a fingerprint has been visualized, it must be preserved by _____.

39. The image produced from a digital file is composed of numerous square electronic dots called _____.

40. A (high-pass filter, frequency Fourier transform analysis) is used to identify repetitive patterns such as lines or dots that interfere with the interpretation of a digitized fingerprint image.

application and critical thinking

1. Classify each of the prints shown below as loop, whorl, or arch.

2. A description of the types of prints from the fingers of a criminal suspect appears. Using the FBI system, determine the primary classification of this individual.

3. While searching a murder scene, you find the following items that you believe may contain latent fingerprints. Indicate whether prints on each item should be developed using fingerprint powder or chemicals.

   a. A leather sofa

   b. A mirror

   c. A painted wooden knife handle

   d. Blood-soaked newspapers

   e. A revolver

4. Criminalist Frank Mortimer is using digital imaging to enhance latent fingerprints. Indicate which features of digital imaging he would most likely use for each of the following tasks:

   a. Isolating part of a print and enlarging it for closer examination

   b. Increasing the contrast between a print and the background surface on which it is located

   c. Examining two prints that overlap one another

(1) _____

(2) _____

(3) _____

(4) _____

(5) _____

(6) _____

Finger	Right Hand	Left Hand
Thumb	Whorl	Whorl
Index	Loop	Whorl
Middle	Whorl	Arch
Ring	Whorl	Whorl
Little	Arch	Whorl

further references

Cowger, James E., *Friction Ridge Skin*. Boca Raton, Fla.: Taylor & Francis, 1992.

Komarinski, Peter, *Automated Fingerprint Identification Systems (AFIS)*. Burlington, Mass.: Elsevier Academic Press, 2004.

Lee, H. C., and R. E. Gaensleen, eds., *Advances in Fingerprint Technology*, 2nd ed. Boca Raton, Fla.: Taylor & Francis, 2001.

Lennard, C., M. Margot, C. Stoilovic, and C. Champod, eds., *Fingerprints and Other Ridge Skin Impressions*. Boca Raton, Fla.: Taylor & Francis, 2004.

U.S. Department of Justice, *The Science of Fingerprints*. Washington, D.C.: U.S. Government Printing Office, 1990.

U.S. Department of Justice, *The Fingerprint Sourcebook*, http://www.OJP.usdoj.gov/nij/pubs-sum/225320.htm

answers to review questions

Odd-Numbered Review Questions

1. Alphonse Bertillion
3. Sir Edward Richard Henry
5. is not
7. Fingerprints
9. dermal papillae
11. loops; whorls; arches
13. arch
15. type lines
17. one
19. plain whorl

21. do not have
23. 1/1
25. True
27. Plastic
29. powder
31. Iodine
33. Physical Developer
35. superglue fuming
37. alternate light sources
39. pixels

Application and Critical Thinking

1. a. Whorl
   b. Arch
   c. Loop
   d. Whorl
   e. Whorl
   f. Arch
2. The primary classification for this individual would be as follows:

$$\frac{0\ +\ 8\ +\ 4\ +\ 0\ +\ 1}{16\ +\ 8\ +\ 0\ +\ 2\ +\ 1}$$

   Thus, the classification would be 13/27.
3. a. Chemicals
   b. Powder
   c. Powder
   d. Chemicals
   e. Chemicals
4. a. Scaling and resizing
   b. Spatial filtering
   c. Frequency analysis, or frequency Fourier transform (FFT)

firearms, tool marks, and other impressions

From Chapter 17 of *Criminalistics: An Introduction to Forensic Science*, Tenth Edition. Richard Saferstein. Copyright © 2011 by Pearson Education, Inc. Published by Pearson Prentice Hall. All rights reserved.

The Beltway Snipers

During a three-week period in October 2002, ten people were killed and three others were wounded as two snipers terrorized the region in and around the Baltimore–Washington metropolitan area. The arrest of John Allen Muhammad, 41, and Lee Boyd Malvo, 17, ended the ordeal. The semiautomatic .223-caliber rifle seized from them was ultimately linked by ballistics tests to eight of the ten killings. The car that Muhammad and Malvo were driving had been specially configured with one hole in the trunk through which a rifle barrel could protrude, so that a sniper could shoot from inside a slightly ajar trunk.

The major break in the case came when a friend of Muhammad's called police suggesting that Muhammad and his friend Malvo were the likely snipers. Muhammad's automobile records revealed numerous traffic stops in the Beltway area during the time of the shootings. Another break in the case came when Malvo called a priest to boast of a killing weeks before in Montgomery, Alabama. Investigators traced the claim to a recent liquor store holdup that left one person dead. Fortunately, the perpetrator of this crime left a latent fingerprint at the murder scene. Authorities quickly tracked the print to Malvo, a Jamaican citizen, through his fingerprints on file with the Immigration and Naturalization Service. A description of Muhammad's car was released to the media, leading to tips from alert citizens who noticed the car parked in a rest area with both occupants asleep.

The motive for the shooting spree was believed to be a planned plot to extort $10 million from local and state governments. Muhammad was recently executed, and Malvo is currently serving life imprisonment without parole.

firearms, tool marks, and other impressions

After studying this chapter you should be able to:

- Describe techniques for rifling a barrel

- Recognize the class and individual characteristics of bullets and cartridge cases

- Understand the use of the comparison microscope to compare bullets and cartridge cases

- Explain the concept of the NIBIN database

- Explain the procedure for determining how far a weapon was fired from a target

- Identify the laboratory tests for determining whether an individual has fired a weapon

- Explain the forensic significance of class and individual characteristics to the comparison of tool mark, footwear, and tire impressions

- List some common field reagents used to enhance bloody footprints

KEY TERMS

bore
breechblock
caliber
choke
distance determination
ejector
extractor
firearms identification
gauge
Greiss test
grooves
lands
rifling

Just as natural variations in skin ridge patterns and characteristics provide a key to human identification, minute random markings on surfaces can impart individuality to inanimate objects. Structural variations and irregularities caused by scratches, nicks, breaks, and wear permit the criminalist to relate a bullet to a gun; a scratch or abrasion mark to a single tool; or a tire track to a particular automobile. Individualization, so vigorously pursued in all other areas of criminalistics, is frequently attainable in firearms and tool mark examination.

Although a portion of this chapter will be devoted to the comparison of surface features for the purposes of bullet identification, a complete description of the services and capabilities of the modern forensic firearms laboratory cannot be restricted to just this one subject, important as it may be. The high frequency of shooting cases means that the science of **firearms identification** must extend beyond mere comparison of bullets to include knowledge of the operation of all types of weapons, restoration of obliterated serial numbers on weapons, detection and characterization of gunpowder residues on garments and around wounds, estimation of muzzle-to-target distances, and detection of powder residues on hands. Each of these functions will be covered in this chapter.

Bullet and Cartridge Comparisons

The inner surface of the barrel of a gun leaves its markings on a bullet passing through it. These markings are peculiar to each gun. Hence, if one bullet found at the scene of a crime and another test-fired from a suspect's gun show the same markings, the suspect is linked to the crime. Because these inner surface striations are so important for bullet comparison, it is important to know why and how they originate.

The Gun Barrel

The gun barrel is produced from a solid bar of steel that has been hollowed out by drilling. The microscopic drill marks left on the barrel's inner surface are randomly irregular and in themselves impart a uniqueness to each barrel. However, the manufacture of a barrel requires the additional step of impressing its inner surface with spiral **grooves**, a step known as **rifling**. The surfaces of the original **bore** remaining between the grooves are called **lands** (see Figure 1). As a fired bullet travels through a barrel, it engages the rifling grooves; these grooves then guide the bullet through the barrel, giving it a rapid spin. This is done because a spinning bullet does not tumble end over end on leaving the barrel, but remains instead on a true and accurate course.

The diameter of the gun barrel, sketched in Figure 2, measured between opposite lands, is known as the **caliber** of the weapon. Caliber is normally recorded in hundredths of an inch or in millimeters—for example, .22 caliber and 9 mm. Actually, the term *caliber*, as it is commonly applied, is not an exact measurement of the barrel's diameter; for example, a .38-caliber weapon may actually have a bore diameter that ranges from 0.345 to 0.365 inch.

RIFLING METHODS Before 1940, barrels were rifled by having one or two grooves at a time cut into the surface with steel hook cutters. The cutting tool was rotated as it passed down the barrel, so that the final results were grooves spiraling either to the right or left. However, as the need for

firearms identification
A discipline mainly concerned with determining whether a bullet or cartridge was fired by a particular weapon; it is not to be confused with ballistics, which is the study of a projectile in motion

grooves
The cut or low-lying portions between the lands in a rifled bore

rifling
The spiral grooves formed in the bore of a firearm barrel that impart spin to the projectile when it is fired

bore
The interior of a firearm barrel

lands
The raised portion between the grooves in a rifled bore

caliber
The diameter of the bore of a rifled firearm; the caliber is usually expressed in hundredths of an inch or millimeters—for example, .22 caliber and 9 mm

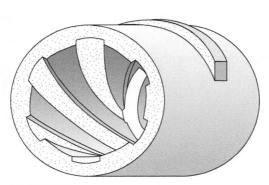

FIGURE 1
Interior view of a gun barrel, showing the presence of lands and grooves.

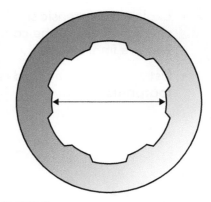

FIGURE 2
Cross section of a barrel with six grooves. The diameter of the bore is the caliber.

increased speed in the manufacture of weapons became apparent, newer techniques were developed that were far more suitable for the mass production of weapons.

The broach cutter, shown in Figure 3, consists of a series of concentric steel rings, with each ring slightly larger than the preceding one. As the broach passes through the barrel, it simultaneously cuts all grooves into the barrel at the required depth. The broach rotates as it passes through the barrel, giving the grooves their desired direction and rate of twist.

In contrast to the broach, the button process involves no cuttings. A steel plug or "button" impressed with the desired number of grooves is forced under extremely high pressures through the barrel. A single pass of the button down the barrel compresses the metal to create lands and grooves on the barrel walls that are negative forms of those on the button. The button rotates to produce the desired direction and rate of twist (see Figure 4).

Like the button process, the mandrel rifling or hummer forging process involves no cutting of metal. A mandrel is a rod of hardened steel machined so its form is the reverse impression of

FIGURE 3

A segment of a broach cutter.
Courtesy Susan Walsh, AP Wide World Photos

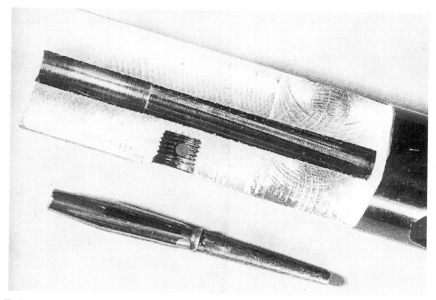

FIGURE 4

(top) Cross-section of a .22-caliber rifled barrel. *(bottom)* A button used to produce the lands and grooves in the barrel.

the rifling it is intended to produce. The mandrel is inserted into a slightly oversized bore, and the barrel is compressed with hammering or heavy rollers into the mandrel's form.

Every firearms manufacturer chooses a rifling process that is best suited to meet the production standards and requirements of its product. Once the choice is made, however, the class characteristics of the weapon's barrel will remain consistent; each will have the same number of lands and grooves, with the same approximate width and direction of twist. For example, .32-caliber Smith & Wesson revolvers have five lands and grooves twisting to the right. On the other hand, Colt .32-caliber revolvers exhibit six lands and grooves twisting to the left. Although these class characteristics permit the examiner to distinguish one type or brand name of weapon from another, they do not impart individuality to any one barrel; no class characteristic can do this.

If one could cut a barrel open lengthwise, a careful examination of the interior would reveal the existence of fine lines, or *striations*, many running the length of the barrel's lands and grooves. These striations are impressed into the metal as the negatives of minute imperfections found on the rifling cutter's surface, or they are produced by minute chips of steel pushed against the barrel's inner surface by a moving broach cutter. The random distribution and irregularities of these markings are impossible to duplicate exactly in any two barrels. **No two rifled barrels, even those manufactured in succession, have identical striation markings.** These striations form the individual characteristics of the barrel.

COMPARING BULLET MARKINGS As the bullet passes through the barrel, its surface is impressed with the rifled markings of the barrel. The bullet emerges from the barrel carrying the impressions of the bore's interior surface; these impressions reflect both the class and individual characteristics of the barrel (see Figure 5). Because there is no practical way of making a direct comparison between the markings on the fired bullet and those found within a barrel, the examiner must obtain test bullets fired through the suspect barrel for comparison. To prevent damage to the test bullet's markings and to facilitate the bullet's recovery, test firings are normally made into a recovery box filled with cotton or into a water tank.

FIGURE 5

A bullet is impressed with the rifling markings of the barrel when it emerges from the weapon.

The number of lands and grooves, and their direction of twist, are obvious points of comparison during the initial stages of the examination. Any differences in these class characteristics immediately eliminate the possibility that both bullets traveled through the same barrel. A bullet with five lands and grooves could not possibly have been fired from a weapon of like caliber with six lands and grooves, nor could one having a right twist have come through a barrel impressed with a left twist. If both bullets carry the same class characteristics, the analyst must begin to match the striated markings on both bullets. This can be done only with the assistance of the comparison microscope.

Modern firearms identification began with the development and use of the comparison microscope. This instrument is the most important tool at the disposal of the firearms examiner. The test and evidence bullets are mounted on cylindrical adjustable holders beneath the objective lenses of the microscope, each pointing in the same direction (see Figure 6). Both bullets are observed simultaneously within the same field of view, and the examiner rotates one bullet until a well-defined land or groove comes into view. Once the striation markings are located, the other bullet is rotated until a matching region is found. Not only must the lands and grooves of the test and evidence bullet have identical widths, but the longitudinal striations on each must coincide. When a matching area is located, the two bullets are simultaneously rotated to obtain additional matching areas around the periphery of the bullets. Figure 7 shows a typical photomicrograph of a bullet match as viewed under a comparison microscope.

CONSIDERATIONS IN BULLET COMPARISON Unfortunately, the firearms examiner rarely encounters a perfect match all around the bullet's periphery. The presence of grit and rust can alter the markings on bullets fired through the same barrel. More commonly, recovered evidence bullets may become so mutilated and distorted on impact as to yield only a small area with intact markings.

Furthermore, striation markings on a barrel are not permanent structures; they are subject to continuing change and alteration through wear as succeeding bullets traverse the length of the barrel. Fortunately, in most cases, these changes are not dramatic and do not prevent the matching of two bullets fired by the same weapon. As with fingerprint comparison, there are no hard-and-fast rules governing the minimum number of points required for a bullet comparison. The final opinion must be based on the judgment, experience, and knowledge of the expert.

Frequently, the firearms examiner receives a spent bullet without an accompanying suspect weapon and is asked to determine the caliber and possible make of the weapon. If a bullet appears not to have lost its metal, its weight may be one factor in determining its caliber. In some instances, the number of lands and grooves, the direction of twist, and the widths of lands and grooves are useful class characteristics for eliminating certain makes of weapons from consideration. For example, a bullet that has five lands and grooves and twists to the right could not come from a weapon manufactured by Colt because Colts are not manufactured with these class characteristics.

Sometimes a bullet has rifling marks that set it apart from most other manufactured weapons, as in the case of Marlin rifles. These weapons are rifled by a technique known as *microgrooving* and may have 8 to 24 grooves impressed into their barrels; few other weapons are manufactured in this fashion. In this respect, the FBI maintains a record known as the *General Rifling Characteristics File*. This file contains listings of class characteristics, such as land and groove width dimensions, for known weapons. It is periodically updated and distributed to the law enforcement community to help identify rifled weapons from retrieved bullets.

As previously discussed, unlike rifled firearms, a shotgun has a smooth barrel. It therefore follows that projectiles passing through a shotgun barrel are not impressed with any characteristic markings that can later be related back to the weapon. Shotguns generally fire small lead balls or pellets contained within a shotgun shell (see Figure 8). A paper or plastic wad pushes the pellets through the barrel on ignition of the cartridge's powder charge. By weighing and measuring the diameter of the shot recovered at a crime scene, the examiner can usually determine the size of shot used in the shell. The size and shape of the recovered wad may also reveal the gauge of the shotgun used and, in some instances, may indicate the manufacturer of the fired shell.

The diameter of the shotgun barrel is expressed by the term **gauge**.[1] The higher the gauge number, the smaller the barrel's diameter. For example, a 12-gauge shotgun has a bore diameter of 0.730 inch as contrasted to 0.670 inch for a 16-gauge shotgun. The exception to this rule is the .410-gauge shotgun, which refers to a barrel 0.41 inch in diameter.

---

[1] Originally, the number of lead balls with the same diameter as the barrel would make a pound. For example, a 20-gauge shotgun has an inside diameter equal to the diameter of a lead ball that weighs 1/20 of a pound.

mycrimekit

WEBEXTRA 17.1
Practice Matching Bullets with the Aid of a 3-D Interactive Illustration
www.mycrimekit.com

mycrimekit

WEBEXTRA 17.2
3-D Shotshell Illustrations
www.mycrimekit.com

gauge
Size designation of a shotgun, originally the number of lead balls with the same diameter as the barrel that would make a pound; for example, a 12-gauge shotgun would have a bore diameter of a lead ball 1/12 pound in weight; the only exception is the .410 shotgun, in which bore size is 0.41 inch

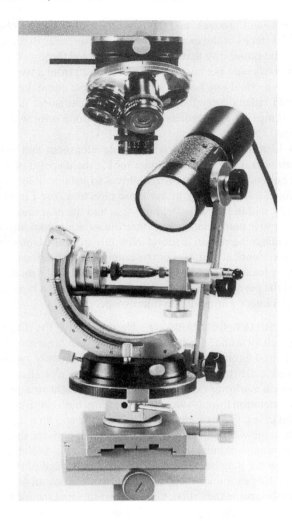

FIGURE 6

A bullet holder beneath the objective lens of a comparison microscope.
Courtesy Leica Microsystems, Buffalo, N.Y., www.leica-microsystems.com

FIGURE 7

Photomicrograph of two bullets through a comparison microscope. The test bullet is on the right; the questioned bullet is on the left.
Courtesy Philadelphia Police Department Laboratory

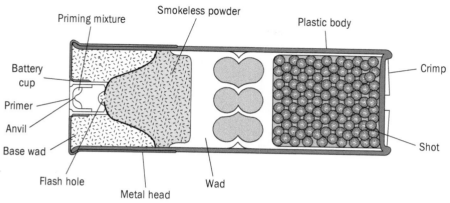

FIGURE 8

Cross-section of a loaded shotgun shell.

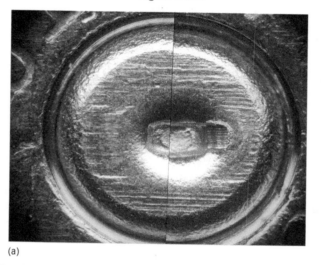

(a)

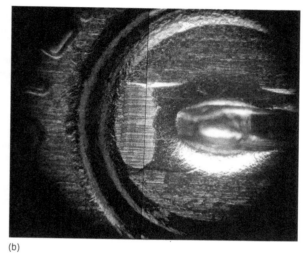

(b)

FIGURE 9

Comparison microscope photomicrograph showing a match between (a) firing pin impressions and (b) the breechblock markings on two shells.

Courtesy Ronald Welsh, Bureau of Forensic Services, Central Valley Laboratory, Ripon, Calif.

Cartridge Cases

The act of pulling a trigger releases the weapon's firing pin, causing it to strike the primer, which in turn ignites the powder. The expanding gases generated by the burning gunpowder propel the bullet forward through the barrel, simultaneously pushing the spent cartridge case or shell back with equal force against the **breechblock**. As the bullet is marked by its passage through the barrel, the shell is also impressed with markings by its contact with the metal surfaces of the weapon's firing and loading mechanisms. As with bullets, these markings can be reproduced in test-fired cartridges to provide distinctive points of comparison for individualizing a spent shell to a rifled weapon or shotgun.

The shape of the firing pin is impressed into the relatively soft metal of the primer on the cartridge case, revealing the minute distortions of the firing pin. These imperfections may be sufficiently random to individualize the pin impression to a single weapon. Similarly, the cartridge case, in its rearward thrust, is impressed with the surface markings of the breechblock. The breechblock, like any machined surface, is populated with random striation markings that become a highly distinctive signature for individualizing its surface. Other distinctive markings that may appear on the shell as a result of metal-to-metal contact are caused by the **extractor** and **ejector** mechanism and the magazine or clip, as well as by imperfections on the fire chamber walls. Photomicrographs in Figure 9 reveal a comparison of the firing pin and breechblock impressions on evidence and test-fired shells.

breechblock
The rear part of a firearm barrel

mycrimekit™

WEBEXTRA 17.3
3-D Revolver Cartridge Illustrations
www.mycrimekit.com

extractor
The mechanism in a firearm by which a cartridge of a fired case is withdrawn from the chamber

ejector
The mechanism in a firearm that throws the cartridge or fired case from the firearm

Sacco and Vanzetti

In 1920, two security guards were viciously gunned down by unidentified assailants. The security guards were transporting shoe factory payroll, nearly $16,000 in cash, at the time of the robbery-murder. Eyewitnesses described the assailants as "Italian-looking," one with a full handlebar mustache. The robbers had used two firearms, leaving behind three different brands of shells.

Two suspects were identified and arrested—Nicola Sacco and his friend, the amply mustachioed Bartolomeo Vanzetti. After denying owning any firearms, each was found to be in possession of a loaded pistol. In fact, Sacco's pistol was .32 caliber, the same caliber as the crime-scene bullets. In Sacco's pockets were found 23 bullets matching the brands of the empty shells found at the murder scene.

This case coincided with the "Red Scare," a politically turbulent time in post–World War I America. Citizens feared socialist zealots, and the media played up these emotions. Political maneuvering and the use of the media muddied the waters surrounding the case, and the fact that both suspects belonged to anarchist political groups that advocated revolutionary violence against the government only incited public animosity toward them. Sympathetic socialist organizations attempted to turn Sacco and Vanzetti into martyrs, calling their prosecution a "witch hunt."

The outcome of the trial ultimately depended on whether the prosecution could prove that Sacco's pistol fired the bullets that killed the two security guards. At trial, the ballistics experts testified that the bullets used were no longer in production and they

Sacco and Vanzetti.
Courtesy Corbis/Bettman

could not find similar ammunition to use in test firings—aside from the unused cartridges found in Sacco's pockets. A forensics expert for the prosecution concluded that a visual examination showed that the bullets matched, leading the jury to return a verdict of guilty. Sacco and Vanzetti were sentenced to death.

Because of continued public protests, a committee was appointed in 1927 to review the case. Around this time, Calvin Goddard, at the Bureau of Forensic Ballistics in New York, perfected the comparison microscope for use in forensic firearms investigations. With this instrument, two bullets are viewed side by side to compare the striations imparted to a bullet's surface as it travels through the gun's barrel. The committee asked Goddard to examine the bullets in question. A test-fired bullet from Sacco's weapon was matched conclusively by Goddard to one of the crime-scene bullets. The fates of Sacco and Vanzetti were sealed and they were put to death in 1927.

Firing pin, breechblock, extractor, and ejector marks may also be impressed onto the surface of the brass portion of shells fired by a shotgun. These impressions provide points for individualizing the shell to a weapon that are just as valuable as cartridge cases discharged from a rifled firearm. Furthermore, in the absence of a suspect weapon, the size and shape of a firing pin impression and/or the position of ejector marks in relationship to extractor and other markings may provide some clue to the type or make of the weapon that may have fired the questioned shell, or at least may eliminate a large number of possibilities.

Automated Firearms Search Systems

The use of firearms, especially semiautomatic weapons, during the commission of a crime has significantly increased throughout the United States. Because of the expense of such firearms, the likelihood that a specific weapon will be used in multiple crimes has risen. The advent of computerized imaging technology has made possible the storage of bullet and cartridge surface characteristics in a manner analogous to the storage of automated fingerprint files. Using this concept, crime laboratories can be networked, allowing them to share information on bullets and cartridges retrieved from several jurisdictions.

Search Systems

The effort to build a national computerized database for firearms evidence in the United States had a rather confusing and inefficient start in the early 1990s. Two major federal law enforcement agencies, the FBI and the ATF, offered the law enforcement community competing and incompatible computerized systems.

EARLY SYSTEMS The automated search system developed for the FBI was known as *DRUGFIRE*. This system emphasized the examination of unique markings on the cartridge casings expended by the weapon. The specimen was analyzed through a microscope attached to a video camera. The magnification allowed for a close-up view to identify individual characteristics. The image was captured by a video camera, digitized, and stored in a database. Although DRUGFIRE emphasized cartridge-case imagery, the images of highly characteristic bullet striations could also be stored in a like manner for comparisons.

The *Integrated Ballistic Identification System (IBIS)*, developed for the Bureau of Alcohol, Tobacco, Firearms and Explosives, processed digital microscopic images of identifying features found on both expended bullets and cartridge casings. IBIS incorporated two software programs: Bulletproof, a bullet-analyzing module, and Brasscatcher, a cartridge-case-analyzing module. A schematic diagram of Bulletproof's operation is depicted in Figure 10.[2]

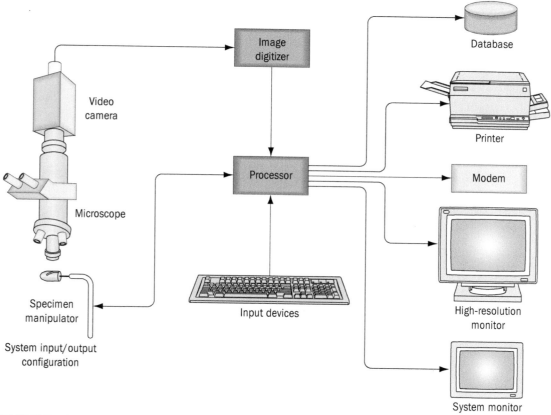

FIGURE 10

Bulletproof configuration. The sample is mounted on the specimen manipulator and illuminated by the light source from a microscope. The image is captured by a video camera and digitized. This digital image is then stored in a database, available for retrieval and comparison. The search for a match includes analyzing the width of land and groove impressions along with both rifling and individual characteristics. The Brasscatcher software uses the same system configuration but emphasizes the analysis of expended cartridge casings rather than the expended bullets.
Courtesy Forensic Technology (WAI) Inc., Côte St-Luc, Quebec, Canada

[2] R. E. Tontarski, Jr., and R. M. Thompson, "Automated Firearms Evidence Comparison: A Forensic Tool for Firearms Identification—An Update," *Journal of Forensic Sciences* 43 (1998): 641.

NIBIN   In 1999, members of the FBI and ATF joined forces to introduce the *National Integrated Ballistics Information Network (NIBIN)* program to the discipline of firearms examination. NIBIN guides and assists federal, state, and local laboratories interested in housing an automated search system. The new unified system incorporates both DRUGFIRE and IBIS technologies available in prior years. ATF has the overall responsibility for the system sites, whereas the FBI is responsible for the communications network.

Agencies using the new IBIS technology produce database files from bullets and cartridge casings retrieved from crime scenes or test fires from retrieved firearms. More than two hundred law enforcement agencies worldwide have adapted to this technology. The success of the system has been proven with more than 800,000 images compiled; nationwide, law enforcement agencies have connected more than 28,000 bullets and casings to more than one crime (see Figure 11).

For example, in a recent case, a Houston security guard was shot and killed during a botched armed robbery. A bullet and .40-caliber Smith & Wesson cartridge casing were recovered and

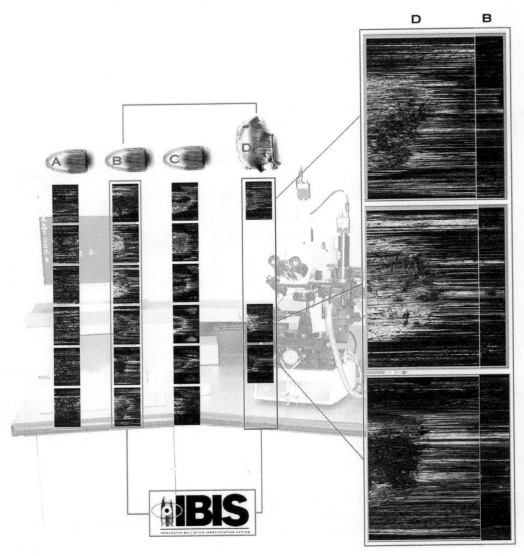

FIGURE 11

Bullets A, B, C, and D were acquired in the IBIS database at different times from different crime scenes. D is a fragmented bullet that had only three land impressions available for acquisition. Upon the entry of bullet D, IBIS found a potential matching candidate in the database: B. On the far right, bullet D is compared to bullet B using the IBIS imaging software. Finally, a forensic firearms examiner using the actual evidence under a conventional comparison microscope will confirm the match between B and D.
Courtesy Forensic Technology WAI Inc.

imaged into NIBIN. Earlier that day, a robbery-turned-double-homicide left two store clerks dead. Again, two bullets and two .40-caliber Smith & Wesson cartridge casings were recovered. Once they were processed into NIBIN, a correlation was found with the murder of the security officer and a separate aggravated robbery that occurred two weeks prior. All three crimes were linked with a firearm believed to be a .40-caliber Smith & Wesson pistol.

Further investigation into the use of a victim's credit card aided police in locating two suspects. In the possession of one suspect was a .40-caliber Smith & Wesson pistol. Once retrieved, the gun was test-fired and imaged into NIBIN. The casing from the test-fired weapon matched the evidence obtained in the robbery and the aggravated robbery-homicides. The associations were verified by traditional firearms examination comparisons performed by a firearms examiner. Before this computerized technology was developed, it would have taken years, or may have been impossible, to link all of these shootings to one single firearm.

In another example, the ATF laboratory in Rockville, Maryland, received 1,466 cartridge casings from the Ovcara mass burial site in Bosnia. After processing and imaging profiles for all casings, the examiners determined that 18 different firearms were used at the site. With the help of NIBIN technology and competent examiners, jurists were able to try and convict an individual for war crimes.

NIBIN serves only as a screening tool for firearms evidence. A computerized system does not replace the skills of the firearms examiner. NIBIN can screen hundreds of unsolved firearms cases and may narrow the possibilities to several firearms. However, the final comparison will be made by the forensic examiner through traditional microscopic methods.

Ballistic Fingerprinting

Participating crime laboratories in the United States are building databases of bullet and cartridge cases found at crime scenes and those fired in tests of guns seized from criminals. As these databases come online and prove their usefulness in solving crimes, law enforcement officials and the political community are scrutinizing the feasibility of scaling this concept up to create a system of *ballistic fingerprinting*. This system would entail the capture and storage of appropriate markings on bullets and cartridges test-fired from handguns and rifles before they are sold to the public. Questions regarding who will be responsible for collecting the images and details of how they will be stored are but two of many issues to be determined. The concept of ballistic fingerprinting is an intriguing one for the law enforcement community and promises to be explored and debated intensely in the future.

Gunpowder Residues

In incidents involving gunshot wounds, it is often necessary to determine the distance from which the weapon was fired. Frequently, in incidents involving a shooting death, the individual apprehended and accused pleads self-defense as the motive for the attack. Such claims are fertile grounds for **distance determinations** because finding the proximity of the parties involved in the incident is necessary to establish the facts of the incident. Similarly, careful examination of the wounds of suicide victims usually reveals characteristics associated with a very close-range gunshot wound. The absence of such characteristics is a strong indication that the wound was not self-inflicted and signals the possibility of foul play.

distance determination
The process of determining the distance between the firearm and a target, usually based on the distribution of powder patterns or the spread of a shot pattern

Distance Determination

Modern ammunition is propelled toward a target by the expanding gases created by the ignition of smokeless powder or nitrocellulose in a cartridge. Under ideal circumstances, all of the powder would be consumed in the process and converted into the rapidly expanding gases. However, in practice the powder is never totally burned. When a firearm is discharged, unburned and partially burned particles of gunpowder in addition to smoke are propelled out of the barrel along with the bullet toward the target. If the muzzle of the weapon is sufficiently close, these products are deposited onto the target. The distribution of gunpowder particles and other discharge residues around the bullet hole permits an assessment of the distance from which a handgun or rifle was fired.

The accuracy of a distance determination varies according to the circumstances of the case. When the investigator is unable to recover a suspect weapon, the best that the examiner can do is to state whether a shot could have been fired within some distance interval from the target. More exact opinions are possible only when the examiner has the suspect weapon in hand and has knowledge of the type of ammunition used in the shooting.

HANDGUNS AND RIFLES The precise distance from which a handgun or rifle has been fired must be determined by careful comparison of the powder-residue pattern on the victim's clothing or skin against test patterns made when the suspect weapon is fired at varying distances from a target. A white cloth or a fabric comparable to the victim's clothing may be used as a test target (see Figure 12). Because the spread and density of the residue pattern vary widely between weapons and ammunition, such a comparison is significant only when it is made with the suspect weapon and suspect ammunition, or with ammunition of the same type and make. By comparing the test and evidence patterns, the examiner may find enough similarity in shape and density on which to judge the distance from which the shot was fired.

Without the weapon, the examiner is restricted to looking for recognizable characteristics around the bullet hole. Such findings are at best approximations made as a result of general observations and the examiner's experience. However, some noticeable characteristics should be sought. For instance, when the weapon is held in contact with or less than 1 inch from the target, a heavy concentration of smokelike vaporous lead usually surrounds the bullet entrance hole. Often, loose fibers surrounding a contact hole show scorch marks from the flame discharge of the weapon, and some synthetic fibers may show signs of being melted as a result of the heat from the discharge. Furthermore, the blowback of muzzle gases may produce a stellate (star-shaped) tear pattern around the hole. Such a hole is invariably surrounded by a rim of a smokelike deposit of vaporous lead (see Figure 13).

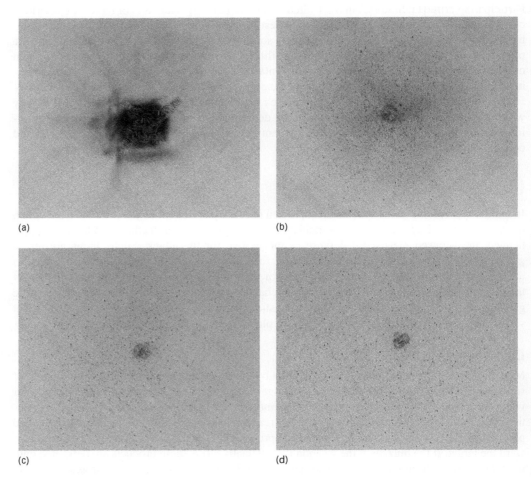

(a)

(b)

(c)

(d)

FIGURE 12

Test powder patterns made with a Glock 9mm luger fired at the following distances: (a) contact, (b) 6 inches, (c) 12 inches, and (d) 18 inches.
Courtesy Michelle D. Miranda, MS, D-ABC

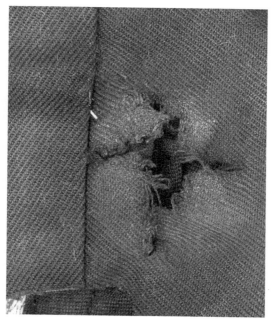

FIGURE 13
A contact shot.
Courtesy Michelle D. Miranda, MS, D-ABC

A halo of vaporous lead (smoke) deposited around a bullet hole normally indicates a discharge 12 to 18 inches or less from the target. The presence of scattered specks of unburned and partially burned powder grains without any accompanying soot can often be observed at distances up to approximately 25 inches. Occasionally, however, scattered gunpowder particles are noted at a firing distance as far out as 36 inches. With ball powder ammunition, this distance may be extended to 6 to 8 feet.

Finally, a weapon that has been fired more than 3 feet from a target usually does not deposit any powder residues onto the target's surface. In these cases, the only visual indication that the hole was made by a bullet is a dark ring, known as *bullet wipe*, around the perimeter of the entrance hole. Bullet wipe consists of a mixture of carbon, dirt, lubricant, primer residue, and lead wiped off the bullet's surface as it passes through the target. Again, in the absence of a suspect weapon, these observations are general guidelines for estimating target distances. Numerous factors—barrel length, caliber, type of ammunition, and type and condition of the weapon fired—influence the amount of gunpowder residue deposited on a target.

SHOTGUNS The determination of firing distances involving shotguns must again be related to test firings performed with the suspect weapon, using the same type of ammunition known to be used in the crime. In the absence of a weapon, the muzzle-to-target distance can be estimated by measuring the spread of the discharged shot. With close-range shots varying in distance up to 4 to 5 feet, the shot charge enters the target as a concentrated mass, producing a hole somewhat larger than the bore of the barrel. As the distance increases, the pellets progressively separate and spread out. Generally speaking, the spread in the pattern made by a 12-gauge shotgun increases 1 inch for each yard of distance. Thus, a 10-inch pattern would be produced at approximately 10 yards. Of course, this is only a rule of thumb; normally, a great number of variables can affect the shot pattern. Other factors to consider include the barrel length, the size and quantity of the pellets fired, the quantity of powder charge used to propel the pellets, and the choke of the gun under examination. **Choke** is the degree of constriction placed at the muzzle end of the barrel. The greater the choke, the narrower the shotgun pattern and the faster and farther the pellets will travel.

choke
An interior constriction placed at or near the muzzle end of a shotgun's barrel to control shot dispersion

Powder Residues on Garments

When garments or other evidence relevant to a shooting are received in the crime laboratory, the surfaces of all items are first examined microscopically for gunpowder residue. These particles may be identifiable by their characteristic colors, sizes, and shapes. However, the absence of visual indications does not preclude the possibility that gunpowder residue is present. Sometimes the lack of color contrast between the powder and garment or the presence of heavily encrusted

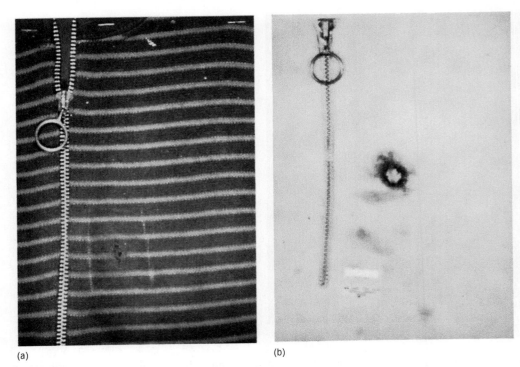

(a)   (b)

FIGURE 14

(a) A shirt bearing a powder stain, photographed under normal light. (b) An infrared photograph of the same shirt.

deposits of blood can obscure the visual detection of gunpowder. Often, an infrared photograph of the suspect area overcomes the problem. Such a photograph may enhance the contrast, thus revealing vaporous lead and powder particles deposited around the hole (see Figure 14). In other situations, this may not help, and the analyst must use chemical tests to detect gunpowder residues.

Nitrites are one type of chemical product that results from the incomplete combustion of smokeless (nitrocellulose) powder. One test method for locating powder residues involves transferring particles embedded on the target surface to chemically treated gelatin-coated photographic paper. This procedure is known as the **Greiss test**. The examiner presses the photographic paper onto the target with a hot iron; once the nitrite particles are on the paper, they are made easily visible by chemical treatment.[3] In addition, comparing the developed nitrite pattern to nitrite patterns obtained from test firings at known distances can be useful in determining the shooting distance from the target. A second chemical test is then performed to detect any trace of lead residue around the bullet hole. The questioned surface is sprayed with a solution of sodium rhodizonate, followed by a series of oversprays with acid solutions. This treatment causes lead particles to exhibit a pink color, followed by a blue-violet color.

Greiss test

A chemical test used to develop patterns of gunpowder residues around bullet holes

Primer Residues on the Hands

The firing of a weapon not only propels residues toward the target, but also blows gunpowder and primer residues back toward the shooter (see Figure 15). As a result, traces of these residues are often deposited on the firing hand of the shooter, and their detection can provide valuable information as to whether an individual has recently fired a weapon.

[3] P. C. Maiti, "Powder Patterns around Bullet Holes in Bloodstained Articles," *Journal of the Forensic Science Society* 13 (1973): 197.

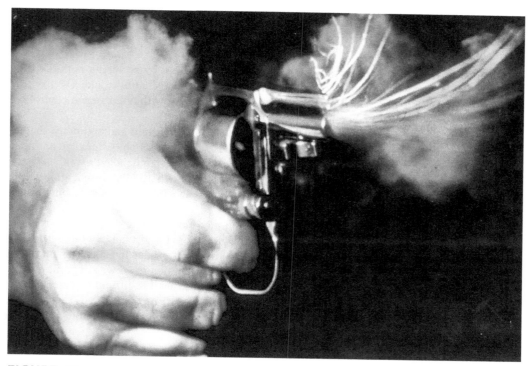

FIGURE 15

When a handgun is fired, gunpowder and primer residues are normally blown back toward the hand of the shooter.
Courtesy Forensic Technology WAI Inc.

Detecting Primer Residues

Early efforts at demonstrating powder residues on the hands centered on chemical tests that could detect unburned gunpowder or nitrates. For many years, the *dermal nitrate test* enjoyed popularity. It required the application of hot paraffin or wax to the suspect's hand with a paintbrush. After drying into a solid crust, the paraffin was removed and tested with diphenylamine. A blue color was taken as an indication of a positive reaction for nitrates. However, the dermal nitrate test has fallen into disfavor with law enforcement agencies, owing mainly to its lack of specificity. Common materials such as fertilizers, cosmetics, urine, and tobacco all give positive reactions that are indistinguishable from that obtained for gunpowder by this test.

Efforts to identify a shooter now center on the detection of primer residues deposited on the hand of a shooter at the time of firing. With the exception of most .22-caliber ammunition, primers currently manufactured contain a blend of lead styphnate, barium nitrate, and antimony sulfide. Residues from these materials are most likely to be deposited on the thumb web and the back of the firing hand of a shooter because these areas are closest to gases escaping along the side or back of the gun during discharge. In addition, individuals who handle a gun without firing it may have primer residues deposited on the palm of the hand coming in contact with the weapon.

However, with the handling of a used firearm, the passage of time, and the resumption of normal activities following a shooting, gunshot residues from the back of the hand are frequently redistributed to other areas, including the palms. Therefore, it is not unusual to find higher levels of barium and antimony on the palms than on the backs of the hands of known shooters. Another possibility is the deposition of significant levels of barium and antimony on the hands of an individual who is near a firearm when it is discharged.

Tests for Primer Residues

Determination of whether a person has fired or handled a weapon or has been near a discharged firearm is normally made by measuring the presence and possibly the amount of barium and antimony on the relevant portions of the suspect's hands. A variety of materials and techniques are used for removing these residues. The most popular approach, and certainly the most convenient for the field investigator, requires the application of an adhesive tape or adhesive to the hand's surface in order to remove any adhering residue particles.

SWABBING Another approach is to remove any residues present by swabbing both the firing and nonfiring hands with cotton that has been moistened with 5 percent nitric acid. The front and back of each hand are separately swabbed. All four swabs, along with a moistened control, are then forwarded to the crime laboratory for analysis.

In any case, once the hands are treated for the collection of barium and antimony, the collection medium must be analyzed for the presence of these elements. High barium and antimony levels on the suspect's hand(s) strongly indicate that the person fired or handled a weapon or was near a firearm when it was discharged. Because these elements are normally present after a firing in small quantities (less than 10 micrograms), only the most sensitive analytical techniques can detect them.

Unfortunately, even though most specimens submitted for this type of analysis have been from individuals strongly suspected of having fired a gun, there has been a low rate of positive findings. The major difficulty appears to be the short time that primer residues remain on the hands. These residues are readily removed by intentional or unintentional washing, rubbing, or wiping of hands. In fact, one study convincingly demonstrated that it is difficult to detect primer residues on cotton hand swabs taken as soon as two hours after firing a weapon.[4] Hence, some laboratories do not accept cotton hand swabs taken from living subjects six or more hours after a firing has occurred.

In cases that involve suicide victims, a higher rate of positives for the presence of gunshot residue is obtained when the hand swabbing is conducted before the person's body is moved or when the hands are protected by paper bags.[5] However, hand swabbing or the application of an adhesive cannot be used to detect firings with most .22-caliber rim-fire ammunition. Such ammunition may contain only barium or neither barium nor antimony in its primer composition.

SEM TESTING Most laboratories possessing gunshot residue detection capabilities require the application of an adhesive to the shooter's hands.[6] Microscopic primer and gunpowder particles on the adhesive are then located with the aid of a scanning electron microscope (SEM). These particles have a characteristic size and shape that readily distinguish them from other contaminants present on the hands (see Figure 16). When the SEM is linked to an X-ray analyzer, an elemental analysis of the particles can be conducted. A finding of a select combination of elements (lead, barium, and antimony) confirms that the particles were indeed primer residue (see Figure 17). Appendix "Instructions for Collecting Gunshot Residue (GSR)" contains a detailed description of the SEM residue collection procedure.

The major advantage of the SEM approach for primer residue detection is its enhanced specificity over hand swabbing. The SEM characterizes primer particles by their size and shape as well as by their chemical composition. Unfortunately, the excessive operator time required to search out and characterize gunshot residue has deterred this technique's use. The availability of automated particle search and identification systems for use with scanning electron microscopes may overcome this problem. Results of work performed with automated systems show it to be significantly faster than a manual approach for searching out gunshot residue particles.[7]

[4] J. W. Kilty, "Activity after Shooting and Its Effect on the Retention of Primer Residues," *Journal of Forensic Sciences* 29 (1975): 219.

[5] G. E. Reed et al., "Analysis of Gunshot Residue Test Results in 112 Suicides," *Journal of Forensic Sciences* 35 (1990): 62.

[6] G. M. Woiten et al., "Particle Analysis for the Detection of Gunshot Residue, I: Scanning Electron Microscopy/Energy Dispersive X-Ray Characterization of Hand Deposits from Firing," *Journal of Forensic Sciences* 24 (1979): 409.

[7] R. S. White and A. D. Owens, "Automation of Gunshot Residue Detection and Analysis by Scanning Electron Microscopy/Energy Dispersive X-Ray Analysis (SEM/EDX)," *Journal of Forensic Sciences* 32 (1987): 1595; and W. L. Tillman, "Automated Gunshot Residue Particle Search and Characterization," *Journal of Forensic Sciences* 32 (1987): 62.

FIGURE 16

An SEM view of gunshot residue particles.
Courtesy Foster and Freeman Limited, Worchester Shine, UK, www.fosterfreeman.co.uk

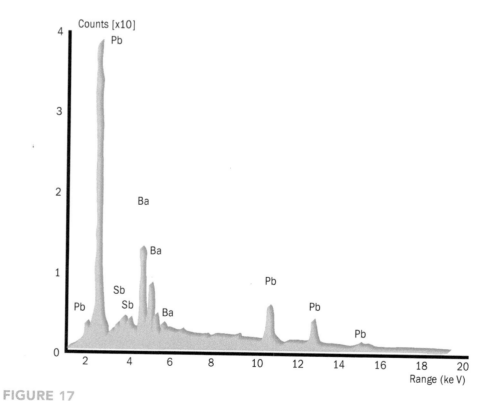

FIGURE 17

Spectrum showing the presence of lead, barium, and antimony in gunshot residue.
Courtesy Jeol USA Inc., Peabody, Mass., www.jeolusa.com

Serial Number Restoration

Today, many manufactured items, including automobile engine blocks and firearms, are impressed with a serial number for identification. Increasingly, the criminalist is asked to restore such a number when it has been removed or obliterated by grinding, rifling, or punching.

Serial numbers are usually stamped on a metal body or frame, or on a plate, with hard steel dies. These dies strike the metal surface with a force that allows each digit to sink into the metal at a prescribed depth. Serial numbers can be restored because the metal crystals in the stamped zone are placed under a permanent strain that extends a short distance beneath the original numbers. When a suitable etching agent is applied, the strained area dissolves faster than the unaltered metal, thus revealing the etched pattern in the form of the original numbers. However, if the zone of strain has been removed, or if the area has been impressed with a different strain pattern, the number usually cannot be restored.

Before any treatment with the etching reagent, the obliterated surface must be thoroughly cleaned of dirt and oil and polished to a mirrorlike finish. The reagent is swabbed onto the surface with a cotton ball. The choice of etching reagent depends on the type of metal surface being worked on. A solution of hydrochloric acid (120 mL), copper chloride (90 g), and water (100 mL) generally works well for steel surfaces.

Collection and Preservation of Firearms Evidence

Firearms

The Hollywood image of an investigator picking up a weapon by its barrel with a pencil or stick in order to protect fingerprints must be avoided. This practice only disturbs powder deposits, rust, or dirt lodged in the barrel, and consequently may alter the striation markings on test-fired bullets. If recovery of latent fingerprints is a primary concern, hold the weapon by the edge of the trigger guard or by the checkered portion of the grip, which usually does not retain identifiable fingerprints.

The most important consideration in handling a weapon is safety. Before any weapon is sent to the laboratory, all precautions must be taken to prevent an accidental discharge of a loaded weapon in transit. In most cases, it will be necessary to unload the weapon. If this is done, a record should first be made of the weapon's hammer and safety position; likewise, the location of all fired and unfired ammunition in the weapon must be recorded.

When a revolver is recovered, the chamber position in line with the barrel should be indicated by a scratch mark on the cylinder. Each chamber is designated with a number on a diagram, and as each cartridge or casing is removed, it should be marked to correspond to the numbered chambers in the diagram. Knowledge of the cylinder position of a cartridge casing may be useful for later determination of the sequence of events, particularly in shooting cases when more than one shot was fired. Place each round in a separate box or envelope. If the weapon is an automatic, the magazine must be removed and checked for prints and the chamber then emptied.

As with any other type of physical evidence recovered at a crime scene, firearms evidence must be marked for identification and a chain of custody must be established. Therefore, when a firearm is recovered, an identification tag should be attached to the trigger guard. The tag should be marked to show appropriate identifying data, including the weapon's serial number, make, and model and the investigator's initials. The firearm itself may be further identified by being marked directly with a sharp-pointed scriber in an inconspicuous area of the weapon—for example, the inside of the trigger guard. This practice will avoid any permanent defacement of the weapon.

When a weapon is recovered from an underwater location, no effort must be made to dry or clean it. Instead, the firearm should be transported to the laboratory in a receptacle containing enough of the same water necessary to keep it submerged. This procedure prevents rust from developing during transport.

Ammunition

Protection of class and individual markings on bullets and cartridge cases must be the primary concern of the field investigator. Thus, extreme caution is needed when removing a lodged bullet from a wall or other object. If the bullet's surface is accidentally scratched during this operation, valuable striation markings could be obliterated. It is best to free bullets from their target by carefully breaking away the surrounding support material while avoiding direct contact with the projectile.

Bullets recovered at the crime scene are scribed with the investigator's initials, on either the base or the nose of the bullet (see Figure 18). Again, obliteration of any striation markings on the bullet must be scrupulously avoided. If the bullet is badly deformed and there is no apparent place for identification, it should just be placed in a container that is appropriately marked for identification. In any case, the investigator must protect the bullet by wrapping it in tissue paper before placing it in a pillbox or an envelope for shipment to the crime laboratory.

In handling the bullet, the investigator should be conscious of the possibility that minute traces of evidence, such as paint and fibers, may be adhering to the bullet. Care must be taken to leave these trace materials intact. Similarly, a fired casing must be identified so as to avoid destroying marks impressed on it from the weapon. The investigator's initials should be placed near the outside or inside mouth of the shell (see Figure 19). Discharged shells from shotguns are initialed with ink or indelible pencil on the paper or plastic tube remaining on the shell or on the metal nearest the mouth of the shell.

In addition, when semiautomatic or automatic weapons have been fired, the ejection pattern of the casings can help establish the relationship of the suspect to his or her victim. For this reason, the exact location of the place from which a shell casing was recovered is important information that must be noted by the investigator.

In incidents involving shotguns, any wads recovered are to be packaged and sent to the laboratory. An examination of the size and composition of the wad may reveal information about the type of ammunition used and the gauge of the shotgun.

Gunpowder Deposits

The clothing of a firearms victim must be carefully preserved so as to prevent damage or disruption to powder residues deposited around a bullet or shell hole. The cutting or tearing of clothing in the area of the holes must be avoided as the clothing is being removed. All wet clothing should be air-dried out of direct sunlight and then folded carefully so as not to disrupt the area around the bullet hole. Each item should be placed in a separate paper bag.

Tool Marks

A *tool mark* is any impression, cut, gouge, or abrasion caused by a tool coming into contact with another object. Most often, tool marks are encountered at burglary scenes that involve forcible entry into a building or safe. Generally, these marks occur as indented impressions into a softer surface or as abrasion marks caused by the tool cutting or sliding against another object.

Comparing Tool Marks

Typically, an indented impression is left on the frame of a door or window as a result of the prying action of a screwdriver or crowbar. A careful examination of these impressions can reveal important class characteristics—that is, the size and shape of the tool. However, they rarely reveal any significant individual characteristics that could permit the examiner to individualize the mark to a single tool. Such characteristics, when they do exist, usually take the form of discernible random nicks and breaks that the tool has acquired through wear and use (Figure 20).

Just as the machined surfaces of a firearm are impressed with random striations during its manufacture, the edges of a pry bar, chisel, screwdriver, knife, or cutting tool likewise display a series of microscopic irregularities that look like ridges and valleys. Such markings are left as a result of the machining processes used to cut and finish tools. The shape and pattern of such minute imperfections are further modified by damage and wear during the life of the tool. Considering the unending variety of patterns that the hills and valleys can assume, it is highly unlikely

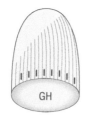

FIGURE 18

Discharged evidence bullets should be marked on the base or nose. When there is more than one bullet, a number should accompany the initials. *Never* mark bullets on the side.

FIGURE 19

Discharged evidence shells should be marked on the outside or inside, as close as possible to the mouth of the shell. Discharged shotgun shells should be marked on the brass, close to the paper or plastic. *Never* mark the shells where the firing pin strikes the primer.

FIGURE 20

A comparison of a tool mark with a suspect screwdriver. Note how the presence of nicks and breaks on the tool's edge helps individualize the tool to the mark.

that any two tools will be identical. Hence, these minute imperfections impart individuality to each tool.

If the edge of a tool is scraped against a softer surface, it may cut a series of striated lines that reflect that pattern of the tool's edge. Markings left in this manner are compared in the laboratory through a comparison microscope with test tool marks made from the suspect tool. The result can be a positive comparison, and hence a definitive association of the tool with the evidence mark, when a sufficient quantity of striations match between the evidence and test markings.

One of the major problems associated with tool mark comparisons is the difficulty in duplicating in the laboratory the tool mark left at the crime scene. A thorough comparison requires the preparation of a series of test marks obtained by applying the suspect tool at various angles and pressures to a soft metal surface (lead is commonly used). This approach gives the examiner ample opportunity to duplicate many of the details of the original evidence marking. A photomicrograph of a typical tool mark comparison is illustrated in Figure 21.

Collecting Tool Mark Evidence

Whenever practical, the entire object or the part of the object bearing a tool mark should be submitted to the crime laboratory for examination. When removal of the tool mark is impractical, the only recourse is to photograph the marked area to scale and make a cast of the mark. Under these circumstances, liquid silicone casting material has been found to be the most satisfactory for reproducing most of the fine details of the mark. See Figure 22. However, even under the most optimum conditions, the clarity of many of the tool mark's minute details will be lost or obscured in a photograph or cast. Of course, this will reduce the chance of individualizing the mark to a single tool.

The crime-scene investigator must never attempt to fit the suspect tool into the tool mark. Any contact between the tool and the marked surface may alter the mark and will, at the least, raise serious questions about the integrity of the evidence. The suspect tool and mark must be packaged in separate containers, with every precaution taken to avoid contact between the tool or mark and another hard surface. Failure to properly protect the tool or mark from damage could result in the destruction of its individual characteristics.

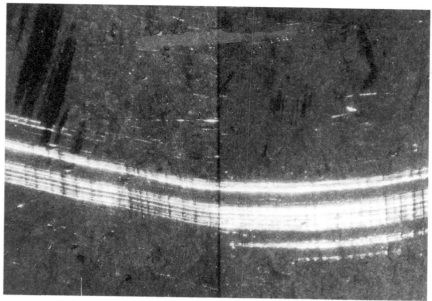

FIGURE 21

A photograph of a tool mark comparison seen under a comparison microscope.
Courtesy Leica Microsystems, Buffalo, N.Y., www.leica-microsystems.com

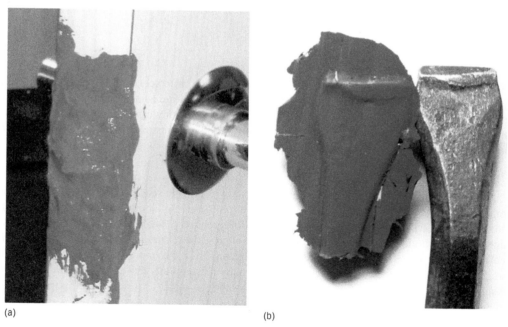

(a)   (b)

FIGURE 22

(a) Casting a tool mark impression with a silicone-based putty. (b) Impression alongside suspect tool.
Courtesy Sirchie Finger Print Laboratories, Inc., Youngsville, N.C., www.sirchie.com

Furthermore, the tool or its impression may contain valuable trace evidence. Chips of paint adhering to the mark or tool provide perhaps the best example of how the transfer of trace physical evidence can occur as a result of using a tool to gain forcible entry into a building. Obviously, the presence of trace evidence greatly enhances the evidential value of the tool or its mark and requires special care in handling and packaging the evidence to avoid losing or destroying these items.

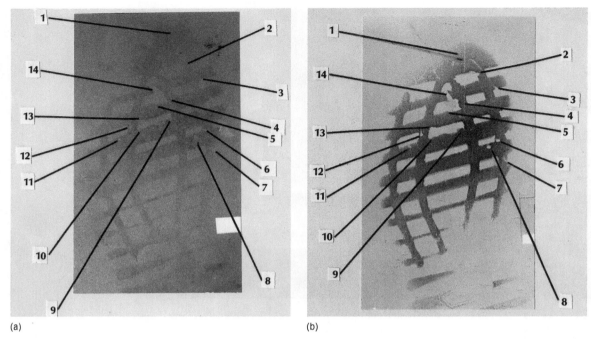

(a)   (b)

FIGURE 23

(a) Impression of shoe found at a crime scene. (b) Test impression made with suspect shoe. A sufficient number of points of comparison exist to support the conclusion that the suspect shoe left the impression at the crime scene.

Other Impressions

From time to time, impressions of another kind are left at a crime scene. This evidence may take the form of a shoe, tire, or fabric impression and may be as varied as a shoe impression left on a piece of paper at the scene of a burglary (Figure 23), a hit-and-run victim's garment that has come into violent contact with an automobile (Figure 24), or the impression of a bloody shoe print left on a floor or carpet at a homicide scene (Figure 25).

Preserving Impressions

The primary consideration in collecting impressions at the crime scene is the preservation of the impression or its reproduction for later examination in the crime laboratory. Before any impression is moved or otherwise handled, it must be photographed (a scale should be included in the picture) to show all the observable details of the impression. Several shots should be taken directly over the impression as well as at various angles around the impression. The skillful use of side lighting for illumination will help highlight many ridge details that might otherwise remain obscured. Photographs should also be taken to show the position of the questioned impression in relation to the overall crime scene.

Although photography is an important first step in preserving an impression, it must be considered merely a backup procedure that is available to the examiner if the impression is damaged before reaching the crime laboratory. Naturally, it is preferable for the examiner to receive the original impression for comparison to the suspect shoe, tire, garment, and so forth. In most cases when the impression is on a readily recoverable item, such as glass, paper, or floor tile, little or no difficulty is presented in transporting the evidence intact to the laboratory.

Lifting Impressions

If an impression is encountered on a surface that cannot be submitted to the laboratory, the investigator may be able to preserve the print in a manner that is analogous to lifting a fingerprint. This is especially true of impressions made in light deposits of dust or dirt. A lifting material large

FIGURE 24

A small child was found dead at the edge of a rural road near a railroad crossing, the victim of a hit-and-run driver. A local resident was suspected, but he denied any knowledge of the incident. The investigating officer noted what appeared to be a fabric imprint on the bumper of the suspect's automobile. The weave pattern of the clothing of the deceased was compared with the imprint on the bumper and was found to match. When the suspect was confronted with this information, he admitted his guilt.
Courtesy Centre of Forensic Sciences, Toronto, ON, Canada

enough to lift the entire impression should be used. Carefully place the lifting material over the entire impression. Use a fingerprint roller to eliminate any air pockets before lifting the impression off the surface.

A more exotic approach to lifting and preserving dust impressions involves the use of a portable electrostatic lifting device.[8] The principle employed is similar to that of creating an electrostatic charge on a comb and using the comb to lift small pieces of tissue paper. A sheet of mylar film is placed on top of the dust mark, and the film is pressed against the impression with the aid of a roller. The high-voltage electrode of the electrostatic unit is then placed in contact with the film while the unit's earth electrodes are placed against a metal plate (earth plate) (see Figure 26). A charge difference develops between the mylar film and the surface below the dust mark so that the dust is attached to the lifting film. In this manner, dust prints on chairs, walls, floors, and the like, can be transferred to the mylar film. Floor surfaces up to 40 feet long can be covered with a mylar sheet and searched for dust impressions. The electrostatic lifting technique is particularly helpful in recovering barely visible dust prints on colored surfaces. Dust impressions can also be enhanced through chemical development (see Figure 27).[9]

[8] See R. Milne, "Electrostatic Lifting of Marks at Crime Scenes and the Development of Pathfinder," *Science & Justice* 38 (1998): 135.
[9] B. Glattstein, Y. Shor, N. Levin, and A. Zeichner, "pH Indicators as Chemical Reagents for the Enhancement of Footwear Marks," *Journal of Forensic Sciences* 41 (1996): 23.

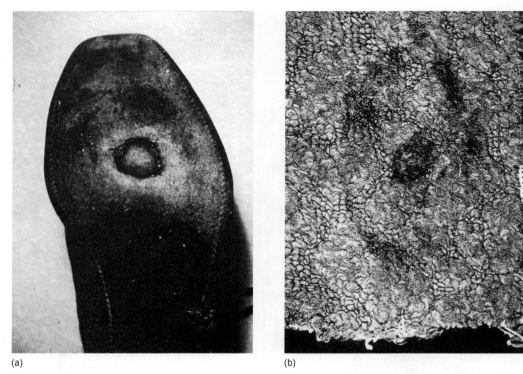

(a)   (b)

FIGURE 25

An imprint of a shoe was found on the carpet in the home of a homicide victim (b). The suspect's shoe, shown in (a), made the impression. Note the distinctive impression of the hole present in the shoe's sole.
Courtesy of Dade County Crime Lab.

FIGURE 26

Electrostatic lifting of a dust impression off a floor using an electrostatic unit.
Courtesy Sirchie Finger Print Laboratories, Inc., Youngsville, N.C., www.sirchie.com

Casting Impressions

When shoe and tire marks are impressed into soft earth at a crime scene, their preservation is best accomplished by photography and casting.[10] Class I dental stone, a form of gypsum, is widely recommended for making casts of shoe and tire impressions. A series of photographs clearly illustrating the steps to be carried out in the casting of an impression are shown in Figure 28.

[10] D. S. Hilderbrand and M. Miller, "Casting Materials—Which One to Use?" *Journal of Forensic Identification* 45 (1995): 618.

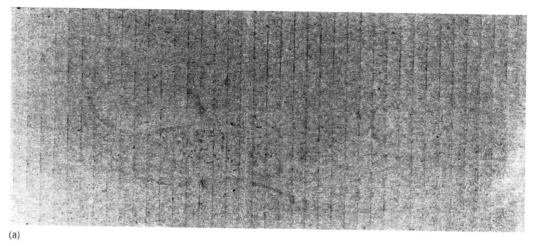

(a)

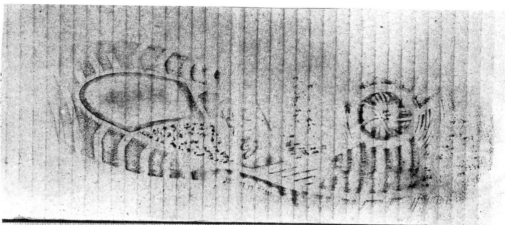

(b)

FIGURE 27

(a) A dust impression of a shoe print on cardboard before enhancement. (b) Shoe print after chemical enhancement with Bromophenol Blue and exposure to water vapor.
Courtesy Division of Identification and Forensic Science (DIFS), Israel Police Headquarters, Jerusalem, Israel

The cast should be allowed to air-dry for 24 to 48 hours before it is shipped to the forensic science laboratory for examination. Figure 29 illustrates a cast made from a shoe print in mud. The cast compares to the suspect shoe. An aerosol product known as Snow Impression Wax is available for casting snow impressions.[11] The recommended procedure is to spray three light coats of the wax at an interval of one to two minutes between layers and then let it dry for ten minutes. A viscous mixture of Class I dental stone is then poured onto the wax-coated impression. After the casting material has hardened, the cast can be removed.

A number of chemicals can be used to develop and enhance footwear impressions made with blood. In areas where a bloody footwear impression is very faint or where the subject has tracked through blood leaving a trail of bloody impressions, chemical enhancement can visualize latent or nearly invisible blood impressions (see Figure 30). A number of chemical formulas useful for bloody footwear impression development are listed in Appendix "Chemical Formulas for Development of Footwear Impressions in Blood".

A number of blood enhancement chemicals have been examined for their impact on STR DNA typing. None of the chemicals examined had a deleterious effect, on a short-term basis, on the ability to carry out STR DNA typing on the blood.[12]

[11] Available from Sirchie Finger Print Laboratories, Inc., Youngsville, N.C.
[12] C. J. Frégeau et al., "Fingerprint Enhancement Revisited and the Effects of Blood Enhancement Chemicals on Subsequent Profiler Plus™ Fluorescent Short Tandem Repeat DNA Analysis of Fresh and Aged Bloody Fingerprints," *Journal of Forensic Sciences* 45 (2000): 354.

FIGURE 28

Casting a footwear impression at a crime scene. (a) The impression is hardened using aerosol hairspray. (b) The correct amount of water is added to a known amount of dental stone. (c) The mixture is kneaded by hand until the desired (pancake batter–like) consistency is reached. (d) The dental stone is poured into the impression using a spoon as a medium to disperse the flow. (e) The impression is filled with dental stone and allowed to dry before removal.

Courtesy Sirchie Finger Print Laboratories, Inc., Youngsville, N.C., www.sirchie.com

Comparing Impressions

Whatever the circumstances, the laboratory procedures used for examining any type of impression remain the same. Of course, a comparison is possible only when an item suspected of having made the impression is recovered. Test impressions may be necessary to compare the characteristics of the suspect item with the evidence impression.

The evidential value of the impression is determined by the number of class and individual characteristics that the examiner finds. Agreement with respect to size, shape, or design may

(a)

(b)

(c)

FIGURE 29

(a) Shoe impression in mud. (b) Cast of shoe impression. (c) Shoe suspected of leaving muddy impression.

Courtesy Sirchie Finger Print Laboratories, Inc., Youngsville, N.C., www.sirchie.com

permit the conclusion that the impression could have been made by a particular shoe, tire, or garment; however, one cannot entirely exclude other possible sources from having the same class characteristics. More significant is the existence of individual characteristics arising out of wear, cuts, gouges, or other damage. A sufficient number or the uniqueness of such points of comparison support a finding that both the evidence and test impressions originated from one and only one source.

When tire tread impressions are left at a crime scene, the laboratory can examine the design of the impression and possibly determine the style and/or manufacturer of the tire. This may be particularly helpful to investigators when a suspect tire has not yet been located.

New computer software may be able to help the forensic scientist make shoe print comparisons. For example, an automated shoe print identification system developed in England, called Shoeprint Image Capture and Retrieval (SICAR), incorporates multiple databases to search known and unknown footwear files for comparison against footwear specimens. Shoe print images can be entered into SICAR by either a scanner or a digital camera. This product has a comprehensive shoe sole database (Solemate ™) that includes more than 17,000 footwear entries, representing more than 700 shoe brands, providing investigators with a means for linking a crime scene footwear impression to a particular shoe manufacturer.

Using the SICAR system, an impression from a crime scene can be compared to a reference database to find out what type of shoe caused the imprint. That same impression can also be searched in the suspect and crime databases to reveal whether that shoe print matches the shoes of a person who has been in custody or the shoe prints left behind at another crime scene. When matches are made during the searching process, the images are displayed side by side on the computer screen.

Human bite mark impressions on skin and foodstuffs have proven to be important items of evidence for convicting defendants in a number of homicide and rape cases in recent years. If a sufficient number of points of similarity between test and suspect marks are present, a forensic odontologist may conclude that a bite mark was made by one particular individual (see Figure 31).

mycrimekit™

WEBEXTRA 17.7
Casting a Footwear Impression
www.mycrimekit.com

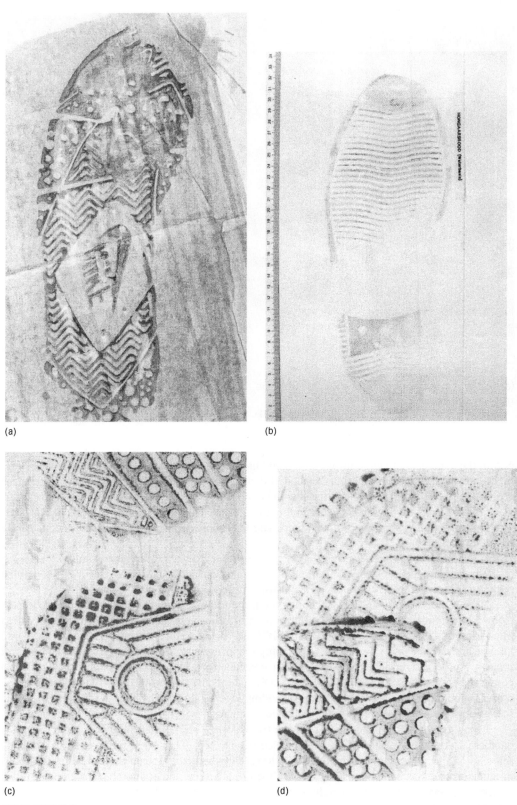

(a)

(b)

(c)

(d)

FIGURE 30

(a) Bloody footprint on cardboard treated with amido black. (b) Bloody footprint treated with Hungarian Red dye. (c) Bloody footprint visualized with leucocrystal violet. (d) Bloody footprint enhanced with patent blue.

(a) Courtesy Dwane S. Hilderbrand and David P. Coy, Scottsdale Police Crime Laboratory, Scottsdale, Ariz.
(b) Courtesy Safariland, Jacksonville, Fla.., South Paris, Maine (c–h) Courtesy William Bodziak, FBI Laboratory

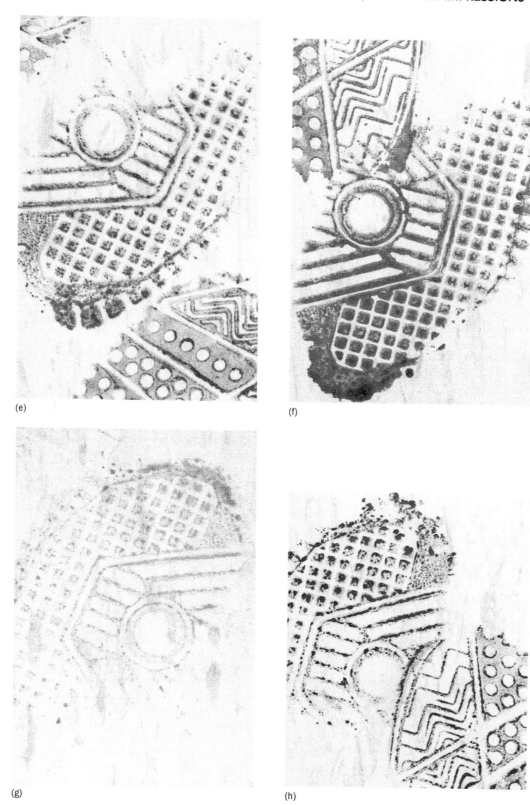

(e)

(f)

(g)

(h)

FIGURE 30 (Continued)

(e) Bloody foot impression treated with amido black. (f) Bloody footprint visualized with fushin acid dye. (g) Bloody foot impression visualized with tartrazine. (h) Bloody footprint treated with diaminobenzidine.

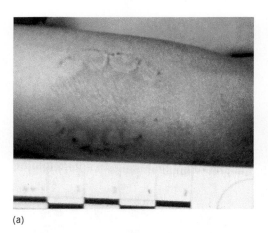
(a)

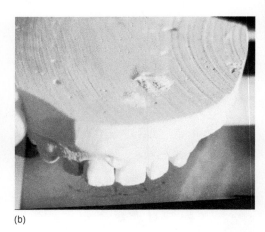
(b)

FIGURE 31

(a) Bite mark impression on the victim's forearm. (b) Upper dental model from the teeth of the suspect matches the individual teeth characteristics of the bite marks.
Courtesy Haskell Askin, D.D.S., Forensic Odontologist, Brick Town, NJ 08724

> >

case study

The O. J. Simpson Trial—Who Left the Impressions at the Crime Scene?

On the night of June 12, 1994, Nicole Brown—ex-wife of football star O. J. Simpson—and her friend Ron Goldman were brutally murdered on the grounds outside her home in Brentwood, California. O. J. Simpson was arrested for their murders, but professed his innocence. At the crime scene, investigators found bloody shoe impressions along the concrete walkway leading up to the front door of Brown's condominium. These shoe impressions were of extremely high quality and of intricate detail. The news media broadcast countless images of these bloody shoe prints on television, making it obvious to the killer that those shoes would surely link him to the crime.

Famed FBI shoe print examiner William J. Bodziak investigated the footwear evidence from the scene. His first task was to identify the brand of shoe that made the marks. Because the pattern was clear and distinct, with complete toe-to-heel detail, this seemed a simple task at first. Bodziak compared this pattern to the thousands of sole patterns in the FBI's database. None matched. He then went to his reference collection of books and trade show brochures, again with no success.

Bodziak's experience told him that these were expensive, Italian-made casual dress shoes with a sole made from synthetic material. Using this knowledge, he shopped the high-end stores for a similar tread pattern, but still was unable to identify the shoes. He then drew a composite sketch of the sole and faxed the image to law enforcement agencies and shoe manufacturers and distributors worldwide. The owner of the American distributing company for Bruno Magli shoes was the only one to respond.

Further exhaustive investigation revealed that these were extremely rare shoes. There were two styles of shoe bearing this exact sole design. They were available for only two years, and from a mere forty stores in the United States and Puerto Rico. The Lorenzo style shoe had a bootlike upper that came to the ankle. The Lyon style shoe had the lower, more typical dress shoe cut. The impressions were made by a size 12 shoe, and it was later determined that only 299 pairs of size 12 with this tread pattern were sold in the United States.

Simpson flatly denied ever owning these shoes, adding that he would never wear anything so ugly. However, he was known to wear a size 12, and photographs taken almost nine months before the murders show Simpson wearing a pair of black leather Bruno Magli Lorenzo shoes. These shoes were available in several colors, so this narrows the number of shoes matching Simpson's pair of Lorenzos (this size, color, and style) sold in the United States to twenty-nine pairs.

Proving that Simpson owned a pair of shoes that had the exact pattern found printed in blood at the crime scene was an essential component of the case, but it was not done in time to be used during the criminal prosecution. The photographs of Simpson in his Bruno Magli shoes were released after the culmination of the criminal trial, so the jury never heard the direct evidence that Simpson owned these shoes. However, this proved to be an important link uniting Simpson with the crime scene in the civil trial. Although O. J. Simpson was acquitted of the murders of Nicole Brown and Ron Goldman in the criminal trial, he was judged responsible for their murders in the civil court case.

chapter summary

> > > > > > > > > > >

Structural variations and irregularities caused by scratches, nicks, breaks, and wear permit the criminalist to relate a bullet to a gun, a scratch or abrasion mark to a single tool, or a tire track to a particular automobile.

The manufacture of a barrel requires impressing its inner surface with spiral grooves, a step known as rifling. The surfaces of the original bore remaining between the grooves are called lands. No two rifled barrels, even those manufactured in succession, have identical striation markings. These striations form the individual characteristics of the barrel. The inner surface of the barrel of a gun leaves its striation markings on a bullet passing through it. The number of lands and grooves and their direction of twist are obvious points of comparison during the initial stages of an examination. Any differences in these class characteristics immediately eliminate the possibility that both bullets traveled through the same barrel.

The comparison microscope is the most important tool to a firearms examiner. Two bullets can be observed and compared simultaneously within the same field of view. Not only must the lands and grooves of the test and evidence bullet have identical widths, but the longitudinal striations on each must coincide. The firing pin, breechblock, and ejector and extractor mechanism also offer a highly distinctive signature for individualization of cartridge cases. The advent of computerized imaging technology has made possible the storage of bullet and cartridge surface characteristics in a manner analogous to automated fingerprint files. However, the final comparison will be made by the forensic examiner through traditional microscopic methods.

The distribution of gunpowder particles and other discharge residues around a bullet hole permits an assessment of the distance from which a handgun or rifle was fired. The firing of a weapon not only propels residues toward the target, but also blows gunpowder and primer residues back toward the shooter. As a result, traces of these residues are often deposited on the firing hand of the shooter, and their detection can provide valuable information as to whether an individual has recently fired a weapon. Examiners measure the amount of barium and antimony on the relevant portion of the suspect's hands or characterize the morphology of particles containing these elements to determine whether a person has fired or handled a weapon, or was near a discharged firearm.

Increasingly, the criminalist is asked to restore a serial number that has been obliterated by grinding, rifling, or punching. Restoration of serial numbers is possible through chemical etching because the metal crystals in the stamped zone are placed under a permanent strain that extends a short distance beneath the original numbers.

A tool mark is any impression, cut, gouge, or abrasion caused by a tool coming into contact with another object. Hence any minute imperfections on a tool impart individuality to that tool. The shape and pattern of such imperfections are further modified by damage and wear during the life of the tool. The comparison microscope is used to compare crime-scene tool marks with test impressions made with the suspect tool. When shoe and tire marks are impressed into soft earth at a crime scene, their preservation is best accomplished by photography and casting. In areas where a bloody footwear impression is very faint or where the subject has tracked through blood, leaving a trail of bloody impressions, chemical enhancement can visualize latent or nearly invisible blood impressions. A sufficient number of points of comparison or the uniqueness of such points support a finding that both the questioned and test impressions originated from one and only one source.

review questions

1. The _____ is the original part of the bore left after rifling grooves are formed.

2. The diameter of the gun barrel is known as its _____.

3. True or False: The number of lands and grooves is a class characteristic of a barrel. _____

4. The _____ characteristics of a rifled barrel are formed by striations impressed into the barrel's surface.

5. The most important instrument for comparing bullets is the _____.

6. To make a match between a test bullet and a recovered bullet, the lands and grooves of the test and evidence bullet must have identical widths, and the longitudinal _____ on each must coincide.

7. True or False: It is always possible to determine the make of a weapon by examining a bullet it fired. _____

8. A shotgun has a _____ barrel.

9. The diameter of a shotgun barrel is expressed by the term _____.

10. True or False: Shotgun pellets can be individualized to a single weapon. _____

11. True or False: A cartridge case can be individualized to a single weapon. _____

12. The automated firearms search system developed by the FBI and ATF as a unified system incorporating both DRUGFIRE and IBIS technologies available in prior years is known as _____.

13. True or False: The distribution of gunpowder particles and other discharge residues around a bullet hole permits an approximate determination of the distance from which the gun was fired. _____

14. True or False: Without the benefit of a weapon, an examiner can make an exact determination of firing distance. _____

15. A halo of vaporous lead (smoke) deposited around a bullet hole normally indicates a discharge _____ to _____ inches from the target.

16. If a firearm has been fired more than 3 feet from a target, usually no residue is deposited but a dark ring, known as _____, is observed.

17. As a rule of thumb, the spread in the pattern made by a 12-gauge shotgun increases 1 inch for every _____ of distance from the target.

18. A(n) _____ photograph may help visualize gunpowder deposits around a target.

19. True or False: One test method for locating powder residues involves transferring particles embedded on the target surface to chemically treated photographic paper. _____

20. Current methods for identifying a shooter rely on the detection of _____ residues on the hands.

21. Determining whether an individual has fired a weapon is done by measuring the elements _____ and _____ present on the hands.

22. True or False: Firings with all types of ammunition can be detected by hand swabbings with nitric acid. _____

23. Microscopic primer and gunpowder particles on the adhesives applied to a suspected shooter's hand can be found with a(n) _____.

24. True or False: Restoration of serial numbers is possible because in the stamped zone the metal is placed under a(n) permanent strain that extends beneath the original numbers. _____

25. True or False: It is proper to insert a pencil into the barrel when picking up a crime-scene gun. _____

26. Recovered bullets are initialed on either the _____ or _____ of the bullet.

27. True or False: Because minute traces of evidence such as paint and fibers may be adhering to a recovered bullet, the investigator must take care to remove these trace materials immediately. _____

28. True or False: Cartridge cases are best marked at the base of the shell. _____

29. The clothing of the victim of a shooting must be handled so as to prevent disruption of _____ around bullet holes.

30. A(n) _____ is any impression caused by a tool coming into contact with another object.

31. Tool marks compare only when a sufficient number of _____ match between the evidence and test markings.

32. Objects bearing tool marks should be submitted intact to the crime lab or a(n) _____ should be taken of the tool mark.

33. An imprint may be lifted using lifting sheets or a(n) _____.

34. Shoe and tire marks impressed into soft earth at a crime scene are best preserved by _____ and _____.

35. A wear pattern, cut, gouge, or other damage pattern can impart _____ characteristics to a shoe.

application and critical thinking

1. From each of the following descriptions of bullet holes, use general guidelines to estimate the distance from the shooter to the target.

   a. A few widely scattered gunpowder particles with no soot around the entrance hole

   b. A dark ring around the bullet hole, but no soot or gunpowder particles

   c. A halo of soot surrounding the entrance hole along with scattered specks of powder grains

   d. Scorch marks and melted fibers surrounding the entrance hole

2. You are investigating a shooting involving a 12-gauge shotgun with a moderately high choke. The spread of the pattern made by the pellets measures 12 inches. In your opinion, which of the following is probably closest to the distance from the target to the shooter? Explain your answer and explain why the other answers are likely to be incorrect.

   a. 18 yards

   b. 12 yards

   c. 6 yards

   d. 30 yards

3. Criminalist Ben Baldanza is collecting evidence from the scene of a shooting. After locating the revolver suspected of firing the shots, Ben picks the gun up by the grip, unloads it, and places the ammunition in an envelope. He then attaches an identification tag to the grip. Searching the scene, Ben finds a bullet lodged in the wall. He uses pliers to grab the bullet and pull it from the wall, then inscribes the bullet with his initials and places it in an envelope. What mistakes, if any, did Ben make in collecting this evidence?

4. How would you go about collecting impressions in each of the following situations?

    a. You discover a shoe print in dry dirt.

    b. You discover a tool mark on a windowsill.

    c. You discover tire marks in soft earth.

    d. You discover a shoe print on a loose piece of tile.

    e. You discover a very faint shoe print in dust on a colored linoleum floor.

further references

Bodziak, William J., *Footwear Impression Evidence*, 2nd ed. Boca Raton, Fla.: Taylor & Francis, 1999.

Bodziak, William J., *Tire Tread and Tire Track Evidence: Recovery and Forensic Examination.* Boca Raton, Fla.: Taylor & Francis, 2008

Heard, B.J., *Handbook of Firearms and Ballistics: Examining and Interpreting Forensic Evidence.* 2nd ed. Chichester, West Sussex, U.K., 2008.

An Introduction to Forensic Firearm Identification, http://www.firearmsid.com.

Rowe, Walter F., "Firearms Identification," in R. Saferstein, ed., *Forensic Science Handbook*, vol. 2, 2nd ed., Upper Saddle River, N.J.: Prentice Hall, 2005.

Schehl, S. A., "Firearms and Toolmarks in the FBI Laboratory," *Forensic Science Communications* 2, no. 2 (2000), http://www.fbi.gov/hq/lab/fsc/backissu/april2000/schehl1.htm.

answers to review questions

Odd-Numbered Review Questions

1. land
3. True
5. comparison microscope
7. False
9. gauge
11. True
13. True
15. 12; 18
17. yard
19. True
21. barium; antimony
23. scanning electron microscope
25. False
27. False
29. gunpowder residue
31. striations
33. electrostatic lifting device
35. individual

Application and Critical Thinking

1. a. 18–36 inches
   b. More than 36 inches
   c. 12–18 inches or less
   d. 1 inch or less

2. The correct answer is (a), 18 yards. A 12-gauge shotgun with no choke would be expected to produce a spread of about 1 inch for each yard from the shooter to the target. Thus, a spread of 12 inches would represent a distance of about 12 yards. A moderately high choke, however, would narrow the spread of the pattern somewhat. This means that at a distance of 12 yards, the spread would be less than 12 inches. At a distance of 6 yards, the spread would be much less than 12 inches. Answers (b) and (c), therefore, must be wrong. The distance in answer (d), 30 yards, is probably too far. Although the choke would narrow the spread of the pellets, it would probably not narrow it to such a great extent.

3. Ben made several errors. Before unloading the revolver, Ben should have indicated the chamber position in line with the barrel by scratching a mark on the cylinder. He then should have made a diagram of the gun, designating each chamber with a number. As he removed each cartridge, he should have marked it to correspond to the numbered chambers in the diagram. Ben also should have placed each cartridge in a separate envelope and he should have put the tag on the trigger guard, not the grip. Instead of using pliers to grab the bullet and pull it from the wall, Ben should have carefully broken away the surrounding wall material while avoiding direct contact with the bullet. Finally, he should have wrapped the bullet in tissue paper before placing it in an envelope.

4. a. Photograph the print.
   b. Photograph the tool mark, then make a cast of it.
   c. Photograph the tire marks, then make a cast of them.
   d. Photograph the shoe print, then bring the tile bearing the print to the laboratory.
   e. Photograph the print, then use an electrostatic lifting device to lift it off the surface.

computer forensics

The BTK Killer

Dennis Rader was arrested in February 2005 and charged with committing ten murders since 1974 in the Wichita, Kansas, area. The killer, whose nickname stands for "bind, torture, kill," hadn't murdered since 1991, but resurfaced in early 2004 by sending a letter to a local newspaper taking credit for a 1986 slaying. Included with the letter were a photocopy of the victim's driver's license and three photos of her body. The BTK killer was back to his old habit of taunting the police. Three months later another letter surfaced. This time the letter detailed some of the events surrounding BTK's first murder victims. In 1974, he strangled Joseph and Julie Otero along with two of their children. Shortly after those murders occurred, BTK sent a letter to a local newspaper in which he gave himself the name BTK. In December 2004, a package found in a park contained the driver's license of another BTK victim along with a doll whose hands were bound with pantyhose and that was covered with a plastic bag.

The major break in the case came when BTK sent a message on a floppy disk to a local TV station. "Erased" information on the disk was recovered and restored by forensic computer specialists, and the disk was traced to the Christ Lutheran Church in Wichita. The disk was then quickly linked to Dennis Rader, the church council president. The long odyssey of the BTK killer was finally over.

computer forensics

by Andrew W. Donofrio

Learning Objectives

After studying this chapter you should be able to:

- List and describe the hardware and software components of a computer

- Understand the difference between read-only memory and random-access memory

- Describe how a hard disk drive is partitioned

- Describe the proper procedure for preserving computer evidence at a crime scene

- Understand the difference between and location of visible and latent data

- List the areas of the computer that will be examined to retrieve forensic data

- Relate various areas found on the computer where a user's Internet activities can be investigated

- Describe how e-mails, chat, and instant messages on the Internet can be traced and recovered

- List and describe three locations where investigators may pinpoint the origin of a hacker

KEY TERMS

bit
bookmark
byte
central processing
　unit (CPU)
cluster
cookies
file slack
firewall
hacking
hard disk drive (HDD)
hardware
Internet cache
Internet history
latent data
Message Digest 5
　(MD5)/secure hash
　algorithm (SHA)
motherboard
operating system (OS)
partition
RAM slack
random-access
　memory (RAM)
sector
software
swap file
temporary files
unallocated space
visible data

Andrew W. Donofrio is a detective sergeant with the Prosecutor's Office in Bergen County, New Jersey, and is a leading computer forensics examiner for Bergen County, with more than 18 years' experience in the field of law enforcement. He has conducted more than five hundred forensic examinations of computer evidence and frequently lectures on the subject throughout the state, as well as teaching multiday courses on computer forensics and investigative topics at police academies and colleges in New Jersey. Det. Sgt. Donofrio writes regularly on Internet-related and computer forensics issues for a number of law enforcement publications and has appeared as a guest expert on Internet-related stories on MSNBC.

Since the 1990s, few fields have progressed as rapidly as computer technology. Computers are no longer a luxury, nor are they in the hands of just a select few. Technology and electronic data are a part of everyday life and permeate all aspects of society. Consequently, computers have become increasingly important as sources of evidence in an ever-widening spectrum of criminal activities.

Investigators frequently encounter computers and other digital devices in all types of cases. As homicide investigators sift for clues they may inquire whether the method for a murder was researched on the Internet; whether signs of an extramarital affair can be found in e-mail or remnants of instant messages, which may provide motive for a spouse killing or murder for hire; or whether threats were communicated to the victim before a murder by an obsessed stalker. Arson investigators want to know whether financial records on a computer may provide a motive in an arson-for-profit fire. A burglary investigation would certainly be aided if law enforcement determined that the proceeds from a theft were being sold online—perhaps through eBay or a similar online auction site.

Accessibility to children and the perception of anonymity has given sexual predators a way to seek out child victims online. The vulnerability of computers to hacker attacks is a constant reminder of security issues surrounding digitally stored data. Finally, the fact that computers control most of our critical infrastructure makes technology an appetizing target for would-be terrorists.

Computer forensics involves the preservation, acquisition, extraction, analysis, and interpretation of computer data. Although this is a simple definition, it gets a bit more complicated. Part of this complication arises from technology itself. More and more devices are capable of storing electronic data: cell phones, personal digital assistants (PDAs), iPods, digital cameras, flash memory cards, smart cards, jump drives, and many others. Methods for extracting data from these devices each present unique challenges. However, sound forensic practices apply to all these devices. The most logical place to start to examine these practices is with the most common form of electronic data: the personal computer.

From Input to Output: How Does the Computer Work?

Hardware versus Software

Before we get into the nuts and bolts of computers, we must establish the important distinction between hardware and software. **Hardware** comprises the physical components of the computer: the computer chassis, monitor, keyboard, mouse, hard disk drive, random-access memory (RAM), central processing unit (CPU), and so on (see Figure 1). The list is much more extensive, but generally speaking, if it is a computer component or peripheral that you can see, feel, and touch, it is hardware.

Software, conversely, is a set of instructions compiled into a program that performs a particular task. Software consists of programs and applications that carry out a set of instructions on the hardware. Operating systems (Windows, Mac OS, Linux, Unix), word-processing programs (Microsoft Word, WordPerfect), Web-browsing applications (Internet Explorer, Safari, Firefox), and accounting applications (Quicken, QuickBooks, Microsoft Money) are all examples of software.

It is important not to confuse software with the physical media that it comes on. When you buy an application such as Microsoft Office, it comes on a compact disc (CD). The CD containing this suite of applications is typically referred to as software, but this is technically wrong. The CD is external computer media that contains the software; it is a container for and a medium to load the set of instructions onto the hard disk drive (the hardware).

Hardware Components

COMPUTER CASE/CHASSIS   The case is the physical box holding the fixed internal computer components in place. Cases come in many shapes and sizes: a full upright tower chassis, a slim desktop model sitting on the desktop, or an all-in-one monitor/computer case like the iMac. For our purposes, the term *system unit* is probably most appropriate when describing a chassis seized as evidence. The term *system unit* accurately references the chassis, including the motherboard and other internal components.

hardware

The physical components of a computer: case, keyboard, monitor, motherboard, RAM, HDD, mouse, and so on; generally speaking, if it is a computer component you can touch, it is hardware

software

A set of instructions compiled into a program that performs a particular task; software consists of programs and applications that carry out a set of instructions on the hardware

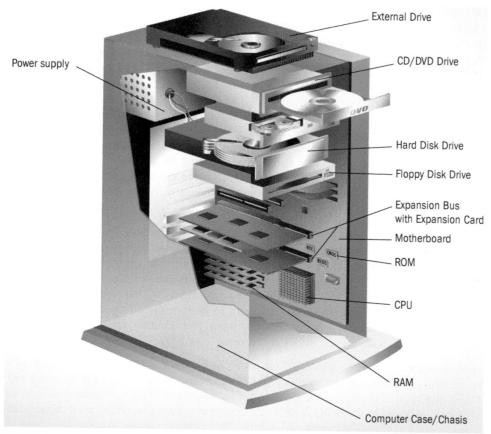

External Drive

CD/DVD Drive

Power supply

Hard Disk Drive

Floppy Disk Drive

Expansion Bus
with Expansion Card

Motherboard

ROM

CPU

RAM

Computer Case/Chasis

FIGURE 1

Cutaway diagram of a personal computer showing the tangible hardware components of a computer system.
Courtesy Tim Downs

POWER SUPPLY   The term *power supply* is actually a misnomer because it doesn't actually supply power—the power company does that. Rather, a computer's power supply converts power from the wall outlet to a usable format for the computer and its components. Different power supplies have different wattage ratings. The use, or more specifically, the components, of the computer dictate the appropriate power supply.

MOTHERBOARD   The main circuit board in a computer (or other electronic devices) is referred to as the **motherboard**. Motherboards contain sockets for chips and slots for add-on cards. Examples of add-on cards are a video card to connect the computer to the monitor, a network card or modem to connect to an internal network or the Internet, and a sound card to connect to speakers. Sockets on the motherboard typically accept things like random-access memory (RAM) or the central processing unit (CPU). The keyboard, mouse, CD-ROM drives, floppy disk drives, monitor, and other peripherals or components connect to the motherboard in some fashion through a direct wired or wireless connection.

SYSTEM BUS   Contained on the motherboard, the system bus is a vast complex network of wires that carry data from one hardware device to another. This network is analogous to a complex highway. Data is sent along the bus in the form of ones and zeros (or, more appropriately stated, as electrical impulses representing an "on" or "off" state—this two-state computing is also known as *binary computing*).

READ-ONLY MEMORY (ROM)   This rather generic term describes special chips on the motherboard. ROM chips store programs called *firmware*, used to start the boot process and configure a computer's components. Today's ROM chips, termed *flash ROM*, are a combination of two types

motherboard
The main system board of a computer (and many other electronic devices); it delivers power, data, and instructions to the computer's components; every component in the computer connects to the motherboard, either directly or indirectly

of chips used in past motherboard technologies. The first was known as the *system ROM*, which was responsible for booting the system and handling the "assumed" system hardware present in the computer. As the system ROM, generally speaking, could not be altered, and because as technology matured changes to the "assumed" hardware were more common, a different type of chip was introduced. The *complementary metal-oxide semiconductor* (CMOS) was a separate chip that allowed the user to exercise setup control over several system components. Regardless of how this technology is present on the motherboard, it can be referred to as the BIOS, for *basic input-output system*. The operation of the BIOS is relevant to several computer forensic procedures, particularly the boot sequence. It is the set of routines associated with the BIOS in ROM that initiates the booting process and enables the computer to communicate with various devices in the system such as disk drives, keyboard, monitor, and printer. As will become clear later, it is important not to boot the actual computer under investigation to the original hard disk drive. This would cause changes to the data, thus compromising the integrity of evidence. The BIOS allows investigators to control the boot process to some degree.

central processing unit (CPU)
The main chip within the computer; also referred to as the brain of the computer; this microprocessor chip handles most of the operations (code and instructions) of the computer

CENTRAL PROCESSING UNIT (CPU) The **central processing unit (CPU)**, also referred to as a processor, is essentially the brain of the computer. It is the main (and typically the largest) chip that plugs into a socket on the motherboard. The CPU is the part of the computer that actually computes. Basically, all operations performed by the computer are run through the CPU. The CPU carries out the program steps to perform the requested task. That task can range from opening and working in a Microsoft Word document to performing advanced mathematical algorithms. CPUs come in various shapes, sizes, and types. Intel Pentium chips and Advanced Micro Devices (AMD) chips are among the most common.

random-access memory (RAM)
The volatile memory of the computer; when power is turned off, its contents are lost; programs and instructions are loaded into RAM while they are in use

RANDOM-ACCESS MEMORY (RAM) This is one of the most widely mentioned types of computer memory. **Random-access memory (RAM)** takes the burden off the computer's processor and hard disk drive (HDD). If the computer had to access the HDD each time it wanted data, it would run slowly and inefficiently. Instead the computer, aware that it may need certain data at a moment's notice, stores the data in RAM. It is helpful to envision RAM as chips that create a large spreadsheet, with each cell representing a memory address that the CPU can use as a reference to retrieve data. RAM is referred to as *volatile memory* because it is not permanent; its contents undergo constant change and are forever lost once power is taken away from the computer. RAM takes the physical form of chips that plug into the motherboard; SIMMs (single inline memory modules), DIMMs (dual inline memory modules), and SDRAM (synchronous dynamic random-access memory) are just a few of the types of chips. Today's computers come with various denominations of RAM: 2 GB (gigabyte) is the most common.[1]

INPUT DEVICES Input devices are used to get data into the computer or to give the computer instructions. Input devices constitute part of the "user" side of the computer. Examples include the keyboard, mouse, joystick, and scanner.

OUTPUT DEVICES Output devices are equipment through which data is obtained from the computer. Output devices are also part of the "user" side of the computer, and provide the results of the user's tasks. They include the monitor, printer, and speakers.

hard disk drive (HDD)
Typically the main storage location within the computer; consists of magnetic platters contained in a case (usually 3.5" in a desktop computer and 2.5" in a laptop); the HDD is usually where the operating system, applications, and user data are stored

HARD DISK DRIVE (HDD) Generally speaking, the **hard disk drive (HDD)** is the primary component of storage in the personal computer (Figure 2). It typically stores the operating system (Windows, Mac OS, Linux, Unix), the programs (Microsoft Word, Internet Explorer, Open Office for Linux, and so on) and data files created by the user (documents, spreadsheets, accounting information, the company database, and so on). Unlike RAM, the HDD is permanent storage and retains its information even after the power is turned off. HDDs work off a controller that is typically part of the motherboard, but sometimes takes the form of an add-on (expansion) card plugged into the motherboard. The most common types of HDD controllers are integrated drive electronics (IDE), small computer system interface (SCSI), and serial ATA (SATA). Each HDD type has a different interface that connects it to the controller. Regardless of the type of controller, the data is basically stored in the same fashion. HDDs are mapped (formatted) and

[1] A megabyte (MB) is approximately one million bytes (discussed later in the chapter), a gigabyte (GB) is approximately one billion bytes, or 1,000 megabytes.

FIGURE 2

An inside view of the platter and read/write head of a hard disk drive.
Courtesy Corbis RF

have a defined layout. They are logically divided into sectors, clusters, tracks, and cylinders. (See the section titled "How Data Is Stored" for further information).

NETWORK INTERFACE CARD (NIC)   Very rarely do we find a computer today that doesn't have a NIC. Whether they are on a local network or the Internet, when computers need to communicate with each other, they typically do so through a NIC. NICs come in many different forms: add-on cards that plug into the motherboard, hard-wired devices on the motherboard, add-on cards (PCMCIA) for laptops, and universal serial bus (USB) plug-in cards, to name a few. Some are wired cards, meaning they need a physical wired connection to participate on the network, and others are wireless, meaning they receive their data via radio waves.

OTHER COMMON STORAGE DEVICES   Although the HDD is the most common storage device for the personal computer, many others exist. Methods for storing data and the layout of that data can vary from device to device. A CD-ROM, for example, uses a different technology and format for writing data than a floppy disk or USB thumb drive. Fortunately, regardless of the differences among devices, the same basic forensic principles apply for acquiring the data. Common storage devices include the following:

CD-R/RW (COMPACT DISC-RECORD/REWRITE) AND DVD-R/RW (DVD-RECORD/REWRITE)
Compact discs (CDs) and digital video discs (DVDs) are two of the most common forms of storing external data. They are used to store a wide variety of information, such as music, video, and data files. A largely plastic disc with an aluminum layer is read by laser light in the CD/DVD reader. Different CDs are encoded in different ways, making the job of the forensic examiner difficult at times.

FLOPPY DISKS   Though "floppies" are not as common as they once were, forensic examiners still encounter the 3.5-inch floppy disk. Floppy disks can be used to boot an operating system or to store data. They are constructed of hard plastic with a thin plastic disk on the inside. That thin plastic disk is coated with a magnetic iron oxide material. The disk is mapped and stores data in a similar fashion to the hard disk drive. By today's standards, floppy disks don't hold much data.

USB THUMB DRIVES AND SMART MEDIA CARDS   These devices can store a large amount of data—some as much as 64 GB. They are known as solid-state storage devices because they have no moving parts. Smart media cards are typically found in digital cameras and PDAs, whereas USB thumb drives come in many shapes, sizes, and storage capacities.

TAPES Tapes come in many different formats and storage capacities. Each typically comes with its own hardware reader and sometimes a proprietary application to read and write its contents. Tapes and thumb drives are typically used for backup purposes and consequently have great forensic potential.

Putting It All Together

A person approaches the computer, sits down, and presses the power button. The power supply wakes up and delivers power to the motherboard and all of the hardware connected to the computer. At this point the flash ROM chip on the motherboard (the one that contains the BIOS) conducts a power-on self test (POST) to make sure everything is working properly.

The flash ROM also polls the motherboard to check the hardware that is attached and follows its programmed boot order, thus determining from what device it should boot. Typically the boot device is the HDD, but it can also be a floppy disk, CD, or USB drive. If it is the HDD, the HDD is then sent control. It locates the first sector of its disk (known as the master boot record), determines its layout (partition[s]), and boots an operating system (Windows, Mac OS, Linux, Unix). The person is then presented with a computer work environment, commonly referred to as a desktop.

Now ready to work, the user double-clicks an icon on the desktop, such as a Microsoft Word shortcut, to open the program and begin to type a document. The CPU processes this request, locates the Microsoft Word program on the HDD (using a predefined map of the drive called a *file system table*), carries out the programming instructions associated with the application, loads Microsoft Word into RAM via the system bus, and sends the output to the monitor by way of the video controller, which is either located on or attached to the motherboard.

The user then begins to type, placing the data from the keyboard into RAM. At the end, the user may print the document or simply save it to the HDD for later retrieval. If printed, the data is taken from RAM, processed by the CPU, placed in a format suitable for printing, and sent through the system bus to the external port where the printer is connected. If the document is saved, the data is taken from RAM, processed by the CPU, passed to the HDD controller (IDE, SCSI, or SATA) by way of the system bus, and written to a portion of the HDD. The HDD's file system table is updated so it knows where to retrieve that data later. In actuality, the boot process is more complex than the way it has been described here and requires the forensic examiner to possess an in-depth knowledge of its process.

The preceding example illustrates how three components perform most of the work: the CPU, RAM, and system bus. The example can get even more complicated as the user opens more applications and performs multiple tasks simultaneously (*multitasking*). Several tasks can be loaded into RAM at once, and the CPU is capable of juggling them all. This allows for the multitasking environment and the ability to switch back and forth between applications. All of this is orchestrated by the operating system and is written in the language of the computer—ones and zeros. The only detail missing, and one that is important from a forensic standpoint, is a better understanding of how data is stored on the hard disk drive.

Storing and Retrieving Data

operating system (OS)
The software that provides the bridge between the system hardware and the user; the OS lets the user interact with the hardware and manages the file system and applications; some examples are Windows (XP, Vista and Windows 7), Linux, and Mac OS

partition
A contiguous set of blocks that are defined and treated as an independent disk

Before beginning to understand how data is stored on a hard disk drive (HDD), it is first important to understand the role of the **operating system (OS)**. An OS, such as Windows, Mac OS, Linux, or Unix, is the bridge between the human user and the computer's electronic components. It provides the user with a working environment and facilitates interaction with the system's components. Each OS supports certain types of file systems that store data in different ways, but some support the methods of others.

Formatting and Partitioning the HDD

Generally speaking, before an OS can write to a HDD it must first be formatted. But even before it can be formatted, a partition must be defined. A **partition** is nothing more than a contiguous set of blocks that are defined and treated as an independent disk. This means that a hard disk drive can hold several partitions, making a single HDD appear as several disks.

Partitioning a drive can be thought of as dividing a container that begins as nothing more than four sides with empty space on the inside. We then cut a hole in the front of it and place inside two drawers containing the hardware to open and close them. We have just created a two-drawer filing cabinet and defined each drawer as contiguous blocks of storage. A partitioning utility such as Disk Manager or fdisk defines the drawer or drawers (partitions) that will later hold the data on the HDD. Just as the style, size, and shape of a filing cabinet drawer can vary, so too can partitions.

After a hard drive is partitioned, it is typically formatted. (At this point it is a high-level format, not to be confused with low-level formatting, which is generally done by the manufacturer of the HDD.) The formatting process initializes portions of the HDD and creates the structure of the file system. The file system can be thought of as the system for storing and locating data on a storage device. Some of the file system types are FAT12 (typically on floppy disks), FAT16 (older DOS and older Windows partitions), FAT32 (Windows file systems), NTFS (most current Windows systems—2000 and XP), EXT2 and EXT3 (Linux systems), and HPFS (some Macintosh systems).

Each of these file systems has a different way of storing, retrieving, and allocating data. So, in summary, a drive is prepared in three processes: low-level formatting (typically done by the manufacturer, dividing the platters into tracks and sectors), partitioning (accomplished through a utility such as fdisk or Disk Manager, defining a contiguous set of blocks), and formatting (initializing portions of the disk and creating the file system structure). Although the process is a bit more technical and detailed, at the conclusion of these steps, the drive is logically defined. We say "logically" because no real divisions are made. If you were to crack open the HDD before or after partitioning and formatting, to the naked eye the platters would look the same.

Mapping the HDD

As shown in Figure 3, HDDs contain several platters stacked vertically that are logically divided into sectors, clusters, tracks, and cylinders. **Sectors** are typically 512 bytes in size (a **byte** is eight bits; a **bit** is a single one or zero). **Clusters** are groups of sectors; their size is defined by the file system, but they are always in sector multiples of two. (Although an NTFS partition does permit a one-sector-per-cluster scenario, such a scenario is not usually chosen.) A cluster, therefore, consists of two, four, six, or eight sectors, and so on. (With modern file systems, the user can exercise some control over the number of sectors per cluster.) *Tracks* are concentric circles that are defined around the platter. *Cylinders* are groups of tracks that reside directly above and below each other.

Additionally, the HDD has a file system table (map) of the layout of the defined space in that partition. FAT file systems use a *file allocation table* (which is where the acronym *FAT* comes

sector
The smallest addressable unit of data by a hard disk drive; generally consists of 512 bytes

byte
A group of eight bits

bit
Short for binary digit; taking the form of either a one or a zero, it is the smallest unit of information on a machine

cluster
A group of sectors in multiples of two; cluster size varies from file system to file system and is typically the minimum space allocated to a file

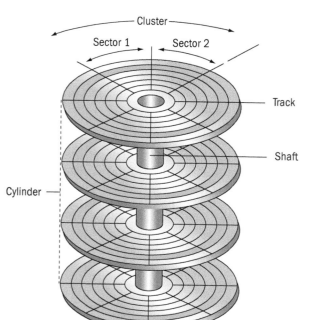

FIGURE 3

Partitions of a hard disk drive.

from) to track the location of files and folders (data) on the HDD, whereas NTFS file systems (used by most current Windows systems—Vista and XP) use, among other things, a *master file table (MFT)*. Each file system table tracks data in different ways, and computer forensic examiners should be versed in the technical nuances of the HDDs they examine. It is sufficient for our purposes here, however, to merely visualize the file system table as a map where the data is located. This map uses the numbering of sectors, clusters, tracks, and cylinders to keep track of the data.

One way to envision a partition and file system is as a room full of safe-deposit boxes. The room itself symbolizes the entire partition and the boxes symbolize clusters of data. In order to determine who rented which box, and subsequently where their property is, a central database is needed. This is especially true if a person rented two boxes located in opposite ends of the room (noncontiguous data on the HDD). The database tracking the locations of the safe-deposit boxes is much like a file system table tracking the location of data within the clusters.

This example is also useful to understand the concept of reformatting a HDD. If the database managing the locations of the safe-deposit boxes were wiped out, the property in them would still remain; we just wouldn't know what was where. So too with the hard disk drive. If a user were to wipe the file system table clean—for example, by reformatting it—the data itself would not be gone. Both the database tracking the locations of the safe-deposit boxes and the file system table tracking the location of the data in the cluster are maps—not the actual contents. (Exceptions exist with some file systems, such as an NTFS file system, which stores data for very small files right in its file system table, known as the master file table).

Processing the Electronic Crime Scene

Processing the electronic crime scene has a lot in common with processing a traditional crime scene. The investigator must first ensure that the proper legal requirements (search warrant, consent, and so on) have been met so that the scene can be searched and the evidence seized. The investigator should then devise a plan of approach based on the facts of the case and the physical location. The scene should be documented in as much detail as possible before disturbing any evidence, and before the investigator lays a finger on any computer components. Of course, there are circumstances in which an investigator may have to act quickly and pull a plug before documenting the scene, such as when data is in the process of being deleted.

Documenting the Crime Scene

Crime-scene documentation is accomplished through two actions: sketching and photographing. The electronic crime scene is no different. The scene should be sketched in a floor plan fashion (see Figure 4) and then overall photographs of the location taken. In the case of a network, a technical network sketch should also be included if possible.

After photographs have been taken of the overall layout, close-up photographs should be shot. A close-up photograph of any running computer monitor should be taken. All the connections to the main system unit, such as peripheral devices (keyboard, monitor, speakers, mouse, and so on), should be photographed. If necessary, system units should be moved delicately and carefully to facilitate the connections photograph. (See Figure 5.) Close-up photographs of equipment serial numbers should be taken if practical.

At this point, investigators must decide whether to perform a live acquisition of the data, perform a system shutdown (as in the case of server equipment), pull the plug from the back of the computer,[2] or a combination thereof. Several factors influence this decision. For example, if encryption is being used and by pulling the plug the data will encrypt, rendering it unreadable without a password or key, pulling the plug would not be prudent. Similarly, if crucial evidentiary data exists in RAM and has not been saved to the HDD, the data will be lost. Hence, if power to the system is discontinued, another option must be considered. Regardless, the equipment will most likely be seized. Exceptions exist in the corporate environment, where servers are fundamental to business operations.

---

[2] Pulling the plug should always be done by removing the plug from the back of the computer. If the plug is removed from the wall, a battery backup (UPS) might be in place, causing an alert to the system and keeping the unit powered on.

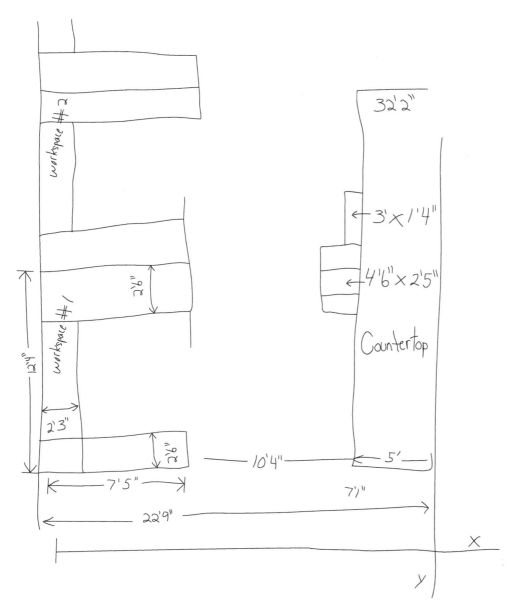

FIGURE 4

Rough sketch made at a crime scene with necessary measurements included.

After the photographs and sketches are complete, but before disconnecting the peripherals from the computer, a label should be placed on the cord of each peripheral, with a corresponding label placed on the port to which it is connected. A numbering scheme should be devised to identify the system unit if several computers are at the scene (Figure 6). The combination of sketching, photographing, and labeling should adequately document the scene, prevent confusion of which component went with which system unit, and facilitate reconstruction if necessary for lab or courtroom purposes.

Forensic Image Acquisition

Now that the items have been seized, the data needs to be obtained for analysis. The number of electronic items that potentially store evidentiary data are too vast to cover in this section. The hard disk drive will be used as an example, but the same "best practices" principles apply for other electronic devices as well.

Throughout the entire process, the computer forensic examiner must use the least intrusive method. The goal in obtaining data from a HDD is to do so without altering even one bit of data.

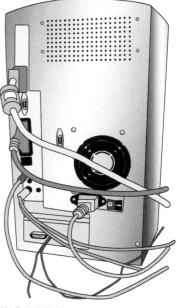

FIGURE 5

Back of a computer showing all connections.

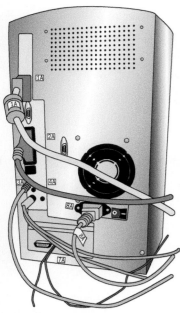

FIGURE 6

Back of a computer with each component correlated with its port through the use of a labeling scheme.

Message Digest 5 (MD5)/Secure Hash Algorithm (SHA)

A software algorithm used to "fingerprint" a file or contents of a disk; used to verify the integrity of data; in forensic analysis it is typically used to verify that an acquired image of suspect data was not altered during the process of imaging

Because booting a HDD to its operating system changes many files and could potentially destroy evidentiary data, obtaining data is generally accomplished by removing the HDD from the system and placing it in a laboratory forensic computer so that a forensic image can be created. However, the BIOS of the seized computer sometimes interprets the geometry of the HDD differently than the forensic computer does. In these instances, the image of the HDD must be obtained using the seized computer. Regardless, the examiner must ensure that the drive to be analyzed is in a "write-blocked," read-only state when creating the forensic image. Furthermore, the examiner needs to be able to prove that the forensic image he or she obtained includes every bit of data and caused no changes (writes) to the HDD.

To this end, a sort of fingerprint of the drive is taken before and after imaging. This fingerprint is taken through the use of a **Message Digest 5 (MD5), Secure Hash Algorithm (SHA),** or similar validated algorithm. Before imaging the drive the algorithm is run and a 32-character alphanumeric string is produced based on the drive's contents. The algorithm is then run against the resulting forensic image; if nothing changed, the same alphanumeric string is produced, thus demonstrating that the image is all-inclusive of the original contents and that nothing was altered in the process.

A forensic image of the data on a HDD (and the same holds true for floppy disks, CDs, DVDs, tapes, flash memory devices, and any other storage medium) is merely an exact duplicate of the entire contents of the drive. In other words, all portions of the drive are copied from the first bit (one or zero) to the last. Why would investigators want to copy what appears to be blank or unused portions of the HDD? The answer is simple: to preserve latent data, discussed later in the chapter. It suffices to say here that data exists in areas of the drive that are, generally speaking, unknown and inaccessible to most end users. This data can be valuable as evidence. Therefore, a forensic image—one that copies every single bit of information on the drive—is necessary.[3] A forensic image differs from a backup or standard copy in that it takes the entire contents, not only data the operating system is aware of.

Many forensic software packages come equipped with a method to obtain the forensic image. The most popular software forensic tools—EnCase, Forensic Toolkit (FTK), Forensic Autopsy (Linux-based freeware), and SMART (Linux-based software by ASR Data)—all include a method to obtain a forensic image. All produce self-contained image files that can then be interpreted and analyzed. They also allow image compression to conserve storage. The fact that self-contained, compressed files are the result of forensic imaging allows many images from different cases to be stored on the same forensic storage drive. This makes case management and storage much easier (see Figure 7).

Analysis of Electronic Data

Analysis of electronic data is virtually limitless and bound only to the level of skill of the examiner. The more familiar an examiner is with computers, operating systems, application software, data storage, and a host of other disciplines, the more prepared he or she will be to look for evidentiary data.

Because computers are vast and complex, discussing each area, file, directory, log, or computer process that could potentially contain evidentiary data is beyond the scope of one chapter—and may be beyond the scope of an entire book. What follows are some of the more common areas of analysis. While reading this section, reflect on your own knowledge of computers and consider what other data might be of evidentiary value and where it might be found.

Visible Data

The category of **visible data** includes all information that the operating system is presently aware of and thus is readily accessible to the user. Here we present several common types of visible data considered in many investigations. This list is by no means exhaustive and can include any information that has value as evidence.

visible data

All data that the operating system is presently aware of and thus is readily accessible to the user

---

[3] In this instance, *bit* is both metaphorical and literal. Every bit of information is needed, so we must get it all. So too every bit, as in the smallest unit of data storage—a one or a zero—must be imaged.

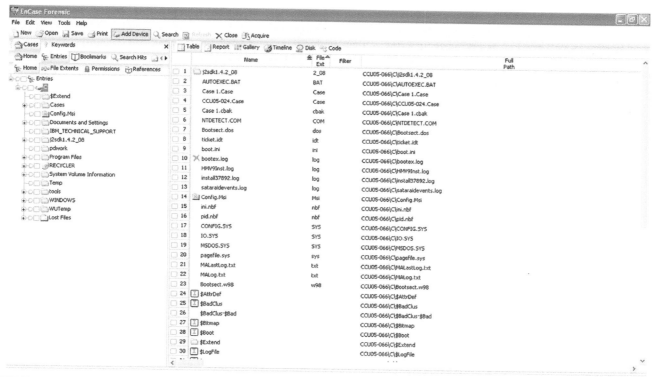

FIGURE 7

Screen shot of EnCase Software. EnCase is a common forensic software application
capable of imaging and assisting in the analysis of data.
Courtesy of Guidance Software, www.guidancesoftware.com

DATA/WORK PRODUCT FILES One place to find evidence is in documents or files produced by
the suspect. This category is extremely broad and can include data from just about any software
program. Microsoft Word and WordPerfect word-processing programs typically produce text-
based files such as typed documents and correspondence. These programs, and a host of other
word-processing programs, have replaced the typewriter. They are common sources of evidence
in criminal cases, particularly those involving white-collar crime.

Also relevant in white-collar crime and similar financial investigations are any data related
to personal and business finance. Programs such as QuickBooks and Peachtree accounting packages can run the entire financial portion of a small to midsize business. Similarly, it is not
uncommon to find personal bank account records in the computer that are managed with personal
finance software such as Microsoft Money and Quicken. Moreover, criminals sometimes use
these programs as well as spreadsheet applications to track bank accounts stolen from unsus-
pecting victims. Computer forensic examiners should familiarize themselves with these
programs, the ways in which they store data, and methods for extracting and reading the data.

Advances in printer technology have made high-quality color printing both affordable and
common in many homes. Although this is a huge benefit for home office workers and those
interested in graphic arts, the technology has been used for criminal gain. Counterfeiting and
check and document fraud are easily perpetrated by most home computer users. All that is
required is a decent ink-jet printer and a scanner. Including the computer, a criminal could set up
a counterfeiting operation for less than $1500. Examiners must learn the graphics and photo-
editing applications used for nefarious purposes. Being able to recognize the data produced by
these applications and knowing how to display the images is key to identifying the evidence.

SWAP FILE DATA When an application is running, the program and the data being accessed are
loaded into RAM. A computer's RAM is much faster than the "read" speed of the hard disk drive,
and that's why the programs are loaded here—for fast access and functioning. RAM, however,
has its limits. Some computers have 256 MB of RAM, others 512 MB, and still others as much
as a gigabyte or two. Regardless of the amount, though, most operating systems (Windows,

swap file

A file or defined space on the HDD used to conserve RAM; data is swapped (paged) to this file/space to free RAM for applications that are in use

Linux, and so on) are programmed to conserve RAM when possible. This is where the **swap file** comes in. The operating system attempts to keep only data and applications that are presently being used in RAM. Other applications that were started, but are currently waiting for user attention, may be swapped out of RAM and written to the swap space on the hard disk drive.[4]

For example, a manager of a retail store may want to type a quarterly report based on sales. The manager starts Microsoft Word and begins his report. Needing to incorporate sales figure data from a particular spreadsheet, he opens Microsoft Excel. Depending on what is running on the computer, the original Word document may be swapped from RAM to the swap space on the HDD to free up space for Excel. As the manager goes back and forth between the programs (and maybe checks his e-mail in between) this swapping continues. Data that is swapped back and forth is sometimes left behind in the swap space. Even as this area is constantly changed, some of the data is orphaned in unallocated space, an area of the HDD discussed later in this chapter.

Swap file or space can be defined as a particular file or even a separate HDD partition, depending on the operating system and file system type (FAT, NTFS, EXT2, and so on). For Windows systems either the swap file *Win386.sys* or *pagefile.sys* is used, depending on the specific Windows version and file system type. Linux systems can create partitions just for swapping data in and out of RAM. Data in the swap space can be read by examining the HDD through forensic software or a utility that provides a binary view, such as Norton Disk Editor or WinHex (see Figure 8).

temporary files

Files temporarily written by an application to perform a function; for applications, such as Microsoft Word and Excel, temporary files are created to provide a "backup" copy of the work product should the computer experience a catastrophic failure

TEMPORARY FILES Any user who has suffered a sudden loss of power in the middle of typing a document can attest to the value of a **temporary file**. Most programs automatically save a copy of the file being worked on in a temporary file. After typing a document, working on a spreadsheet, or working on a slide presentation, the user can save the changes, thus promoting the temporary copy to an actual file. This is done as a sort of backup on the fly. If the computer experiences a sudden loss of power or other catastrophic failure, the temporary file can be recovered, limiting the amount of data lost. The loss is limited because the temporary file is not updated in real time. Rather, it is updated periodically (typically defaulted to every ten minutes in most programs), depending on the application's settings.

Temporary files can sometimes be recovered during a forensic examination. Additionally, some of the data that may have been orphaned from a previous version may be recoverable, if not the complete file. This is true even when a document has been typed and printed, but never saved. The creation of the temporary file makes it possible for some of this "unsaved" data to be recovered during analysis.

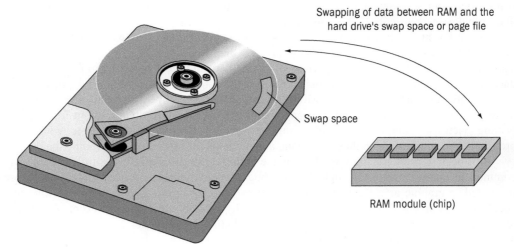

Swapping of data between RAM and the hard drive's swap space or page file

Swap space

RAM module (chip)

FIGURE 8

As a user switches between applications and performs multiple tasks, data is swapped back and forth between RAM and the computer's hard drive. This area on the hard drive is referred to as either *swap space* or a *paging file*.

[4] Actually, the more appropriate term is probably *paging* as opposed to *swapping*. This is because entire programs are typically not swapped in and out of memory to the swap space; rather, *pages* of memory are placed there.

Another type of temporary file valuable to the computer investigator is the print spool file. When a print job is sent to the printer, a spooling process delays the sending of the data to the printer. This happens so the application can continue to work while the printing takes place in the background. To facilitate this, a temporary print spool file is created; this file typically includes the data to be printed and information specific to the printer. There are different methods for accomplishing this, and thus the files created as a result of this process vary. It is sometimes possible to view the data in a readable format from the files created during the spooling process.

Latent Data

The term **latent data** includes data that are obfuscated (not necessarily intentionally) from a user's view. It includes areas of files and disks that are typically not apparent to the computer user but contain data nonetheless. Latent data are one of the reasons a forensic image of the media is created. If a standard copy were all that was produced, only the logical data (that which the operating system is aware of) would be captured. Getting every bit of data ensures that potentially valuable evidence in latent data is not missed.

Once the all-inclusive forensic image is produced, how is the latent data viewed? Utilities that allow a user to examine a hard disk drive on a binary (ones and zeros) level are the answer. Applications such as Norton Disk Editor and WinHex provide this type of access to a hard disk drive or other computer media. Thus these applications, sometimes also referred to as *hex editors* (for the hexadecimal shorthand of computer language), allow all data to be read on the binary level independent of the operating system's file system table. Utilities such as these can write to the media under examination, thus changing data. Consequently, a software or hardware write-blocker should be used.

A more common option in data forensics is to use specialized forensic examination software. EnCase and Forensic Toolkit for Windows and SMART and Forensic Autopsy for Linux are examples of forensic software. Each allows a search for evidence on the binary level and provides automated tools for performing common forensic processing techniques. Examiners should be cautious, however, about relying too heavily on automated tools. To merely use an automated tool without understanding what is happening in the background and why evidentiary data may exist in particular locations would severely impede the ability to testify to the findings.

SLACK SPACE　Slack space is empty space on a hard disk drive created because of the way the HDD stores files. Recall that, although the smallest unit of data measure is one bit (either a one or a zero), a HDD cannot address or deal with such a small unit. In fact, not even a byte (eight bits) can be addressed. Rather, the smallest unit of addressable space by a HDD is the sector. HDDs typically group sectors in 512-byte increments, whereas CD-ROMs allocate 2,048 bytes per sector.

If the minimum addressable unit of the HDD is 512 bytes, what happens if the file is only 100 bytes? In this instance there are 412 bytes of slack space. It does not end here, however, because of the minimum cluster requirement. As you may recall, clusters are groups of sectors used to store files and folders. The cluster is the minimum storage unit defined and used by the logical partition. It is because of the minimum addressable sector of the HDD and the minimum unit of storage requirement of the volume that we have slack space.

Minimum cluster allocation must be defined in a sector multiple of two. Thus, a cluster must be a minimum of two, four, six, or eight sectors, and so on. Returning to our initial example of the 100-byte file, suppose an HDD has a two-sectors-per-cluster volume requirement. This means that the HDD will isolate a minimum of two 512-byte sectors (a total of 1,024 bytes) of storage space for that 100-byte file. The remaining 924 bytes would be slack space (see Figure 9).

To illustrate this point, let us expand on the previous example of safe-deposit boxes. The bank offers safe-deposit boxes of a particular size. This is the equivalent of the HDD's clusters. A person wanting to place only a deed to a house in the box gets the same size box as a person who wants to stuff it full of cash. The former would have empty space should he or she desire to place additional items in the box. This empty space is the equivalent of slack space. But what if the box becomes full and the person needs more space? That person must then get a second box. Similarly, if a file grows to fill one cluster and beyond, a second cluster (and subsequent clusters as needed) is allocated. The remaining space in the second cluster is slack space. This continues as more and more clusters are allocated depending on file size and file growth.

latent data
Areas of files and disks that are typically not apparent to the computer user (and often not to the operating system) but contain data nonetheless

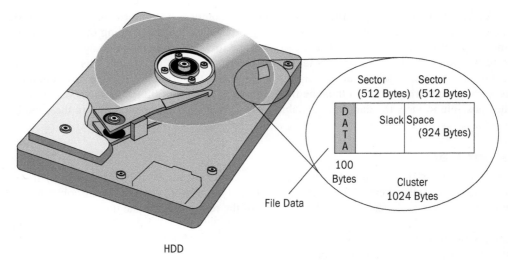

FIGURE 9

Slack space illustrated in a two-sector cluster. Cluster sizes are typically greater than two sectors, but two sectors are displayed here for simplicity.

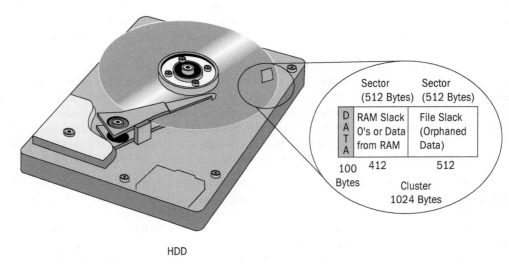

FIGURE 10

File slack.

RAM slack

The area beginning at the end of the logical file and terminating at the end of that sector; in some older operating systems this area is padded with information in RAM

file slack

The area that begins at the end of the last sector that contains logical data and terminates at the end of the cluster

This example is a bit of an oversimplification because there are actually two types of slack space: RAM slack and file slack. **RAM slack** occupies the space from where the actual (logical) data portion of the file ends to where the first allocated sector in the cluster terminates. **File slack**, therefore, occupies the remaining space of the cluster.

Let us go back to the 100-byte file with the two-sectors-per-cluster minimum requirement. Following the end of the logical data (the end of the 100 bytes), the remaining 412 bytes of that sector is RAM slack; the additional 512 bytes completing the cluster is then file slack. See Figure 10 for a visual depiction. The question now becomes: what can I expect to find in slack space and why is this important? The answer: junk—valuable junk.

RAM slack is a concept that was more relevant in older operating systems. Remember that the minimum amount of space the HDD can address is the 512-byte sector. Therefore, if the file size is only 100 bytes, the remaining space must be padded. Some operating systems pad this area with data contained in RAM. This could include Web pages, passwords, data files, or other data that existed in RAM when the file was written. Modern Windows operating systems pad this space with zeros, but some examinations may still yield valuable data in this area.

File slack, on the other hand, can contain a lot of old, orphaned data. To illustrate this point, let's take the 100-byte file example a bit further. Let's say that before the 100-byte file was written to the HDD, occupying one cluster (two sectors totaling 1,024 bytes), a 1,000-byte file occupied this space but was deleted by the user. When a file is "deleted," the data still remains behind, so it is probably a safe bet that data from the original 1,000-byte file remain in the slack space of the new 100-byte file now occupying this cluster. This is just one example of why data exists in file slack and why it may be valuable as evidence.

In one final attempt to illustrate this point, let us again build on our safe-deposit box analogy. Suppose a person rents two safe-deposit boxes, each box representing a sector and the two combined representing a cluster. If that person places the deed to his house in the first box, the remaining space in that box would be analogous to RAM slack. The space in the second box would be the equivalent of file slack. The only difference is that, unlike the empty spaces of the safe-deposit box, the slack space of the file most likely contains data that may be valuable as evidence.

The data contained in RAM and file slack is not really the concern of the operating system. As far as the OS is concerned, this space is empty and therefore ready to be used. Until that happens, however, an examination with one of the aforementioned tools will allow a look into these areas, thus revealing the orphaned data. The same is true for unallocated space.

UNALLOCATED SPACE Latent evidentiary data also resides in **unallocated space**. What is unallocated space, how does data get in there, and what is done to access this space? If we have an 80-GB hard drive and only half of the hard drive is filled with data, then the other half, or 40 GB, is unallocated space. Returning to our safe-deposit box analogy, if the entire bank of safe-deposit boxes contains 100 boxes, but only 50 are currently in use, then the other 50 would be the equivalent of unallocated space. The HDD's unallocated space typically contains a lot of useful data. The constant shuffling of files on the HDD causes data to become orphaned in unallocated space as the logical portion of the file is rewritten to other places. Some examples of how data is orphaned may help.

DEFRAGMENTING Defragmenting a HDD involves moving noncontiguous data back together. Remember that the HDD has minimum space reservation requirements. Again, if the file requires only 100 bytes of space, the operating system may allocate much more than that for use. If the file grows past what has been allocated for it, another cluster is required. If, however, a different file occupies the next cluster in line, then the operating system will have to find another place for that first file on the drive. In this scenario, the file is said to be *fragmented* because data for the same file is contained in noncontiguous clusters. In the case of the HDD, the shuffling of files causes data to be orphaned in unallocated space.

Ultimately fragmentation of numerous files can degrade the performance of a HDD, causing the read/write heads to have to traverse the platters to locate the data. Defragmenting the HDD takes noncontiguous data and rearranges it so it is in contiguous clusters. Building yet again on our safe-deposit box analogy, if a renter eventually needs to store more property than his original box can hold, the bank will rent him a second box. If, however, all the boxes around his are occupied and the only free one is in another section of the room, then his property is "fragmented." The bank would have to "defrag" the safe-deposit boxes to get the property of users with more than one box into adjacent boxes.

SWAP FILE/SWAP SPACE Recall that a computer uses the HDD to maximize the amount of RAM by constantly swapping data in and out of RAM to a predetermined location on the HDD, thus freeing valuable RAM. The constant read and write operations of RAM cause a constant change in the swap file—*WIN386.swp* or *pagefile.sys* in Windows—or swap space on a Linux system. Data can become orphaned in unallocated space from this constant swapping to and from the HDD.

DELETED FILES The deletion of files is another way that data becomes orphaned in unallocated space. Data from deleted files can manifest itself in different ways during a forensic examination. The actions that occur when a file is deleted vary among file systems. What is fairly consistent, though, is that generally speaking the data is not gone. For example, consider what happens when a user or program deletes a file in a Windows operating system with a FAT file system. When a file is deleted, the first character in the file's directory entry (its name) is replaced with the Greek letter sigma. When the sigma replaces the first character, the file is no longer viewable through

unallocated space
The area of the HDD that the operating system (file system table) sees as empty (containing no logical files) and ready for data; simply stated, it is the unused portion of the HDD, but is not necessarily empty

conventional methods and the operating system views the space previously occupied by the file as available. The data, however, is still there.

This example doesn't account for the actions of the Windows Recycle Bin. When the Windows operating system is set up to merely place the deleted file in the Recycle Bin, the original directory entry is deleted and one is created in the Recycle folder for that particular user. The new Recycle folder entry is linked to another file, the *info* or *info2* file, which includes some additional data, such as the location of the file before its deletion should the user wish to restore it to that location. Detailed discussions of the function of the Recycle Bin are beyond the scope of this chapter, but suffice it to say that even when the Recycle Bin is emptied the data usually remains behind until overwritten. Moreover, Windows NTFS partitions and Linux EXT partitions handle deleted files differently, but in both cases data typically remains.

What if a new file writes data to the location of the original file? Generally speaking, the data is gone. This is, of course, unless the new file only partially overwrites the original. In this instance we return to the unallocated-space orphaned-data scenario: if a file that occupied two clusters is deleted, and a new file overwrites one of the clusters, then the data in the second cluster is orphaned in unallocated space. Of course, yet a third file can overwrite the second cluster entirely, but until then the data remains in unallocated space.

Let us once again look to our safe-deposit box analogy. If, for example, the owner of two safe-deposit boxes stopped renting them, the bank would list them as available. If the owner didn't clean them out, the contents would remain unchanged. If a new owner rented one of the boxes, the contents from the former owner would be replaced with the new owner's possessions. The second box would therefore still contain orphaned contents from its previous owner. The contents would remain in this "unallocated box" space until another renter occupies it.

Forensic Analysis of Internet Data

It's important from the investigative standpoint to be familiar with the evidence left behind from a user's Internet activity. A forensic examination of a computer system reveals quite a bit of data about a user's Internet activity. The data described next would be accessed and examined using the forensic techniques outlined in the previous sections of this chapter.

Internet Cache

Evidence of Web browsing typically exists in abundance on the user's computer. Most Web browsers (Internet Explorer, and Firefox) use a caching system to expedite Web browsing and make it more efficient. This was particularly true in the days of dial-up Internet access. When a user accesses a Web site, such as the *New York Times* home page, the data is fed from that server (in this example the *New York Times*), via the Internet service provider, over whatever type of connection the user has, to his or her computer. If that computer is accessing the Internet via a dial-up connection, the transfer of the *New York Times* home page may take a while because the data transfer rate and capabilities (bandwidth) of the telephone system is limited. Even with the high-speed access of a DSL line or cable connection, conservation of bandwidth is always a consideration. Taking that into account, Web browsers store (cache) portions of the pages visited onto the local hard disk drive. This way, if the page is revisited, portions of it can be reconstructed more quickly from this saved data, rather than having to pull it yet again from the Internet and use precious bandwidth.

Internet cache
Portions of visited Web pages placed on the local hard disk drive to facilitate quicker retrieval once revisited

This **Internet cache** is a potential source of evidence for the computer investigator. Portions of, and in some cases, entire visited Web pages can be reconstructed. Even if deleted, these cached files can often be recovered (see the section on deleted data). Investigators must know how to search for this data within the particular Web browser used by a suspect.

Internet Cookies

cookies
Files placed on a computer from a visited Web site; they are used to track visits and usage of that site

Cookies provide another area where potential evidence can be found. To appreciate the value of cookies you must first understand how they get onto the computer and their intended purpose. **Cookies** are placed on the local hard disk drive by Web sites the user has visited, if the user's Web browser (such as Internet Explorer) is set to allow this to happen. Microsoft Internet Explorer places cookies in a dedicated directory. The Web site uses cookies to track certain information about its visitors. This information can be anything, such as history of visits, purchasing habits, passwords, and personal information used to recognize the user for later visits.

Consider a user who registers for an account at the Barnes and Noble bookstore Web site, then returns to the same site from the same computer a few days later. The site will then display "Welcome, *Your User Name*." This data is retrieved from the cookie file placed on the user's hard disk drive by the Web site during the initial visit and registration with the site.

It is helpful to think of cookies almost like a Caller ID for Web sites. The site recognizes and retrieves information about the visitor, as when a salesperson recognizes the caller from a Caller ID display and quickly pulls the client's file. Cookie files can be a valuable source of evidence. In Internet Explorer, they take the form of plain text files, which can typically be opened with a standard text viewer or word-processing program, revealing part of the data. The existence of the files themselves, regardless of the information contained within, can be of evidentiary value to show a history of Web visits. A typical cookie may resemble the following: rsaferstein@ forensicscience.txt. From this we can surmise that someone using the local computer login *rsaferstein* accessed the forensic science Web site. It is possible that the cookie was placed there by an annoying pop-up ad, but considered against other evidence in the computer data, the presence of this cookie may be of corroborative value.

Internet History

Most Web browsers track the history of Web page visits for the computer user. This is probably done merely for a matter of convenience. Like the "recent calls" list on a cell phone, the **Internet history** provides an accounting of sites most recently visited, with some storing weeks' worth of visits. Users can go back and access sites they recently visited just by going through the browser's history. Most Web browsers store this information in one particular file; Internet Explorer uses the *index.dat* file. On a Windows system, an *index.dat* file is created for each login user name on the computer.

Internet history
An accounting of Web sites visited; different browsers store this information in different ways

The history file can be located and read with most popular computer forensic software packages. It displays the uniform resource locator (URL) of each Web site, along with the date and time the site was accessed. An investigation involving Internet use almost always includes an examination of Internet history data.

In some respects, the term "*Internet* history" is wrong because it doesn't encompass all of its functions. Several browsers—Internet Explorer, for one—store other valuable evidence independent of Internet access. It is not uncommon to see files accessed over a network listed in the history. Similarly, files accessed on external media, such as floppy disks, CDs, or thumb drives, may also appear in the history. Regardless, the Internet history data is a valuable source of evidence worthy of examination (see Figure 11).

Bookmarks and Favorite Places

Another way users can access Web sites quickly is to store them in their **bookmarks** or "Favorite Places." Like a preset radio station, Web browsers allow users to bookmark Web sites for future visits (see Figure 12). A lot can be learned from a user's bookmarked sites. You may learn what online news a person is interested in or what type of hobbies he or she has. You may also see that person's favorite child pornography or computer hacking sites bookmarked.

bookmark
A feature that enables the user to designate favorite sites for fast and easy access

In Internet Explorer the favorite places are kept in a folder with link (shortcut) files to a particular URL. They can be organized in subfolders or grouped by type. The same is true for the Firefox Web browser, except that Firefox bookmarks are stored in a document done in hypertext markup language (HTML), the same language interpreted by Web browsers themselves.

Forensic Investigation of Internet Communications

Computer investigations often begin with or are centered on Internet communication. Whether it is a chat conversation among many people, an instant message conversation between two individuals, or the back-and-forth of an e-mail exchange, human communication has long been a source of evidentiary material. *Regardless of the type, investigators are typically interested in communication.*

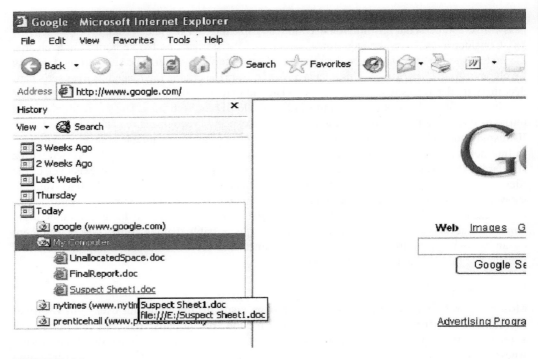

FIGURE 11

The Internet history displays more than just Web browsing activity. Here we see Microsoft Word documents and a picture accessed on the current day.

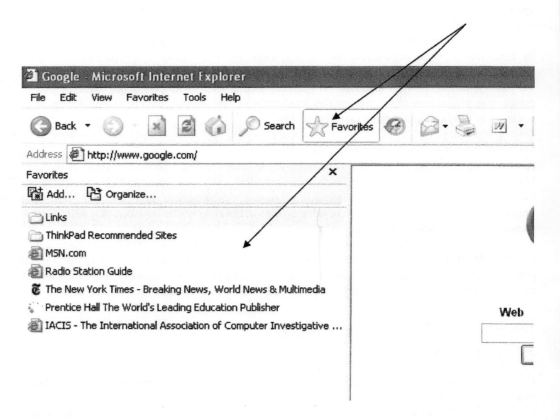

FIGURE 12

Bookmarks or favorite places can be saved for quick access in most Web browsers.

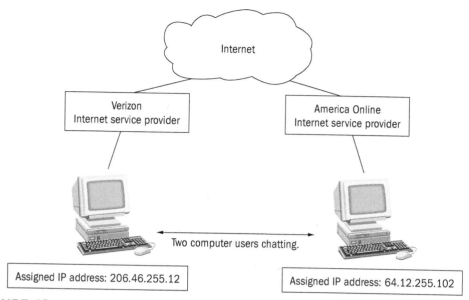

FIGURE 13

Two computers communicating by sending data to each other's IP address via the Internet. An IP address is assigned to each computer by their respective Internet service providers.

Role of the IP

With all of the computer manufacturers and software developers, some rules are necessary for computers to communicate on a global network. Just as any human language needs rules for people to communicate successfully, so does the language of computers. Computers that participate on the Internet, therefore, must be provided with an address known as an Internet protocol (IP) address from the Internet service provider to which they connect.

IP addresses take the form ###.###.###.###, in which, generally speaking, ### can be any number from 0 to 255. A typical IP address might look like this: 66.94.234.13. Not only do IP addresses provide the means by which data can be routed to the appropriate location, but they also provide the means by which most Internet investigations are conducted (see Figure 13). Thus the IP address may lead to the identity of a real person. If an IP address is the link to the identity of a real person, then it is quite obviously valuable for identifying someone on the Internet.

To illustrate, let's assume that a user of the Internet, fictitiously named John Smith, connects to the Internet from his home by way of a Verizon DSL connection. Verizon in this case would be responsible for providing Smith with his IP address. Verizon was issued a bank of IP addresses to service its customers from a regulatory body designed to track the usage of IP addresses (obviously so no two were used at the same time).

Suppose that Smith, while connected to the Internet, decides to threaten an ex-girlfriend by sending her an e-mail telling her he is going to kill her. That e-mail must first pass through Smith's Internet service provider's computers (in this case, Verizon) on its way to its destination—Smith's girlfriend. The e-mail would be stamped by the servers that it passes through, and this stamp would include the IP address given to Smith by Verizon for his session on the Internet.

An investigator responsible for tracking that e-mail would locate the originating IP address stamped in the e-mail header. That IP address could be researched using one of many Internet sites (http://www.samspade.org, http://www.arin.net) to determine which Internet service provider was given this IP as part of a block to service its customers (see Figure 14). The investigator then files a subpoena with the Internet service provider (Verizon) asking which of its customers was using that IP address on that date and time.

IP addresses are located in different places for different methods of Internet communications. E-mail has the IP address in the header portion of the mail. This may not be readily apparent and

FIGURE 14

Sites such as http://www.samspade.org can be used to track the origins of an IP address.
Courtesy Word to the Wise

may require a bit of configuration to reveal. Each e-mail client is different and needs to be evaluated on a case-by-case basis. For an instant message or chat session, the particular provider (the one providing the chat mechanism—AOL, Yahoo, and so on) would be contacted to provide the user's IP address.

E-Mail, Chat, and Instant Messaging

E-mail can be read by a number of *clients* or software programs. Two of the most popular ways to access, read, and store e-mail in today's Internet environment, however, are Microsoft Outlook and through an Internet browser. Some people even use a combination of the two.

If an e-mail account is linked through Microsoft Outlook, then the e-mail is stored in a compound file (a file with several layers). Typically, a compound file exists for received (inbox), sent, and deleted e-mail. Users can also create new categories (shown as folders in Outlook) and categorize saved e-mail there. Most computer forensic software applications can view (mount) these compound files so that the e-mail can be seen, including any file attachments. These files can also be imported into a clean copy (one not attached to an account) of Microsoft Outlook and the e-mail viewed there. Investigators must also be aware that in a computer network environment, the user's Outlook files may not reside on his or her workstation computer, but rather on a central mail or file server.

Most accounts offer the ability to access e-mail through a Web-based interface as well. This way, users can access their e-mail remotely from other computers. For e-mail accessed through a Web browser, the information presented earlier on Internet-based evidence applies. The Web interface converts the e-mail into a document suitable for reading in a Web browser. Consequently, Web-based e-mail is often found in the Internet cache. This is particularly true of free Internet e-mail providers such as Hotmail and Yahoo.

Much of the evidence from Internet communication is also derived from chat and instant message technology. This is particularly true in the world of child sexual exploitation over the Internet. Various technologies provide chat and instant message services. Most chat and instant message conversations are not saved by the parties involved. Although most of the software does allow for conversation archiving, it is typically turned off by default. Therefore, conversations of this nature typically exist in the volatile memory space of random-access memory (RAM).

Recall that RAM is termed volatile because it holds data only if it has power. Unplugging the computer will cause the data located in RAM to be lost. If, however, chat or instant message conversations are relevant as evidence and the computer was turned off, thus erasing the data in RAM, all may not be lost. Remember that there is an interaction between the computer system's RAM and the hard disk drive. RAM is a commodity and therefore the computer's operating system makes an effort to conserve it as best as possible. This is done by swapping/paging that information back and forth into the swap space/paging file. Therefore remnants of chat conversations are often found in the swap space/paging file during a forensic examination of the hard disk drive. These remnants, however, are typically fragmented, disconnected, and incomplete. Therefore if the chat or instant message is still present on the screen (and thus probably still in RAM), the investigator needs a method by which to preserve and collect it.

A detailed discussion of capturing volatile data from RAM is beyond the scope of this chapter. Suffice it to say that many commercial forensic software packages can capture this data. Similarly, Linux-based tools can accomplish this as well. The examiner may even be able to export the data remotely to another device. Regardless of the method, the data needs to be acquired.

Furthermore, many programs such as America Online Instant Messenger, Yahoo Messenger, and mIRC (Internet Relay Chat) create files regarding the rooms or channels a user chatted in or the screen names with which a user sent instant messages. Each application needs to be researched and the computer forensic examination guided by an understanding of how it functions.

Hacking

Unauthorized computer intrusion, more commonly referred to as **hacking**, is the concern of every computer administrator. Hackers penetrate computer systems for a number of reasons. Sometimes the motive is corporate espionage; other times it is merely for bragging rights within the hacker community. Most commonly, though, a rogue or disgruntled employee with some knowledge of the computer network is looking to cause damage. Whatever the motivation, corporate America frequently turns to law enforcement to investigate and prosecute these cases.

Generally speaking, when investigating an unauthorized computer intrusion, investigators concentrate their efforts in three locations: *log files*, *volatile memory*, and *network traffic*. Logs typically document the IP address of the computer that made the connection. Logs can be located in several locations on a computer network. Most servers on the Internet track connections made to them through the use of logs. Additionally the router (the device responsible for directing data) may contain log files detailing connections.

Similarly, devices known as **firewalls** may contain log files listing computers that were allowed access to the network or an individual system. Firewalls are devices (taking the form of either hardware or software) that permit only requested traffic to enter a computer system (or, more appropriately, a network). In other words, if a user didn't send out a request for Internet traffic from a specific system, the firewall should block its entry. If the log files captured the IP address of the intruder, then revealing the user behind the IP is the same process as for e-mail. Investigating a computer intrusion, however, does get a bit more complicated than this.

Frequently, in cases of unlawful access to a computer network, the perpetrator attempts to cover the tracks of his or her IP address. In these instances, advanced investigative techniques may be necessary to discover the hacker's true identity. When an intrusion is in progress, the investigator may have to capture volatile data (data in RAM). The data in RAM at the time of an intrusion may provide valuable clues to the identity of the intruder, or at least his or her method of attack. As in the case of an instant message or chat conversation, the data in RAM needs to be acquired.

Another standard tactic for investigating intrusion cases is to document all programs installed and running on a system in order to discover malicious software installed by the perpetrator to facilitate entry. The investigator uses specialized software to document running processes, registry entries, open ports, and any installed files.

Additionally, the investigator may want to capture live network traffic as part of the evidence collection and investigation process. Traffic that travels the network does so in the form of data packets. In addition to data, these packets also contain source and destination IP addresses. If the

hacking
Has various meanings, but is frequently used as a slang term for an unauthorized computer or network intrusion

firewall
Hardware or software designed to protect intrusions into an Internet network

attack requires two-way communication, as in the case of a hacker stealing data, then data needs to be transmitted back to the hacker's computer using the destination IP address. Once this is learned, the investigation can focus on that system. Moreover, the type of data that is being transmitted on the network may be a clue as to what type of attack is being launched, whether any important data is being stolen, or what types of malicious software, if any, are involved in the attack.

chapter summary >>>>>>>>>>

Computers have permeated society and are used in countless ways with innumerable applications. Similarly, the role of electronic data in investigative work has realized exponential growth in the last decade. Users of computers and other electronic data storage devices leave footprints and data trails behind. Computer forensics involves the preservation, acquisition, extraction, analysis, and interpretation of computer data. In today's world of technology, many devices are capable of storing data and could thus be grouped into the field of computer forensics.

The central processing unit (CPU) is the brain of the computer—the main chip responsible for doing the actual computing. Random-access memory (RAM) is volatile memory containing data that is forever lost when the power is turned off. Programs are loaded into RAM because of its faster read speed. The hard disk drive (HDD) is typically the primary location of data storage within the computer. Different operating systems map out HDDs differently, and examiners must be familiar with the file system they are examining. Evidence exists in many different locations and in numerous forms on a HDD. This evidence can be grouped into two major categories: visible and latent data.

Visible data is data that the operating system is aware of and consequently is easily accessible to the user. From an evidentiary standpoint, it can encompass any type of user-created data, such as word-processing documents, spreadsheets, accounting records, databases, and pictures. Temporary files, created by programs as a sort of backup on the fly, can also prove valuable as evidence.

Finally, data in the swap space (used to conserve the valuable RAM within the computer system) can yield evidentiary visible data.

Latent data, on the other hand, is data that the operating system typically is not aware of. Evidentiary latent data can exist in both RAM slack and file slack. RAM slack is the area from the end of the logical file to the end of the sector. File slack is the remaining area from the end of the final sector containing logical data to the end of the cluster. Another area where latent data may be found is in unallocated space. Unallocated space is space on a HDD that the operating system sees as empty and ready for data. The constant shuffling of data through deletion, defragmentation, and swapping is one of the ways data is orphaned in latent areas. Finally, when a user deletes files the data typically remains behind. Deleted files are therefore another source of latent data to be examined during forensic analysis.

Investigators seeking a history of an Internet user's destinations can take advantage of the fact that computers store or cache portions of Web pages visited, and Web sites often create cookies to track certain information about Web site visitors. An investigator tracking the origin of an e-mail seeks out the sender's IP address in the e-mail's header. Chat and instant messages are typically located in a computer's random-access memory (RAM). Finding the origin of unauthorized computer intrusions (hacking) requires investigation of a computer's log file, RAM, and network traffic, among other things.

review questions

1. Computer forensics involves the _____, _____, _____, _____, and _____ of computer data.

2. True or False: Hardware comprises the physical components of the computer. _____

3. _____ is a set of instructions compiled into a program that performs a particular task.

4. (ROM, RAM) chips store programs used to start the boot process.

5. The term used to describe the chassis, including the motherboard and any other internal components of a personal computer, is _____.

6. True or False: The motherboard is a complex network of wires that carry data from one hardware device to another. _____

7. True or False: The first thing you should do when you encounter a computer system in a forensic investigation is to connect the power supply and boot the system. _____

8. RAM is referred to as volatile memory because it is not _____.

9. The brain of the computer is referred to as the _____.

10. The _____ is the primary component of storage in the personal computer.

11. Personal computers typically communicate with each other through a(n) _____.

12. The computer's _____ permits the user to manage files and applications.

13. A hard drive's partitions are typically divided into _____, _____, _____, and _____.

14. A(n) _____ is a single one or zero in the binary system and the smallest term in the language of computers.

15. A(n) _____ is a group of eight bits.

16. A group of sectors, always units in multiples of two, is called a(n) _____.

17. An exact duplicate of the entire contents of a hard disk drive is known as a(n) _____.

18. All data readily available to a computer user is known as _____ data.

19. A(n) _____ file is created when data is moved from RAM to the hard disk drive to conserve space.

20. Most programs automatically save a copy of a file being worked on into a(n) _____ file.

21. The existence of _____ data is why a forensic image of the media is created.

22. The smallest unit of addressable space on a hard disk drive is the _____.

23. The two types of slack space are _____ slack and _____ slack.

24. _____ slack is the area from the end of the data portion of the file to the end of the sector.

25. The portion of a disk that does not contain stored data is called _____.

26. True or False: Defragmenting a hard disk drive involves moving noncontiguous data back together. _____

27. True or False: A portion of a "deleted" file may be found in a computer's unallocated space. _____

28. A(n) _____ takes the form of a series of numbers to route data to an appropriate location on the Internet.

29. A user's hard disk drive will _____ portions of Web pages that have been visited.

30. A(n) _____ is placed on a hard disk drive by a Web site to track certain information about its visitors.

31. E-mails have the _____ address of the sender in the header portion of the mail.

32. True or False: Chat and instant messages conducted over the Internet are typically stored in RAM storage. _____

33. When investigating a hacking incident, investigators concentrate their efforts on three locations: _____, _____, and _____.

34. Devices that permit only requested traffic to enter a computer system are known as _____.

application and critical thinking

1. If a file system defines a cluster as six sectors, how many bits of information can be stored on each cluster? Explain your answer.

2. Criminalist Tom Parauda is investigating the scene of a crime involving a computer. After he arrives, he photographs the overall scene and takes close-up shots of all the connections to the single computer involved, as well as photos of the serial numbers of the computer and all peripheral devices. Tom then labels the cord to each peripheral device, then disconnects them from the computer. After making sure that all data in RAM has been saved to the hard disk drive, he unplugs the computer from the wall. What mistakes, if any, did Tom make?

3. You are investigating a case in which an accountant is accused of keeping fraudulent books for a firm. Upon examining his computer, you notice that the suspect uses two different accounting programs that are capable of reading the same types of files. Given this information, where would you probably begin to search for latent data on the computer and why?

4. You are examining two computers to determine the IP address from which several threatening e-mails were sent. The first computer uses Microsoft Outlook as an e-mail client and the second uses a Web-based e-mail client. Where would you probably look first for the IP addresses in each of these computers?

case analysis 1

Suspicious circumstances surrounding the death of Ms. Smith in a home fire led the police to suspect her husband of murder. Evidence later recovered from Mr. Smith's computer proved key in solving the case.

1. What did police hope to prove from examining the Microsoft Word files on Mr. Smith's computer? Why did they believe this would implicate him in his wife's murder?

2. How were the documents titled *insurance1.doc* and *WRL1604.tmp* important to tying Mr. Smith to his wife's death?

case analysis 2

When police seized a laptop from a van parked suspiciously outside a local shopping mall, they discovered a cyber counterfeiting ring that employed modern technology to perpetrate this age-old crime.

1. What physical evidence most strongly implicated the driver of the van in a currency counterfeiting operation? What aspect of this evidence confirmed these suspicions?

2. What files located on the suspect's computer indicated that the suspects were producing more than counterfeit currency? What conclusion did the investigators draw from the existence of these files?

further references

Britz, M. T., *Computer Forensics and Cyber Crime,* 2nd ed. Upper Saddle River, N.J.: Prentice Hall, 2008.

Carrier, B., *File System Forensic Analysis.* Upper Saddle River, N.J.: Addison-Wesley, 2005.

Casey, E., *Digital Evidence and Computer Crimes*, 2nd ed. San Diego: Elsevier Academic Press, 2004.

Kruse, W. G., and J. G. Heiser, *Computer Forensics— Incident Response Essentials.* Boston: Addison-Wesley, 2001.

Leshin, C. B., *Internet Investigations in Criminal Justice.* Upper Saddle River, N.J.: Prentice-Hall, 1997.

Nelson, B., A. Phillips, F. Enfinger, and C. Steuart, *Guide to Computer Forensics and Investigations*, 4th ed. Boston: Thomson Course Technology, 2009.

Proise, C., K. Mandia, and B. Pepe, *Incident Response and Computer Forensics*, 2nd ed. New York: McGraw-Hill, 2003.

Computer Forensic Analysis Answers the Question "Arson or Accident?"

Brief

The home of John Smith was destroyed by a fire, which was later determined to be the result of arson. During the fire, Smith's wife, Jane, died. Investigators learned that insurance policies taken against both the home and the life of Jane Smith were recently increased, so Smith stands to receive a very large monetary settlement. This fact, and problems with his purported alibi at the time of the fire, makes him the primary suspect. Smith has steadfastly denied the existence of the insurance policies and offers that his wife must have recently changed the policies.

Further investigation discloses that the couple did not possess a home computer but that Smith uses a computer at work. After applying for and receiving a search warrant for Smith's workplace, the arson investigator seizes the computer system unit from underneath Smith's desk, which he found in a powered-off condition. During execution of the search warrant, the company's computer administrator tells investigators that the computer was used only by Smith. The computer system unit is submitted for forensic analysis.

Analysis Request

Locate any incriminating or exculpatory evidentiary data with respect to Smith's knowledge of changes in his insurance policy. Locate any evidentiary data with respect to motive for the crimes of arson and/or homicide.

Forensic Image Acquisition

1. The computer system was documented and its chassis was opened and a single IDE/ATA hard disk drive (HDD) was located and documented. The HDD was removed from the system and the computer system unit was booted to the BIOS setup program. The system date and time were verified.
2. The HDD was then placed in a forensic workstation, connected to the system using a hardware write-blocking device to ensure that the suspect HDD was not altered in any way.
3. A forensic image of the HDD was acquired using EnCase Version 5. The integrity of this image was verified using the MD5 algorithm inherent in the EnCase program. A date and time analysis was done on all the files, revealing no dates later than the date of the execution of the search warrant.

Courtesy Peter Arnold Inc.

Analysis

1. Deleted files were recovered.
2. A file signature analysis was run.
3. All files, including dates and times, logical and physical sizes, and complete location path, were documented by the EnCase program.
4. User accounts were documented: two default accounts (*Administrator* and *Guest*, SID 500 and 501, respectively) and one user account (*jsmith*).
5. The operating system and file system type were documented: Windows 2000 using an NTFS partition.
6. Keyword text searches, derived from the text of letters received by the insurance company, were conducted.
7. All Microsoft Word documents were examined.
8. All text documents were examined.
9. Print spool files were examined.

Findings

1. A file titled *insurance1.doc* was located in the directory *C:\Documents and Settings\jsmith\junk*. The directory structure *C:\Documents and Settings\jsmith* coincides with a default directory for the user name *jsmith*, which would have been established with that account. The subdirectory *junk* was then added by a user of the *jsmith* account. The text in this file is the same as the one received by the insurance company requesting an increase in homeowner's insurance.

2. Text found in unallocated space matches sections of text in a second letter received by the insurance company requesting an increase in life insurance for Jane Smith.

3. A file titled *WRL1604.tmp* was found in the directory *C:\Documents and Settings\jsmith\junk*. The file matches that of a temporary Microsoft Word file and contains text matching sections of text in the letter received by the insurance company requesting an increase in life insurance for Jane Smith.

4. A file titled *46127a.SPL* was located in the directory *C:\windows\system32\spool\printers*. This file appears to be a print spool file. This file, when viewed as an Enhanced Meta File (EMF), reveals a document exact in composition and similar in layout to the letter received by the insurance company requesting an increase in life insurance for Jane Smith. An EMF is a type of spool file created during the printing process and can be viewed as a Windows picture file in the forensic software.

Conclusion

Based on the forensic examination of the computer data submitted in this case, it can be stated within a reasonable degree of scientific certainty that a user of this computer had knowledgeable interaction with letters very similar in content, composition, and structure to the evidentiary letters submitted as reference for analysis.

Counterfeiting and Fraud:
A Forensic Computer Investigation

Brief

A detective submits a laptop computer for examination and explains that it was seized in connection with a case of counterfeiting and fraud. According to the detective, patrol officers happened upon a large sport-utility vehicle, occupied by one male driver, parked in the lot of a local mall. According to the officers, the driver and the circumstances appeared suspicious.

After investigating further, the officers located a laptop computer, color printer, and scanner in the rear of the vehicle. All equipment was hooked up and running. Additionally, the officers located gift certificates for one of the stores within the mall, which apparently were printed inside the vehicle. Finally, two $100 bills bearing exactly the same serial number were located in the driver's wallet. In response to questioning, the driver admitted using the system to print bogus gift certificates and counterfeit cash, which he then redeemed inside the mall. Prior to submission at the computer forensics laboratory, the equipment was processed for fingerprints at the state Bureau of Criminal Identification (BCI).

Courtesy Getty Images, Inc.—Agence France Presse

Analysis Request

Locate any evidentiary data with respect to the crimes of counterfeiting and fraud. Demonstrate any connection between the recovered printed documents and the electronic equipment seized from the vehicle.

Forensic Image Acquisition

1. The computer system was documented and its case was opened and a single IDE hard disk drive (HDD) was located and documented. The HDD was removed from the system and the computer system unit was booted to the BIOS setup program. The system date and time were verified.
2. The HDD was then placed in a forensic workstation, connected to the system using a hardware write-blocking device to ensure that the suspect HDD was not altered in any way.
3. A forensic image of the HDD was acquired using EnCase Version 5. The integrity of this image was verified using the MD5 algorithm inherent in the EnCase program. A date and time analysis was done on all the files, revealing no dates later than the date of the execution of the search warrant.

Analysis

1. Deleted files were recovered.
2. A file signature analysis was run.
3. All files, including dates and times, logical and physical sizes, and complete location path, were documented by the EnCase program.
4. The operating system and file system type were documented: Windows XP using an NTFS file system.
5. All graphics files were viewed, including ones previously deleted.
6. A graphics finder script was run against unallocated space. The script searched this area to locate file signatures of known graphics files.
7. All print spool files were located and examined.

Findings

1. A file titled *100front.jpg* was located in the directory *C:\Documents and Settings\user1\My Documents*. This file is an image of the front of a $100 bill. The serial number on this image matched the serial number of the suspected counterfeit $100 bills found on the suspect.
2. A file titled *100back.jpg* was located in the directory *C:\Documents and Settings\user1\My Documents*. This file is an image of the back of a $100 bill.
3. A file titled *GapGiftCert1.jpg* was located in the directory *C:\Documents and Settings\user1\My Documents*. This file is an image of the front of a gift certificate for The Gap, a retail store.
4. A file titled *GapGiftCert2.jpg* was located in the directory *C:\Documents and Settings\user1\My Documents*. This file is an image of the back of a gift certificate for The Gap, a retail store.
5. A file titled *thumbs.db* was located in the directory *C:\Documents and Settings\user1\My Documents*. This file, when viewed as a compound file, displayed several images, namely the images in items 1–4.
6. In the folder *C:\Documents and Settings\User1\My Recent Documents*, link files were found to the following:
   a. *C:\Documents and Settings\user1\My Documents\100front.jpg*
   b. *C:\Documents and Settings\user1\My Documents\100back.jpg*
   c. *C:\Documents and Settings\user1\My Documents\GapGiftCert1.jpg*
   d. *C:\Documents and Settings\user1\My Documents\GapGiftCert2.jpg*
7. The submitted scanner and printer were connected to a laboratory computer system and the aforementioned evidentiary files were copied onto the HDD of that system. Several printouts of the images were made. Additionally, test items were scanned and printed. All exemplars produced from the laboratory computer system were submitted to the state Bureau of Criminal Identification. The original counterfeit currency and gift certificates were also submitted to BCI for comparison to the exemplars. BCI was asked to locate any distinguishing characteristics produced by the printer and scanner submitted in this case.

Conclusion

Based on the forensic examination of the computer data submitted in this case, it can be stated within a reasonable degree of scientific certainty that a user of this computer knowingly produced counterfeit currency and counterfeit gift certificates.

answers to review questions

Odd-Numbered Review Questions

1. preserving; acquiring; extracting; analyzing; interpreting
3. Software
5. system unit
7. False
9. CPU
11. network interface card (NIC)
13. sectors; clusters; tracks; cylinders
15. byte
17. forensic image
19. swap
21. latent
23. RAM; file
25. unallocated space
27. True
29. cache
31. IP
33. log files; volatile memory; network traffic

Application and Critical Thinking

1. Because each sector is 512 bytes, a cluster consisting of six sectors would hold 3,072 bytes of data. Because each byte equals 8 bits, each cluster would hold 24,576 bits of data.
2. Tom made several mistakes. When he arrived, he should have sketched the overall layout as well as photographing it. He also should have photographed any running monitors. In addition to labeling the cord of each peripheral, Tom should have placed a corresponding label on the port to which each cord was connected. Before unplugging the computer, he should have checked to ensure that the computer was not using encryption. Finally, he should have removed the plug from the back of the computer, not from the wall.
3. You probably would begin to search for latent data in the swap space on the hard disk drive. If the accountant was keeping fraudulent records, he may well have been transferring data from one accounting program to another. Data from those operations may well be left behind in the swap space, where it later can be retrieved.
4. On the first computer you probably would look first at the compound files created by Microsoft Outlook. On the second computer you probably would look first in the Internet cache.

Case Analysis 1

1. By examining Mr. Smith's computer, police hoped to prove that he had changed his wife's insurance policy shortly before the fire in which she died. They believed this would implicate him in his wife's murder because the increased insurance settlement Mr. Smith would

receive upon his wife's death would serve as a strong motive for murdering her.

2. The documents titled *insurance1.doc* and *WRL1604.tmp* were important to tying Mr. Smith to his wife's death because they proved that he wrote the letter to his insurance company requesting an increase in his wife's life insurance.

Case Analysis 2

1. The physical evidence that most strongly implicated the driver of the van in a counterfeiting operation was the discovery of two $100 bills in his wallet. These suspicions were confirmed by the fact that the bills had identical serial numbers.

2. The documents titled *GapGiftCert1.jpg* and *GapGiftCert2.jpg* indicated that the suspects were producing more than counterfeit currency. From these files, the investigators concluded that the suspects were also producing counterfeit gift certificates to The Gap.

the future

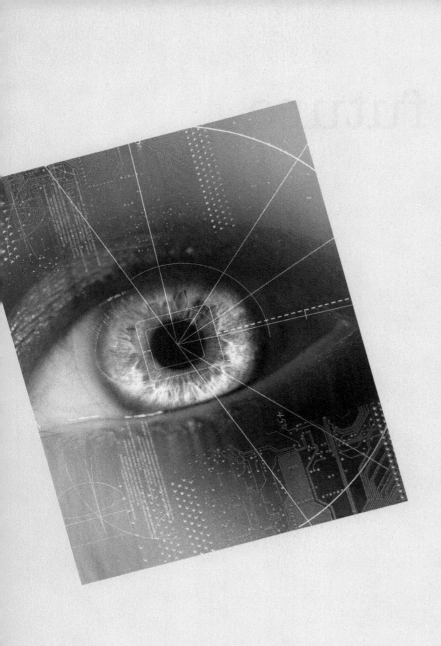

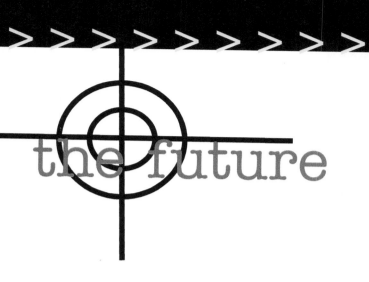

the future

In 1949, Charles O'Hara and James Osterburg, noted criminalistics authors, wrote: "The present position of criminalistics among the sciences may properly be compared with that of chemistry in the nineteenth century." Certainly, in this new millennium, the changes that have taken place since this observation was made have been nothing short of revolutionary. Forensic science may still have many shortcomings, but it has successfully shed the distinction of being a nineteenth-century science.

Crime laboratories have now become the major benefactors of enormous advances in scientific technology. Chromatography and spectrophotometry have already had a tremendous impact on forensic methodology. In a very short span of time, DNA typing has developed into a routine forensic science technique. The future promises even more rapid progress. Mass spectrometry, capillary electrophoresis, and high-performance liquid chromatography, among other developments, are rapidly gaining recognition as essential forensic tools. The scanning electron microscope is already enhancing the application of microscopy to the examination of trace physical evidence. An even more impressive tool is the scanning electron microscope linked to an X-ray microanalyzer. This combination enables forensic scientists to examine very small samples nondestructively while plotting the elemental composition of the specimen in view.

The notion that there is a need for trained and knowledgeable evidence collectors at crime scenes has been a recurring one throughout this text. Once again this requirement must be reiterated. How is the evidence collector or investigator to gain the skill and appreciation for recognizing the value of physical evidence? The trend of events seems to be one of conceding past failings and acknowledging the need for creating specialists to perform evidence-collection functions. In growing numbers, police agencies are training and equipping "evidence-collection technicians" to help criminal investigators retrieve evidence at the crime scene.

If this program is to have a significant impact on investigative procedures, immediate steps must be taken that go beyond mere designation of an evidence-collection unit on a police agency's organization chart. The effectiveness of such a program should not be measured by the number of oversized and overequipped mobile vans at the unit's disposal; instead, a staff of dedicated operators and administrators trained and experienced in evidence collection must be assembled. This unit must be recognized as the essential first step in forensic analysis and must become an integral part, both administratively and functionally, of the total forensic service offered by a law enforcement agency.

The education of evidence collectors and investigators is a critical factor in improving the quality of crime scene investigation. Although continued in-depth training of investigators by forensic scientists is an essential ingredient for the success of such a program, many agencies—for lack of space, time, or desire—have not implemented this training. It is therefore gratifying that colleges and universities are emerging as centers of education for law enforcement personnel. Criminal justice or law enforcement programs provide viable forums for teaching the philosophy and theory of criminal investigation and forensic science. However, academia must strive to supplement, not supplant, police in-service training. Police administrators now have the responsibility for selecting the personnel to perform investigative functions. These administrators cannot abdicate their responsibility to create and foster training programs to ensure competent performance of the investigator's mission.

Whether a college degree will someday be required by all police departments is still a subject of debate, but the trend is certainly in that direction. More than a thousand higher education institutions in the United States offer some sort of law enforcement program. Future generations of criminal investigators and police administrators will be recruited from the ranks of these students. Participation in these programs offers the forensic scientist a unique opportunity to teach, develop, and put into practice the philosophy that science is an integral part of criminal investigation.

Of course education alone will not guarantee the success of the criminal investigator or evidence collector. Experience, perceptive skill, persistence, and precise judgment are all essential ingredients to the makeup of the successful investigator and evidence collector. Combine all of these characteristics with a careful selection process designed to choose only those who qualify for this role, and the result will be substantial enhancement of the quality of criminal investigative services.

Certainly it is not the case that crime laboratories are not being used or that forensic scientists have difficulty justifying a full day's work. On the contrary, these facilities are overworked and understaffed. The demand imposed on them just to complete the examination of drug and blood-alcohol evidence is enough to inundate and preoccupy all but the larger crime laboratories. Most facilities are drowning in a "sea" of drugs. Furthermore, the disproportionate burden placed on the skills, time, and equipment of the laboratory by drug and blood-alcohol evidence has had a detrimental effect on the capacity of the law enforcement system to process physical evidence generated by more serious or violent crimes.

The solution to the problem may seem obvious: more people, larger facilities, and, of course, more money. But crime laboratories must stand in line with other components of the criminal justice system because skyrocketing crime rates have overburdened our police, courts, and correctional institutions. In light of public and political outcries, criminal justice administrators have sought programs geared to producing quick and dramatic reductions in crime rates. In this atmosphere, hiring more scientists or buying a mass spectrometer or a gas chromatograph may hardly seem the best way to reduce crime.

The solution is not a crash program for building crime laboratories or, for that matter, a crash program aimed at improving one segment of the criminal justice community at the expense of the others. Reduction of crime will come about only with a balanced approach to criminal justice, as well as alleviation of social injustices. We must keep the future role of the crime laboratory in its proper perspective while examining the goals and performance that we expect from all components of our criminal justice system.

The size and effectiveness of a crime laboratory directly mirror the capability of the investigative agencies that it serves. If all or even most of the burglaries, homicides, assaults, rapes, and other types of major offenses were investigated with the thoroughness expected of a proper criminal investigation, the quantity of physical evidence collected would require the existence of better staffed and better equipped crime laboratories.

An important impetus behind the expansion of crime laboratory services in the United States has been DNA profiling. The advent of DNA profiling has placed tremendous pressures on crime laboratory services. Laws passed to mandate entry into a DNA database for many convicted offenders and, in some jurisdictions, arrestees, has imposed tremendous workloads on crime laboratories that must also cope with an overwhelming variety of evidence collected at crime scenes for DNA analysis. The high-profile nature of DNA investigations has pressured government officials to expand crime laboratory facilities and to hire adequate staff to deal with the influx of biological evidence.

Although the commitment of police to improve the quality of crime-scene investigation is essential, it must be accompanied by a simultaneous effort to improve the caliber of crime laboratory services. Certainly, thorough collection of crime-scene evidence will require more forensic scientists to handle the increasing caseloads. However, forensic scientists should not be lulled into a false sense of security by believing that the tremendous strides made in the development of analytical instruments and techniques are sufficient to meet the needs and goals of their profession. Progress can be expected only if crime laboratories are staffed with trained and knowledgeable scientists.

Fortunately more colleges and universities are offering courses and degree programs in forensic science or criminalistics. These institutions are beginning to serve as fertile training grounds for new forensic scientists. Although many of these individuals have textbook knowledge of the techniques used in forensic analysis, few arrive at the crime laboratory possessing an understanding of the practical aspects of criminal investigation. This deficiency necessitates a prolonged and time-consuming period of intensive training under the direction of trained criminalists. Not only must the new criminalist learn to apply specialized skills to the responsibilities and objectives of a working crime laboratory, he or she must also acquire a familiarity with all phases of crime laboratory operation.

The extent and depth of versatility expected of the forensic scientist are usually determined by the size of the crime laboratory's staff. Scientists in smaller laboratories are often expected to be generalists, performing a wide variety of tasks in order to fulfill the varied objectives of the laboratory. Their counterparts in larger facilities enjoy the luxury of working in specialized areas, relying on a teamwork approach to provide the spectrum of scientific skills needed for the comparison or identification of physical evidence.

In addition to his or her technical responsibilities, the newly trained criminalist must discover and master the role of expert witness. A good courtroom demeanor and the ability to communicate thoughts and ideas in clear, concise terms are absolutely essential if the scientist's examination and conclusions are to be properly and effectively presented at a hearing or in a courtroom.

The current momentum of forensic research could very well falter unless individuals who possess relevant knowledge and skills are attracted to careers in forensic science. The recognition by a sufficient number of colleges and universities of the need to foster undergraduate and graduate programs in this field is essential for ensuring an ample supply of scientists to meet the anticipated personnel needs of the profession. Furthermore, the establishment of forensic education programs, especially at the graduate level, should be accompanied by the formulation of new academic research programs dedicated to investigating fertile areas of research that are pertinent to the expanding role of forensic science in criminal justice. In a university environment, these research programs can be pursued in an atmosphere unaffected by the pressures of everyday casework, a burden that currently weighs heavily on the working forensic scientist.

The prospects for significant technological advances in forensic science in the near future are great. In fact, the computer-aided search of single latent fingerprints is already a reality in most jurisdictions. The ability to search, in a matter of minutes, files comprising millions of prints in order to ascertain a probable match to a latent fingerprint represents the most significant contribution that forensic science has made to criminal investigation since the introduction of the fingerprint itself. Jurisdictions using this approach have reported startling increases in arrests.

Computerized technology is also helping investigators link multiple unrelated shooting cases to a single firearm. The automated search system NIBIN allows the surface characteristics of a bullet or cartridge case to be scanned and stored in a computerized database that is networked throughout various regions of the United States. An investigator can search the database for entries bearing similar characteristics to the evidential bullet or cartridge case. If a match is made, multiple crimes may be linked and associated with a single firearm.

Almost every week we read in newspapers that researchers are developing new products with their ability to manipulate genes. The ability of scientists to penetrate DNA, the basic building block of genes, provides investigators with a powerful forensic tool to individualize blood, semen, and hair. The FBI has initiated an aggressive forensic research program to develop this technology, along with an ambitious technical training program to instruct personnel of state and local crime laboratories throughout the United States in the use of this technology. DNA typing has already progressed to the level that all states are routinely DNA typing offenders involved in sex-related and other crimes. The technology of DNA profiling has progressed so rapidly that today blood and semen stains recovered from crime scenes are as revealing of human identity as a fingerprint. CODIS is a computer software program developed and maintained by the FBI that links local, state, and national databases of DNA profiles from convicted offenders, unsolved crime-scene evidence, and missing people. CODIS software has enabled local, state, and national crime laboratories to compare DNA profiles electronically. Thousands of matches have linked criminal perpetrators to DNA profiles in CODIS databases.

One unexpected dividend from DNA testing has been the reinvigoration of the investigation of "minor crimes." For decades, police have given the investigation of house burglary scenes and other property crimes low priority. Evidence now suggests that DNA evidence collected at property crime scenes may help law enforcement solve those crimes and identify perpetrators of more serious offenses. According to one state study, more than 50 percent of the DNA database hits against murder and sexual assault cases matched individuals who had prior convictions for burglary.

Apprehending perpetrators of property crimes can certainly discourage criminals from moving on to the commission of more serious violent crimes, and thus can have a dramatic long-term impact on decreasing the overall crime rate. In this respect, it is apparent that DNA collected at burglary scenes is a powerful investigative tool. In one major jurisdiction, DNA evidence from 201 burglaries yielded 86 DNA profiles for entry in CODIS. Most of the profiles resulted in links to multiple unsolved cases. One profile uncovered a five-burglary serial offender. A few were linked to more serious violent crimes such as sexual assault and robbery. Significantly, more than 30 of the burglaries were matched though CODIS to convicted offenders. In Florida jurisdictions, individuals associated with two hundred DNA samples collected from various burglary investigations were identified by CODIS. A more recent study showed that twice as many property crime suspects were identified and arrested when DNA evidence was collected than when crimes were investigated in a more traditional manner.

Unfortunately, in spite of the fact that crime laboratories are equipped with expensive and sophisticated instruments, often a forensic scientist cannot report to a police officer or a jury that a scientific examination of the evidence has itself solved a case. More often than not, a conclusive comparison of evidential and control material cannot exclude other possible sources. To further complicate matters, the statistical data available to support such conclusions are usually sketchy or nonexistent. In such situations, heavy reliance must necessarily be placed on the experience and opinion of the expert in interpreting the significance of the forensic examination.

Although class physical evidence for corroborating investigative findings is an important contribution to any criminal case, its nonexclusive character does not always motivate investigators to go all out in their search for class physical evidence. The items most sought at the crime site are those that possess potential individual characteristics—that is, DNA, fingerprints, firearms, bullets, tool marks, and track impressions—because these are more likely to have a greater impact on an investigation. Once these avenues have been exhausted, there seems to be little desire to progress further. Clearly, future research will have to concentrate on defining the value of class evidence so that these items can become statistically more meaningful and attractive to scientists and investigators alike. However, a salient point of this book is that all physical evidence, whether class or individual in nature, is critical to a properly conducted criminal investigation. Criminalists have become extremely proficient in conducting tests that will narrow the origin of class evidence to a limited number of possibilities. Yet some insist that if a scientist cannot define the significance of a comparison in statistical terms, the evidence should be excluded from consideration. To succumb to this reasoning is tantamount to eviscerating a core principle of criminalistics—the collection and presentation of impartial and objective information for evaluation by an adjudicator of fact. The criminalistic community must aggressively communicate its capabilities and objectives to both the police and legal communities.

A major thrust of forensic research must concentrate on defining the most distinctive properties of evidence and relating these properties to statistics that measure their frequency of occurrence. The creation of data banks to collect, store, and disseminate this kind of information will facilitate the task. Because the responsibility for providing forensic services is spread among more than 350 independent government laboratories in the United States, the task of accumulating meaningful statistical data applicable to the entire country or to large regions is exceedingly difficult. Future progress will depend on the willingness of all crime laboratories to enter into cooperative programs that will ensure uniform standards of analysis as well as providing for the collection and dissemination of analytical and statistical data.

Furthermore, the FBI has encouraged the formation of committees comprising forensic specialists in relevant forensic science disciplines to develop standardized analytical protocols in their field. These committees, known as SWGS (Scientific Working Groups), meet on a regular basis and are constantly fine tuning and updating developments in their respective fields. Their work products are disseminated to the entire forensic community to serve as an impetus for laboratory standardization of forensic technology.

The central role that forensic science has assumed in the criminal justice system led to the creation of a study by the National Academy of Science to assess the current and future roles of forensic science in the criminal justice system. The report was published in 2009 under the title *Strengthening Forensic Science in the United States: A Path Forward.* Some of the report's recommendations were controversial; however, few disagreed with the report's call for creating a culture in forensic science that is strongly rooted in science. The report correctly advocates support for research to address issues of accuracy, reliability, and validity in forensic science disciplines.

The FBI's Forensic Science Research and Training Center is a key ingredient in the development of criminalistics in the United States. The FBI has made a substantial commitment to the center in terms of personnel and equipment. This facility has established a research program concentrated in the areas of biochemistry, immunology, chemistry, and physics. The FBI's program is directed toward the development of new methods for forensic science. The research staff interacts with researchers from academia, industry, and other government and forensic science laboratories. The staff also participates in specialized scientific courses offered by the FBI to state and local crime laboratory personnel. These courses not only have improved the quality of forensic science practices in the United States but have encouraged standardization of many of the scientific procedures used by forensic laboratories throughout the United States.

A foundation of cooperation has been laid; much remains to be accomplished. How successful our profession will be in fulfilling its present and future obligations to justice depends on the skill, dedication, and ingenuity of its practitioners.

further references

Houck, M. M., "Statistics and Trace Evidence: The Tyranny of Numbers," *Forensic Science Communications* 1, no. 3 (1999), www.fbi.gov/programs/lab/fsc/current/backissu.htm

National Research Council, *Strengthening Forensic Science in the United States: A Path Forward,* Washington, D.C.: The National Academies Press, 2009, http://books.nap.edu/openbook.php?record_id=12589&page=R1

Roman, J. K., Reid, S., Reid, J., Chalfin, A. Adams, W., and Knight, C., *The DNA Field Experiment: Cost-Effectiveness Analysis of the Use of DNA in the Investigation of High-Volume Crimes,* www.ncjrs.gov/pdffiles1/nij/grants/222318.pdf

"Status and Needs of Forensic Science Service Providers: A Report to Congress," www.ncjrs.gov/pdffiles1/nij/213420.pdf

Index

Page references followed by "f" indicate illustrated figures or photographs; followed by "t" indicates a table.